THE BOOK OF
The Bothy

About the Author

Having grown up on the edge of Snowdonia National Park in north Wales, Phoebe Smith's love of dramatic landscapes has taken her on walking and backpacking adventures all around the world – from wild camping on Scottish islands and sleeping under a swag in the Australian outback to watching the Northern Lights from a wigwam above the Arctic Circle and sleeping under the stars in Antarctica. She's enjoyed snowshoeing in the Swiss Alps, scrambling in Wadi Rum and canyon walking in the USA. But of all the places she's been, it's the UK that holds the dearest place in her heart. Phoebe is adamant that you don't need to travel far to have an adventure, and when not planning her next escapade she's most likely to be found in the mountains with her trusty tent or beside the fire inside a beloved bothy.

Phoebe is award-winning editor of *Wanderlust* travel magazine and has written extensively for a range of newspapers and magazines, both in the UK and overseas. She was a finalist in the 2015 National Adventurer Awards, and in 2014 became the first woman to camp solo at all the extreme points of mainland Britain on consecutive nights. Her other books include *Extreme Sleeps: Adventures of a Wild Camper*; *Wild Nights: Camping Britain's Extremes*; *The Camper's Friend*; *The Joy of Camping*; and *Wilderness Weekends: Wild Adventures in Britain's Rugged Corners*.

Other Cicerone guides by the author
The Peddars Way and Norfolk Coast Path

THE BOOK OF
The Bothy

by Phoebe Smith

2 POLICE SQUARE, MILNTHORPE, CUMBRIA LA7 7PY
www.cicerone.co.uk

© Phoebe Smith 2015
First edition 2015, reprinted 2016 (with updates)
ISBN: 978 1 85284 756 2
Printed in China on behalf of Latitude Press Ltd
A catalogue record for this book is available from the British Library.
All photographs and illustrations by the author or Neil S Price unless
otherwise stated.

Route mapping by Lovell Johns www.lovelljohns.com
Contains Ordnance Survey data © Crown copyright and
database right 2015. NASA relief data courtesy of ESRI.

DEDICATION

This book is dedicated to the Mountain Bothies Association, which for the past 50 years has protected over 100 of these wonderful shelters for us all to enjoy, and to all the bothy Maintenance Officers (MOs) who work tirelessly to look after their adopted shelters. Finally, it is dedicated to every single person who has, and will, visit a bothy – just like you reading this now; I know you will also work to leave them in better shape then when you arrive, so we can all continue to enjoy them in the years to come.

ACKNOWLEDGEMENTS

Thanks to my walking companions over the years and to all the people I've ever met in bothies – this book would not exist without you. Special thanks to Neil for some of the wonderful photographs and illustrations within these pages.

UPDATES TO THIS GUIDE

While every effort is made by our authors to ensure the accuracy of guidebooks as they go to print, changes can occur during the lifetime of an edition. If we know of any, they will be listed under the Updates tab on this book's page on the Cicerone website (www.cicerone.co.uk/756/updates), so please check before planning your trip. We also advise that you check information about such things as transport, accommodation and shops locally. Even rights of way can be altered over time. We are always grateful for information about any discrepancies between a guidebook and the facts on the ground, sent by email to info@cicerone.co.uk or by post to Cicerone, 2 Police Square, Milnthorpe LA7 7PY, United Kingdom.

Front cover: Shenavall Bothy, Wester Ross, Scotland

Contents

Warning

Mountain walking can be a dangerous activity carrying a risk of personal injury or death. It should be undertaken only by those with a full understanding of the risks and with the training and experience to evaluate them. While every care and effort has been taken in the preparation of this guide, the user should be aware that conditions can be highly variable and can change quickly, materially affecting the seriousness of a mountain walk. Therefore, except for any liability that cannot be excluded by law, neither Cicerone nor the author accept liability for damage of any nature (including damage to property, personal injury or death) arising directly or indirectly from the information in this book.

To call out the Mountain Rescue, ring 999 or the international emergency number 112: this will connect you via any available network. Once connected to the emergency operator, ask for the police.

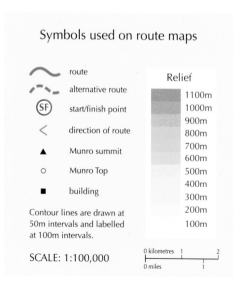

Symbols used on route maps

		Relief
~	route	
‑ ‑ ‑	alternative route	1100m
(SF)	start/finish point	1000m
		900m
<	direction of route	800m
▲	Munro summit	700m
		600m
o	Munro Top	500m
■	building	400m
		300m
Contour lines are drawn at 50m intervals and labelled at 100m intervals.		200m
		100m

SCALE: 1:100,000

```
0 kilometres   1            2
|_____|_____|
0 miles              1
```

Approaching The Schoolhouse bothy, Sutherland

Bothy locations

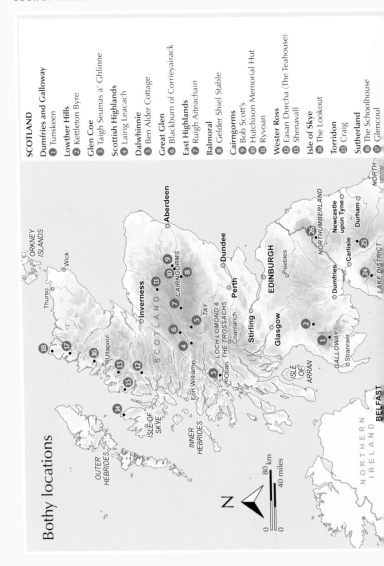

SCOTLAND

Dumfries and Galloway
1 Tunskeen

Lowther Hills
2 Kettleton Byre

Glen Coe
3 Taigh Seumas a' Ghlinne

Scottish Highlands
4 Lairig Leacach

Dalwhinnie
5 Ben Alder Cottage

Great Glen
6 Blackburn of Corrieyairack

East Highlands
7 Ruigh Aiteachain

Balmoral
8 Gelder Shiel Stable

Cairngorms
9 Bob Scott's
10 Hutchison Memorial Hut
11 Ryvoan

Wester Ross
12 Easan Dorcha (The Teahouse)
13 Shenavall

Isle of Skye
14 The Lookout

Torridon
15 Craig

Sutherland
16 The Schoolhouse
17 Glencoul

8

WALES

Brecon Beacons
⑲ Grwyne Fawr

Mid-Wales
⑳ Nant Syddion

Snowdonia
㉑ Arenig Fawr

Carneddau
㉒ Dulyn

ENGLAND

Lake District
㉓ Warnscale Head
㉔ Mosedale Cottage

Pennines
㉕ Greg's Hut

Border Country
㉖ Kershopehead

Glencoul bothy, Sutherland

Preface

From sea to forest, beach to mountain, this assortment of 26 bothies represents a snapshot of what's out there in some of Britain's wildest areas – hopefully enough to whet your appetite and make you want to go and check them out for yourself. It was never my intention to produce a catalogue of all the bothies out there, instead I wanted to provide a big enough selection for everyone to find a bothy that was not too far away, so that you could actually go and stay there. Conversely, I didn't want too large a spread so that there were no new ones for you to discover yourself – that is, after all, the joy of bothying.

The initial basis of the selection was geographical – I don't think anyone would have wanted to read about 26 bothies all within the same mountain range. But within that, it was a personal choice – bothies, much like mountain summits or waterproof jackets, are subjective. One that I might rate highly, others may never want to stay at. The result is a selection in which each bothy offers something slightly different, be it back-story, structure, size or views from the window.

Some bothies described here set the scene for some of the most memorable nights of my life and, as such, are just too good to keep to myself. Other bothies are included because I want more eyes on them – more good people looking out for them so that they remain for years to come. So I share them here, hoping that, like me, you'll discover the magic that bothies can create.

You may disagree with my selection – but that's half the fun. So go forth, find your favourite bothy, share your own adventure in the book you find inside it, and then tell me which bothy you would have included. You can get in touch through Cicerone's Facebook and twitter. I can't wait to hear from you all…

Phoebe Smith, 2015

 ciceronepress

@PhoebeRSmith
@CiceronePress

#BookoftheBothy

Strathchailleach (aka Sandy's Bothy) nestles in the hills beyond Sandwood Bay

Introduction

Welcome to the wonderful world of bothying

Something I love about this bothy, and every bothy, is how a network of adventurers and travellers is created through these pages. We may never meet. David, Owen and their friends who stayed here on the 5th October may never meet the famous Izzy and Rose who stayed here from 1–3 October, but there's a connection there… something happened between them, even though separated by time, they are united by place.

Entry in Grwyne Fawr bothy book, by 'Hannah', 2013

My face appeared orange in the light of the flame. The flickering glow of a dying candle fizzed and spat as I leafed through the pages of a bothy book – the visitors' log that's placed in each and every shelter from the far north of Scotland to the forested valley of mid-Wales which makes up the bothy network. I was, at the particular moment, not really aware of my surroundings. Wasn't taking in the view of the creeping valley at my window as a thin sliver of a river hewed its way through the undergrowth and tipped into the dam below it. Didn't register the shrill hoot of a brown owl on the hunt in the clear sky above my little slate roof. Instead I was lost among the pages of this tome, caught in a space between time by Hannah's words, meeting new people in the ink within the lines of paper. This is the power of the bothy book, and of the bothy itself – this ability for visitors to simultaneously find and lose themselves, to meet and connect with other people in a way that they never could in an office or house surrounded by mod cons and mobile phone reception.

But first, perhaps, I should rewind. I was in a bothy – a mountain hut that's completely free to use as an overnight stop, positioned in a wild and stunning location. Somewhere you could go and stay tomorrow and not pay a penny for the privilege.

I know all too well how novel the idea of a bothy can sound to the uninitiated. The notion that landowners, who will make no money from it, will leave one of their buildings unlocked for walkers, climbers or outdoor enthusiasts to sleep in can sound bizarre. Furthermore, when you learn that an organisation regularly raises money to maintain these buildings and furnishes them with basics like a fireplace or stove, a table and a visitors' book, it seems even more outlandish. But that's exactly what the Mountain Bothies Association (MBA) – a donation-funded and volunteer-run organisation which has just celebrated its 50th anniversary – does to this day.

Bothies have a knack of bringing out both the best and the worst in people. Don't believe me? Head to a popular one, close to a city, on a Monday night, and you might, if you're unlucky, find piles of rubbish on the sleeping platforms, questionable yellow liquid in bottles above the fireplace and a visitors' book filled with senseless scrawl. But, equally, there's not another place in the world I can name where I've arrived in a storm, uninvited, and instantly been offered dry clothes, the comfiest armchair closest to the fire (forcing someone else to stand), and warm food and drink I didn't bring myself.

Two extremes? Definitely. But I stand by my assertion that something happens to us when we venture into the wild, the remote,

the isolated. Social barriers break down, we have time to think, time to reflect, and the opportunity to do things right – not through fear of being punished if we don't, but because we get a feeling so good from doing them that we want to do them more and more. And it's in those places that you'll find bothies.

Until five years ago the MBA didn't publish locations of their bothies online – they remained a secret for members and those in the know. But word got out, as it always does, and so they decided it was time to share them. Some disagree with the idea – think that it's best that few people know their whereabouts because they operate within a system of trust. There's nothing to stop someone ruining them for others.

Given that, you might wonder why I too have decided to publish details of some of these shelters myself in this book. The reason is simple – I want more eyes on them, more eyes to watch over them and keep them safe. The kind of person hell-bent on destroying a bothy is certainly not going to bother with a book when they can find the location of just about any bothy in the country with a quick search on Google.

The kind of person I want to tell about bothies is you. I want to invite you all to fall in love with

Warm fires and mountain adventures are shared by candlelight

these modest shelters as much as I have. I want to share the information I know about them, want to help you reach them the best way possible, would like you to be prepared for staying at them and, finally, I want to take you on a journey to visit them over the next couple of hundred pages so that, even if you don't get chance to visit them all, you'll feel like you have.

As the wise Hannah said – we may never meet, but through these bothies we will be connected, a network of travellers and adventurers created through these pages.

What are bothies?

The easiest way to describe bothies is simply as stone tents. They may look like country cottages from the outside – pretty enough, with a ramshackle type of charm to earn them a spot on chocolate boxes – but inside it's a different story. With no gas, no electric, no running water, no bathroom, no beds and certainly no TV, these are as basic a shelter as they come. But it's amazing what a few candles, a lit fire and good cheer can do to a place.

In terms of size, bothies range from two-person shed-like affairs right up to multi-bedroom house-like structures with several fireplaces and even kitchen areas.

There isn't a standard bothy – they will constantly surprise you – but therein lies their charm.

Best of all they are left unlocked on a trust basis, for wilderness lovers to stay in, so that we might linger in the places we love so well. It's funny how somewhere so basic that it wouldn't even make a hotel grading system can be a place with views that are definitely five star.

Where can I find them?

Bothies can be found all over Britain in wild and remote places. Because of this, most are found in Scotland – arguably home to the wildest tracts of land in mainland Britain – with a few scattered in the north of England and parts of rural Wales.

To give you an idea of their distribution, the MBA has around 100 buildings in its care, of which just eight are in Wales (where the MBA is known as the CLLM) and 10 in England. The selection of bothies in this book reflects this northern bias.

History of bothies

Chatas, Alpenvereinshütten, cabins, wilderness huts, backcountry bunks – even if you've never stayed at a British bothy you will probably have heard of one of their foreign cousins. So the idea of staying out in

Glencoul, in Sutherland, is just one of the many bothies in Scotland that is ideally placed beside a loch

the mountains or wild hinterland is certainly not a new one.

The Swiss Alpine Club has built huts for climbers and walkers since 1863, offering refuge and respite for those far from civilization. The Appalachian Mountain Club in North America constructed its first backcountry shelter in 1888. And places around the world from Norway to New Zealand, and from Poland to Patagonia, are home to a network of cabins that provide a bed for the night for weary travellers.

Where the bothies in Britain differ is that they were never built for that purpose, but rather were appropriated when that need arose. Originally old farmsteads or workers' huts, they existed because employees on big remote estates, or those quarrying or building dams deep in the mountains, needed somewhere to rest or stay nearby – a commute would have been impossible.

However, the arrival of cheaper vehicles, agricultural machinery and greater transport links meant there was no longer a need for people to reside in these far-flung corners of the country. One by one they began to leave their homesteads behind, quarrying fell out of demand and workers' quarters were no longer inhabited.

Around the same time, in the 1930s, came the Great Depression, a time when industrial workers' hours were becoming shorter, giving the working classes more leisure

17

time but little money to spend on it. Most of them were stuck in factories during the hours they did work, and longed to escape the cities. Naturally the mountains were calling. Mass trespasses began to take place – famously in the English Peak District on Kinder Scout, but also beyond – by which men and women demanded their right to roam in the empty swathes of land that surrounded them. Climbing clubs cropped up all over the country, but especially in Scotland, and more specifically Glasgow, where the famous Creagh Dhu club was formed in Clydebank.

For its members, getting into these wild spaces was more than just a hobby, it was what they needed to enable them to survive working in industrialised urban environments for the remaining five (or more) days each week. Putting on shared buses or, more often, hitchhiking, once they got where they needed to go, short on money, they would sleep wherever they could – in barns, under rocky overhangs (known as howffs), in caves and in these abandoned bothies, and they taught themselves to live off the land, so that they could be close to the crags the next day.

Hutchison Memorial Hut in the Cairngorms is popular with climbers

This spawned some of the most famous climbers of the 20th century – from Jimmy Bell (who put up a host of new routes on Ben Nevis and edited the *Scottish Mountaineering Club Journal* for an impressive 24 years) to WH Murray, author of Mountaineering in Scotland (first penned on toilet paper when Murray was a prisoner of war during the Second World War, it was destroyed by his captors, to which he retaliated by writing it again and finally – triumphantly – getting it published in 1947), and Don Whillans (working-class hero, incredible climber, gear inventor and renowned deliverer of the one-liner). For men such as these, bothies were key to enabling them to get into the countryside and stay on the doorstep of the peaks.

In the years after the Second World War society's attitude to the outdoors and, more specifically, outdoor activities was changing too. Soldiers and their families looked to camping as a cheap holiday, and more and more people were discovering that walking was a therapeutic way to spend their increasing free time.

Some more intrepid walkers and mountaineers began to explore their own country's wild corners, and as they did, those other than climbers stumbled upon these abandoned buildings. Giving them a convenient start point for a mountain ascent, walk or crag climb the following day, many began to stay the night in them – sometimes with and sometimes without the landowner's consent. And thus the modern day bothy-er was born.

But an ill-maintained building can survive only so long, and soon many of these bothies crumbled into ruin. Some were adopted by climbing clubs that knew of their importance; others were lucky enough to have landowners who privately maintained them for outdoor enthusiasts and local shepherds. But many others were left abandoned. And so they would have remained were it not for one man, Bernard Heath. It was he who, back in 1965, got together with a group of friends to repair and restore the old farm building in Dumfries and Galloway now known as Tunskeen bothy. Later that year a group of like-minded bothy-lovers joined forces, and the Mountain Bothies Association we know and love was formed.

Membership grew (as did bothy projects), Maintenance Officers (MOs) were appointed in the 1970s, in 1975 the charity was officially registered, in 1991 Bernard and Betty Heath were honoured with a British Empire Medal for their work and

Toilets in or near bothies are a welcome addition – but should by no means be expected!

in 2015 the MBA won the Queen's Award for Voluntary Service.

Changes may have taken place over the years, with health and safety legislation being addressed, complaints procedures being established and company status being updated. But its purpose remains unchanged. Some 100 bothies, over 3000 members, regular work parties and 50 years later, the volunteer-run organisation is still working hard with landowners to preserve and restore 'open shelters for the use and enjoyment of all who love wild and lonely places'. And thank goodness they do.

The association's founders once wrote that: 'Members' only reward will be the knowledge that their efforts have helped save a bothy from ruin.' And how many of us would want anything more?

Facilities to expect

Basically none. In fact, if you get four walls and a roof that doesn't leak then you should count yourself lucky. In my experience it's much better to go with low expectations and be pleasantly surprised, rather than to go expecting a Hilton and find a low-rent shack.

Many bothies will, of course, have something more in them, ranging from the basic (chairs, tables) to the more upmarket (sleeping platforms, a stove, a river nearby) and the downright luxurious (toilet, water pipe just outside, reading material, bed frames).

Go prepared for the worst. Even if you've read something about a bothy in this book, remember that things change, break or are removed – so be prepared. Expect the walk to the nearest water source to be a trek and bring a bigger container to minimise your trips to collect it; assume the fire won't work and bring an extra layer and a hat to sleep in; know that there won't be any toilet paper so bring your own.

Follow this simple rule and you will avoid any disappointment.

Why bothy?

It's a fair question, and one my friends and even family members frequently ask me. Aside from the obvious – that I love them, and once you get the bothy bug you can't stop going to them (I swear it's worse than being a Munro-bagger) – it's really the same reason that you go wild camping, or even just walking. It's to get away from everything and enjoy discovering the uncrowded and rugged corners of a beautiful country.

Of course, you can do exactly the same thing with a trusty bivvy bag or tent, so below is a list I've drawn up to show the pros and cons of staying in a bothy versus a tent. I'll leave it to you to decide the best…

Bothy pros

- Warmth You can have a fire and get warm.
- Space Rather than being stuck in a cramped crouch of a tent, trying to get undressed without touching the sides of your condensation-drenched walls, you have the luxury of space to manoeuvre, stretch – even dance if the mood takes you.
- Drying out Got caught out in the rain? At a bothy you can dry your clothes out above a fire or spread your belongings out on a table and let them dry.
- Escaping midges Bothies are usually home to spiders, and spiders mean fewer midges, so you can cook and eat your evening meal without getting bitten.
- People You may meet people with a similar love of the outdoors.
- Inside information Fellow visitors may share the location of other bothies or wild camp spots for you to discover.

Bothy cons

- Mice A mainstay of nearly every bothy, you are guaranteed to hear at least one at some point in your bothying experiences – make sure you pack your food away before you go to sleep.
- People Although a few like-minded souls can be good, too many can be frustrating – staying up too late, being loud, not understanding the boundaries of personal space, snoring.
- Poop Where there's lots of people there can sometimes be a toilet issue; put a foot wrong and the consequences could be dire.

Conclusion: Do use bothies, but take a tent or bivvy bag as a back-up – that way the choice is yours…

Finding a bothy

If you're serious, the first thing you should do is join the MBA. At the time of writing, membership is a tiny £20 per year, with a reduced rate of £10 to under 16s, over 60s and the unemployed (see www.mountainbothies.org.uk for current prices). The money you give goes straight into the pot to pay for maintenance work – so you can stay at your next bothy and know that your contribution made a difference. You'll get a members' handbook, a regular newsletter and the annual report.

Skirting the reservoir en route to Arenig Fawr bothy, Snowdonia

This book is a good first step to finding a bothy, but before you head out get a good map – Ordnance Survey or Harvey Maps (if available). Using the grid reference find your bothy and then plot the best route there for you, based on your experience.

Then, pack the proper kit (see 'What to take', below) and get out there and find it. I'll warn you – some are easy to find, whereas others are more difficult. Many bothy-lovers will (or at least soon will) know the pain of wandering around tired after a long walk-in, mere metres from the spot where the bothy should be, in horrendous weather, mistaking boulder after boulder as the promised bothy (I'm looking at you, Hutchison Memorial Hut – if you come from the Linn of Dee approach). But the more you visit, the more confident you'll get, and you might even find bothies not under the care of the MBA…

MBA or not?

Not all bothies that exist do so under the umbrella of the MBA. Look at an OS map, in any of the wilder areas of Scotland, Wales and England, away from towns and cities, and you will see a number of tiny shelters marked on it. Of course that doesn't mean that a) it's actually a bothy or, perhaps more importantly, that b) it's even there at all. Time is harsh to buildings in wild places. Wind, rain, ice and snow will eventually take their toll, and many a would-be bothy has been destroyed over the years completely unintentionally, because a landowner cannot afford to maintain a building that has no real purpose for them.

On the other hand, I've often stumbled upon a bothy belonging to a landowner, and equally as often it has been kept beautifully by the walkers who find and use it. The non-MBA bothies, of course, tend to be hard to find. But, and I guarantee this, the more that you use bothies the more you will find that are out there. Bothy-dwellers are a generous bunch, and having sussed out that you're a responsible sort will often share with you other locations. So while all but one of the bothies in this book are maintained by the MBA (as denoted by the circular white MBA sign on the front door), it's hoped that this book will serve as a starting point, a kicking-off into the wonderful world of bothies, from where you will discover more than you ever imagined.

Always take a tent or bivvy in case the bothy is full – particularly when visiting smaller bothies such as the Hutchison Memorial Hut

What to take

- Rucksack (suggest around 40–50 litres)
- Sleeping mat (if yours is inflatable and prone to puncture consider bringing a ground sheet)
- Sleeping bag (in winter consider taking a liner for extra warmth)
- Tent/bivvy (as a back-up)
- Camping stove
- Gas
- Spork (fork, knife, spoon combination)
- Mug
- First aid kit (don't forget the blister plasters and tick remover/tweezers)
- Map (OS Landranger (1:50,000), Explorer (1:25,000) or Harvey – relevant maps are indicated in each chapter)
- Headtorch (with new batteries inside)
- Warm gloves, hat and buff
- Fleece/midlayer
- Waterproof jacket
- Waterproof overtrousers
- Insulated jacket (down or synthetic)
- Dry bag containing: toothbrush and paste, dry socks, change of underwear, tissues
- Toilet paper
- Sanitary products (if applicable)
- Disposal bag for toilet paper/sanitary products/general waste

Craig bothy, Torridon

- Hand sanitiser
- Water bottle (for purified water only)
- Water container (collapsible, wide-mouthed is best) for collecting stream water
- Food
- Candles (tea lights) and lighter/matches
- Fuel (see 'A note on fuel' below) and small amount of kindling for the fire
- Midge repellent (trust me, you'd rather have it and not need it than need it and not have it)
- Pen for filling in the bothy book

Luxury item
- In winter consider taking down booties – those nights can get cold!

A note on fuel

Most (although not all) bothies have either an open fire or a multi-fuel stove. This book indicates whether or not the featured bothies have one. If they do, it's strongly advised that – unless indicated otherwise in the relevant chapter – you take in your own fuel. So what to take? Coal is the obvious choice – it burns longer and hotter than wood and stores heat well – although it is heavy, of course. If you decide on coal, consider getting the smokeless variety. Wood is the other option, although a bag of wood is a lot bulkier than coal. If you decide on wood, a better option is wood briquettes (also known as 'heat logs'), which are compact and often have a guaranteed burn time of 1–2hrs.

If you forget to take fuel, think very carefully about what to use. Never cut live trees – only ever use dead wood. Don't chop up furniture/shelves inside the bothy to burn. It may be annoying to forget fuel – we've all done it – but please still be a responsible user.

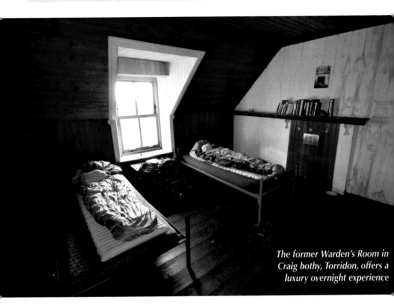

The former Warden's Room in Craig bothy, Torridon, offers a luxury overnight experience

Etiquette

Much like wild camping, to be a good bothy guest you need to follow good etiquette. Members of the MBA follow a Bothy Code of Conduct, but you don't need to be a member to be a responsible bothy user. Simply follow this fairly common-sense set of guidelines.

- **Look after your bothy** From tiding up food after you make it to taking out rubbish some-one else has left behind – it's all about doing as much as you can to make bothying a great experience for everyone else. So if you've got room left in your backpack, take out that rubbish that was there when you arrived – even if it's not yours.

- **…and look after its surroundings** This book indicates when a stove or fireplace is present, and also when you should bring your own fuel – so you can go prepared. Please don't cut live trees or nearby fences for your fire, and don't light a fire outside the bothy.

- **Everybody's got to go, but…** When you need the toilet, be courteous. If there is a toilet (which is rare, but some have them) follow the instructions to the letter. If it says not to drop down anything but tissue and human waste, then don't throw down a wet wipe. If it asks you to refill the bowl from the stream once you've flushed, then fill the bowl from the stream when you've finished – no matter what the weather. In the much more likely case that there is no toilet, note the spade in the corner. It's there for entirely this reason – make sure you use it. When you do, remember these simple steps:

1 Go at least 200m away from the bothy, at least 50m from a path and definitely at least 50m from a watercourse (it is, after all, likely to be the place where you'll want to source your drinking water), and downstream of the bothy.

2 Try to carry your own waste out with you (places like the Cairngorms operate a Poo Pot scheme – pick up a Poo Pot from the ranger base and return it there for disposal – and dry-bag manufacturers make bags for the same purpose).

3 If you can't carry out your own waste, bury it, even in winter. Using the spade, dig a hole at least 15cm deep (if there's snow

on the ground, it needs to be a hole in the ground below the snow to stop an unwelcome surprise for other walkers in spring) and go in that.

4 Carry out all your toilet paper and any sanitary products (remember to take a special bag for this in your rucksack) and cover the hole.

5 Remember to wash your hands – antiseptic hand sanitiser is the best method as no water is required.

• Make sure everyone is welcome It's not first come, first served; bothies are there for everyone to use, so try to accommodate everyone who turns up – no one should be left out in the cold. Don't like crowds? Take your own tent or bivvy to give yourself a Plan B.

• Be generous… to a point While it's good to leave things for the next guest – be sensible. A few pieces of coal, some firelighters or tinder is great; rubbish that you think would work as kindling and can't be bothered to carry out, not so good. Want to share your food? Think about it – what food would you be prepared to eat when you don't know the source? Unopened

This friendly sign hangs on the door of every bothy in the MBA network

M.B.A.

WITH THE OWNERS PERMISSION THIS BOTHY IS MAINTAINED BY THE MOUNTAIN BOTHIES ASSOCIATION

Please keep the place tidy

tinned food – yes; a half-eaten bag of nuts – no. And remember mice are frequent visitors too; don't encourage them by leaving opened food.

• Don't outstay your welcome If an estate asks users not to visit the bothy at certain times of the year, it's for a good reason. So respect their wishes, and if they ask you to call ahead to check it's safe – then do it.

- **Keep it brief** The whole point of a bothy is that it's a temporary refuge for walkers – so keep walking. Don't turn up and set up home there for a week. One or two nights is fine, but any longer and you'll need to ask permission first. There are plenty more bothies anyway, so get exploring rather than settling in the same one.

- **Keep it to the minimum** Bothies are not the place for large groups. With other users turning up all the time, you cannot arrive en masse and expect to fit. A maximum group size should be six or fewer. Any more and you will need to ask for permission from the owner first.

- **When you leave, go gracefully** Check the fire is out, and if it's not, put it out – never leave it unattended. Close the door – cattle, deer and birds can all get inside if you leave it open, but then can't get back out. And take rubbish with you.

Safety issues

Fires

The main risk in a bothy is from the fire. Stoves and open fires are a welcome facility, but if you leave a fire unattended, burn the wrong thing or – worse – have a faulty stove or chimney the consequences can be dire.

Check before you start your fire that there is nothing in the fire/stove that shouldn't be – plastics, tins, and painted or varnished wood are a definite no-no. Remove these if you find them. Make sure there's no masonry from the chimney in the grate – this could be a sign the chimney is faulty.

When you do start the fire keep a lookout for smoke seeping out where it shouldn't – from panels or from part-way up the chimney or flue. If this happens, or if the room fills with smoke, put the fire out, open the windows or doors, leave the bothy and do not enter until it's clear – carbon monoxide poisoning is a killer.

If using a stove make sure the ash pan is empty before you start and empty it the next day before you leave.

Do not leave a fire unattended, and make sure the fire is out when you leave.

Water

Most bothies are near a water source (river or stream), and this is indicated within each bothy chapter. While there are many people who swear they drink from these without treating the water first, and have always been fine, it's best to err on the side of caution.

The simplest way to purify water is by boiling it on your camping stove. Once you've brought it to the boil be sure to let the water roll for a couple of minutes before using it. If you want to save fuel take chlorine tablets with you or consider carrying in a water filter/purifier device, though these can be a bulkier option.

Whatever method you choose, take fast-flowing water (as opposed to standing water) from as close to the source as possible.

The bothy book

As good a read as any book you'll ever find, these wonderful pages contain days', months' and years' worth of other people's adventures. They will sometimes shock, sometimes make you laugh, often be a cryptic puzzle about the person who was here before you, but they are always sure to inspire you to go somewhere new and read another one.

I've seen everything from poetry to illustrations, book extracts and even a 16-page polemic about why the outdoors shouldn't be regulated.

Some bothy locations – such as that of The Lookout on the Isle of Skye – can bring out the artist in us

Each one is a gem that, if I had my way, would find its way into the National Archives. Better yet – they are all unique. They give a sense of the characters who've slept in the same four walls as you and tell a lot about the type of people who seek out the different ones – from the popular bothies, where lots of newcomers visit and Duke of Edinburgh groups stop for lunch, to the hard-to-reach ones where the entries are more sombre affairs full of advice and plans for the days ahead.

In each of the following chapters you'll find my own bothy-book entry – a personal account of a memorable experience at that particular place.

Make sure, whenever you visit a bothy, you fill the bothy book in and become part of the wonderful legacy.

Traditions

Apart from writing in the bothy book – which should be mandatory (consider taking a pen in case there isn't one or it's run out) – many walkers often share whisky from a Sigg bottle, which I've done on more than one occasion. But if you don't fancy that, your tradition could be being kind to any other users who come along. And while we're talking new traditions, the best approach you can take at a bothy – whether you're staying for a couple of minutes to look around, half an hour for a lunch break, or one or two nights – is always to leave it in a better state than when you arrived. Because if we all did that, we'd always find every bothy in a clean and well-maintained state.

How you can help

Bothies are maintained by volunteers, who can't always get out to them as often as they'd like. That means you can be their eyes and ears on the ground. Once you've visited a bothy contact the MBA via the website (www.mountainbothies.org.uk, 'Make a Report' section) and let them know if vital work needs doing. If something's missing – such as a shovel – tell them. If someone's tried to burn a chair – tell them. Or even if everything seems in order just tell them – it's nice for them to know.

Common things that go wrong with bothies are roofs, windows, doors and floors. So on your next visit take a look around. Are there tiles missing on the roof? Is water dripping inside when it rains? Are all the windows intact? Is the door still on the stove? Is the floor OK – no holes or soft spots underfoot? Do any of the walls, ceilings or floors have visible cracks? Is the front door closing properly and staying closed?

Saws, often supplied at the bothy, are useful for cutting dead wood for the bothy fire

If you notice anything tell the MBA so that they can sort it before things get worse – a minor problem can easily develop into a major expense if not addressed.

Then, perhaps consider joining one of the regular work parties held throughout the year all over the bothy network. You can help restore one of your favourite shelters, meet other bothy-goers and get to spend a weekend in one of the best spots in Britain.

SCOTLAND

Looking out to the Rubha Hunish, the northernmost point on the Isle of Skye, en route to The Lookout

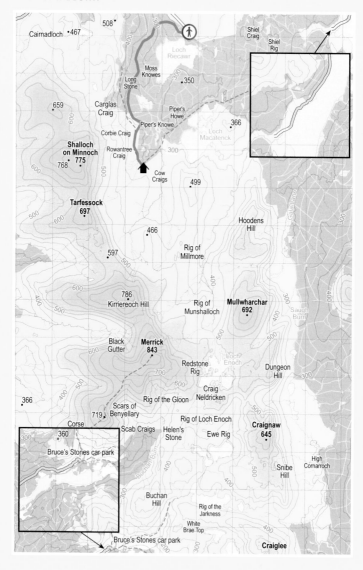

DUMFRIES AND GALLOWAY

Tunskeen

The very first MBA bothy,
situated in the wilds of the Galloway Forest

Tunskeen was the first bothy to be placed under the care of the MBA

I often wonder if, when the idea to begin renovating and protecting old dilapidated buildings in deepest, wildest Scotland was first suggested, anyone thought that it would have grown to the extent it has 50 years later. Thanks to that notion – which must have been looked upon as completely crazy back then – we now have shelters not just spread over Britain's northernmost country, but in England and Wales too.

It all started here...with Tunskeen. The very first Mountain Bothies Association (MBA) project, this building was taken on in 1965 and, courtesy of the small group that started this work, it is still open today for walkers like you and me to enjoy. The original MBA idea was to 'maintain simple shelters in remote country for the use and benefit of all who love wild and lonely places' – and it doesn't come much lonelier and wilder than the Galloway Forest, in which Tunskeen sits.

Music echoed from the stones. It was an almost alien sound to my ears, so unexpected in a place that seems so far from electricity and mod cons. But here it was.

Tunskeen was a start point for me and a friend called Matt. We were there to attempt a crossing of the range of peaks that make up The Awful Hand. We arrived by taxi, to make the crossing easier and, as it was mid-week in September, expected to have it to ourselves, to be able to luxuriate in our own separate sleeping platforms rather than being cramped in, and to enjoy the night sky in this quiet and lonely place. But it was not to be.

When we opened the door to discover the source of the music a single man was sat on the chair. This close the radio sounded tinny and raw, bouncing off the walls in the darkened room; it was like standing in a kitchen and banging pots and pans together.

He didn't smile at first, only stared; I guess we'd ruined his plans as much as he'd ruined ours. But after making introductions, offering him a coffee and sawing up some wood for the fire he'd started, he seemed to warm to us.

It turned out he worked with a lot of troubled youths, and the more he talked, the more it became apparent that he'd come to the bothy to escape the dramas, to 'just' be' without reference to the people who rely on him to offload their problems. Perhaps, I mused as he switched off the radio, the silence and the thinking space had become a little too loud with his own thoughts

The welcome white-washed walls of Tunskeen rise above the heather

and he'd needed some noise to make them stop. Or maybe it was that he just liked music.

Either way, soon the music was replaced by conversation as he and Matt talked well into the night. I squeezed my sleeping mat into a corner and snuggled down into its warmth, the sound of their conversation lulling me to sleep quicker than any song could. Their voices turned to snores as they too retired to bed, and soon the only music was the rhythm of the mouse's feet, pit-patting on the floor as it hunted for comfort in this building. I smiled - it seemed everyone, man and beast, came to bothies in search of something. I just hope we all find it.

Thanks to the lack of light pollution in the area surrounding the forest, this less visited part of southern Scotland, away from the more famous Highlands further north, is officially designated as a Dark Sky Park – the first area in the UK to obtain this designation. Being so far from any towns, it's a great place to watch the night sky. From the bothy doorstep you may see The Plough, from which you can identify the North Star and even, when the cloud stays away, the smear of white that is the Milky Way. In winter there have even been reports of walkers spotting the green and red dazzles of the aurora borealis, aka the Northern Lights.

Did you know?

The range of hills above the bothy that stretch out into a ridge make up what is known as 'The Awful Hand'; it includes The Merrick, Benyellary, Kirriereoch Hill, Tarfessock and Shalloch on Minnoch. It's not particularly tough in terms of technicality, but the descent and re-ascent makes it something of a challenge, as does the amount of boggy ground underfoot.

By far the most famous landmark close to Tunskeen is The Merrick, a high but fairly rounded bump of a hill that most approach from the car park at Glen Trool. But start at this bothy and you can tackle it from the direction that few others bother to.

The area abounds with tantalising names – from the Dungeon Hills, the Murder Hole and even the Grey Man of Merrick – but the one name that will always entice outdoor lovers is Tunskeen. Because without this stone-built legend, the legacy of all the other bothies we know and love may never have existed.

Look out for...

Wildlife: Both roe and fallow deer can be seen among these hills. Watch the sky as night falls for lingering bats. During the day you may see one of the local red kites.

Stars: The Galloway Forest Park was the first Dark Sky Park in Britain. It achieved this accolade because of the lack of light pollution in the area.

Top tip

If the bothy is full there is some space outside for a tent, although the ground is boggy and there's a lot of long grass and ticks are a risk. Make sure you take some tick removers with you, or at least a pair of flat-headed tweezers, in case you need to remove one.

It has been estimated that over 7000 stars can be seen from inside the park, as well as Jupiter – and even the aurora.

How to get there

Quickest: The shortest way in starts from the car park at Loch Riecawr. From there follow the forestry track as it passes above the loch under the cover of woodland. At the fork take the path on your left as it bears south. Ignore any turn-offs and eventually you will emerge from the trees. The path becomes a little rougher and wet, but in just over 1km you'll arrive at the bothy.

Time: 1½hrs

Alternative route

Very hard: If you want to arrive after piling on the miles, then start from the south at Bruce's Stones. From there head up to The Merrick and then follow the ridge along as it stretches over many undulating kilometres with plenty of knee-busting ascent. Eventually, after passing the summit of Tarfessock, continue on to the col between it and the next peak, from where you descend downhill (pathless) to reach the bothy. Make sure you have plenty of time and are confident in navigating using a map and compass even in bad weather.

Tunskeen essentials

Maps	OS Explorer 318; OS Landranger 77
Grid ref	NX 425 906
Terrain	Forestry track, followed by boggy but clear trail to the bothy
Water source	Small stream not far from the bothy
Facilities	Stove (bring your own fuel); saw (if you use firewood left by others make sure you replace it – only with dead wood, do not cut live trees); shovel
Building	Stone/brick construction, tiled roof
Inside	The bothy is made up of just a single room. On arrival you see an L-shaped sleeping platform, a few chairs and a stove. The sleeping platform sleeps four comfortably; the floor space sleeps many more.
Nearby hills	Shalloch on Minnoch, Kirriereoch Hill, The Merrick, Rhinns of Kells

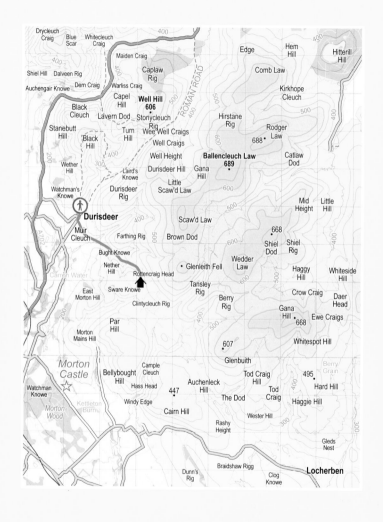

Kettleton Byre

*A cosy one-roomed shelter in the
often-overlooked Lowther Hills*

Kettleton Byre, with its
bright doors, is situated in
the lonely Lowther Hills

When some of us reach the borderland between the Lowther Hills and north-ernmost England we have a tendency to speed up. We're perhaps ending our Highland adventure and keep our foot down, intent on going home, or head-ing north to explore the 'proper' mountains, complete with serrated tops and knife-edged ridges, further north.

However, edged between the speeding cars of the M74 and the Dalveen pass is the mass of undulating humps known as the Lowther Hills, pushing up the moorland like a crumpled blanket. They are not high. But what they lack in pointy summits they make up for in their crowd-free potential.

It wasn't always the case of course. Romans once paced through the land-scape in their efforts to seize Scotland; a battle they would never win. Among the marks left on the scenery, amid the velvet-like collection of knolls and hillocks, are signs of much more recent residents – farm buildings, dry-stone

Recording a stay in Kettleton Byre in the bothy book

walls and…this little bothy. Once part of a series of three little huts, only this sturdy structure remains. The concrete foundation of one of the former buildings sits to its right, then merely the depression of the other to the left.

Surrounded by the empty Lowther Hills, Kettleton Byre offers a doorstep from which to enter into a proper exploration of a small but wild place. Don't expect to see many wild animals – they seem to be tightly controlled with traps by the locals who want to protect the prize grouse that people pay to come and shoot – but do come ready to be the only human soul up in these southern highlands, where paths are few and views are boundless.

Inside your base is a homely, cosy room, lovingly decorated with perhaps the most ornate of all the bothy-book holders, made from brass, and a candlestick with the name of the bothy etched onto it. Best of all, above the bed is a poster that simply tells us to 'colour outside the lines' – as if us bothy-dwellers, especially in a place so overlooked by most hillwalkers, need to be told.

Look out for...

Birds: This is a popular area for grouse shooting. As you head up to the bothy you will no doubt startle a few – which will in turn startle you with their calls of 'go back'.

History: To the north of Durisdeer are the remains of a former Roman road; not just that, there are also the former ramparts and ditch from a Roman fortlet – one of the best preserved in Britain.

Did you know?

The hamlet of Durisdeer, from where this walk starts, is something of a film star, as it appears in 1978 version of the British thriller *The Thirty-Nine Steps*. The little white cottage here stands in as the village post office in Strathallan.

How to get there

Classic: From the nearby village of Durisdeer head down the road towards the cemetery. Turn left on the track just before you reach the cemetery, passing some old farm buildings as you go. Where the path forks keep to the lower one, which stays just above the river. Follow it steadily uphill until you finally come to a large gate. Once through it, after a few steps the bothy is on your left.

Time: 1hr

Heading up the path from Durisdeer to the wild Lowther Hills

I couldn't imagine what it might be like being a child in a bothy, being able to sleep out in a stone shelter in the middle of nowhere, being allowed to stay up late by a fire blazing, drinking a cup of hot chocolate in my pyjamas. So I don't know how a little girl called Ellie

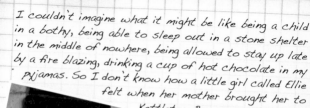

felt when her mother brought her to Kettleton Byre, one summer in 2014, and they spent two nights curled up in their momentary home shut away from the rest of the world, far from TVs and mobile phones.

After reading about their adventure in the bothy book, high above the farming land, I went outside to sit on the little bench. Under the stars I listened to the sounds – a distant 'baa' from a sheep, the swoop of a bat overhead, the 'go-back' call of the grouse among the long tufts of grass. Up here my phone had no reception, I couldn't speak to anyone, couldn't check my email or go on Twitter to share

Always be sure to look for the bothy book when you arrive

my story. I was removed from all the distractions we thrust at ourselves to block out the time we spend alone.

I lingered a while thinking how near I was to the rest of the world, yet how far removed I felt from it. Despite the early autumn warmth I felt myself tingle - a shiver or a burst of excitement, in my current predicament - I know not which one. But there I stayed, dwelling on this sensation just a little longer.

Eventually, I checked the time and was taken aback to realise it was already the next day - five past midnight to be exact. I thought of what other people my age would be doing on this, a Saturday night. Some would be out in the pub, surrounded by snippets of other people's conversations - the yell of an overexcited storyteller in one corner, the hushed toned of a confession in another - others would be at home with their loved ones snuggled up on the couch, with the warmth of central heating, their faces turned multi-coloured by the glow of the light from the television. But me? I was here alone in a bothy, on my own mini-adventure.

I went inside and changed ready for bed, threw another log on the fire and began to boil some water so that I might make some hot chocolate. Then I caught sight of myself in the reflection in the window. I chuckled... I may be a lot older than five but I was lying before - I knew exactly what it felt to be Ellie, and it made me smile.

Alternative route

Hard: If you want to explore some of the Lowther Hills before you reach your shelter, then instead of heading south out of the village of Durisdeer, head north on a track that takes you to the top of Durisdeer Hill. From there follow the fenceline (pathless) first to Little Scaw'd Law, Scaw'd Law and then on to Glenleith Fell. Now pick up a wider track down to Blackhill Moss. Turn right onto the main track and then follow it round to the north, to approach the bothy from the south. It will be on your right.

Top tip

There's lots of flat ground outside the bothy, as this used to be the site of several buildings, and this offers a good Plan B if the building is full. Don't light a fire outside as others clearly have done. Note that during lambing season (15 April to 31 May) the bothy is not available.

Kettleton Byre essentials

Maps	OS Explorer 329; OS Landranger 78
Grid ref	NS 912 020
Terrain	Tarmac to start, then loose stone, followed by grassy Landrover track
Water source	Stream just before the gate to the bothy
Facilities	Stove (no fuel, bring your own); shovel
Building	Stone and brick construction, tile roof
Inside	This bothy is made up of just one room. You enter via a small porchway area, then go through the door to the main room. Here there's an L-shaped raised sleeping platform that comfortably sleeps four. There's also a small table, a couple of chairs and a stove.
Nearby hills	Wedder Law, Scaw'd Law, Little Scaw'd Law

Taigh Seumas a' Ghlinne

*The birthplace of a man once framed for
murder, this bothy has a dark tale to tell*

*Taigh Seumas a' Ghlinne was home to James
of the Glen, who was wrongfully convicted
of the murder of Colin Campbell in 1752*

It's not many a bothy that has an interpretation board outside it. But Taigh Seumas a' Ghlinne is different. For here is the birthplace of a man called James Stewart, aka James of the Glen. His name may not be legendary to many, but dig a little deeper into the tale surrounding the man who used to call this small bothy home and I guarantee you'll be captivated. Indeed, author Robert Louis Stevenson was – for the history that surrounds it formed the basis of his book *Kidnapped*.

Back in 1752, on 14 May, a man called Colin Campbell was murdered – shot in the back in Ballachulish. A search was mounted to bring his killer to justice. The finger was pointed at the Stewarts of Appin, as they had been served eviction notices by none other than Campbell himself. James was the one held accountable and – despite him having an alibi for the time of the

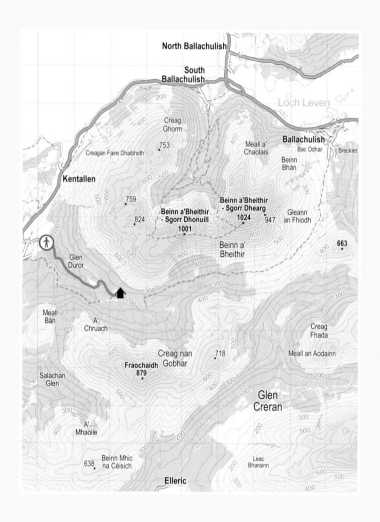

murder – that same year he was found guilty for being an accessory and hung in November at a place called Cnap a'Chaolais.

Stories abound that it was actually Allan Stewart who pulled the trigger that fateful night and that James knew nothing about it, but Stewart absconded and the Campbells wanted to see someone hang. And, as the Campbell Clan Chief served as judge at the trial, and 11 of the 15 jury were also Campbells, it was anything but a fair day in court.

Did you know?

The village of Duror, from where you reach the bothy, and from where the glen gets its name, is home to the oldest 'Parliamentary' church built in Scotland – by none other than Thomas Telford.

Right until the end James protested his innocence. Even as he was hung near the present-day south end of the Ballachulish Bridge he recited a psalm that is now named after him, distraught that history would remember him as a murderer.

In answer to his fears, even as recently as 2008 a movement to get a pardon for James Stewart was put forward to the Scottish Criminal Cases Review Commission. It was thrown out due to the age of the case, but protestors are still trying to make it happen.

So if you go down to the woods today to seek out this tree-lined shelter, remember the man who once called this modest place home and the miscarriage of justice he faced all those years ago.

Look out for…

Wildlife: Keep a lookout in the trees during your walk-in, as you may spot pine marten, owls and red squirrels. Wild cats have been spotted in the area too. Look to the skies and among the sea birds you may – if you're lucky – see raptors or even golden eagles.

History: After a night in the bothy it's worth heading to Duror village to see the Achara Stone, an odd standing stone that sits in a field just off the main road. Investigations by the local community suggest that this particular one (there are many throughout Scotland) was erected during the Bronze Age (1800BC). It's thought to be a 'backsight marker' or viewing point of the moon.

I've never thought of myself as a bad navigator. I like to study a map for hours before I even reach the start of my walk. I stare at the contours and watch as they seem to become 3D in front of me, I picture the ways that the paths will cut into the slopes, imagine the sound of the streams that will appear to my left, visualise the points where confusion is possible and make a mental checklist of the landmarks I should see on my way to ensure I stick to my chosen path.

This usually works well in the mountains, normally ensures that even when weather makes things confusing, I manage to hold my own and get myself in and out of any situation safely. But if there's one thing that strikes real fear in me when planning my route, it's those patches of green that denote forestry land.

I grew up with a pretty patch of woodland behind me - a proper old, oak-filled pocket of wizen trees. I'd spent hours climbing them, running under them and making dens among them. But forestry ones are different. Never have I walked through one and not got lost as the path deviates wildly from what is shown on the OS map.

Unfortunately my trip to this historical bothy was no different. I set off late, knowing the walk-in would be short. How wrong I was. It all started badly to be fair. The route I wanted to take from the car park was roped off, a cartoon forestry working telling me that work was in progress and too dangerous for me to traverse. So I went the other way.

It felt right at first – path junction where it was supposed to be, gradient kicking in where it was meant to. But then the next junction never came. The path just seemed to keep heading upwards, then it swung round to the left; the turning I was waiting for – shown on the map to be a blatant T-junction – needed me to turn right. And that wasn't the only thing that was wrong. I was going higher up too – higher than I felt I should be. Then I reached the age-old dilemma – turn back now and try and search for the missed junction, or continue and hope it would all turn out right. Stupidly I did the latter and soon realised I must have overshot it. Looking at the path I figured out how I should be able to make it right, but then felled trees blocked the path – and I was losing daylight. Refusing at all costs to go back I clambered over the trunks and limbo-ed under others as they creaked, keeping my fingers crossed that they wouldn't choose that moment to fall. Then all of a sudden – the trees were gone.

I felt annoyed, and pushed on convinced I would never find it. Then I spotted it on the hillside above. It couldn't have been more than a couple of hundred metres away, but between me and it was a thicket of small bushes and chopped trees. I did what anyone else would do. I pushed through it. Eventually finding a path made by so many others like me. Until, at last, I reached the bothy.

Inside it was dark like my mood. I immediately went back outside and sat on the bench, rejecting it for causing me so many problems. Soon, however, in the cooling darkness, I went inside to eat, make a fire, and finally fell into a deep sleep.

In the morning all was forgiven. I loved the surroundings, packed away quickly and wondered what all the fuss had been about the night before. Now, I thought picking up my rucksack, all I needed to do was find my way back to the car...

Entering Taigh Seumas a' Ghlinne bothy

The bothy is sparsely furnished but full of history

How to get there

Classic: This is very much dependent on the current state of the footpaths. Forestry work can change them significantly, but in theory the shortest way begins at the car park just outside Achadh nan Darach in Duror and sticks to the lower path, nearest the River Duror. Follow this for about 2km (if you reach a turning to the bridge to take you over the river, then you've gone too far), where you'll see a path leading uphill on your left, bearing northeast. Follow it to a path junction and take the path on your right, leading uphill again. At the final path junction turn right.

The path begins heading southeast and, 500m later, reaches a clearing and the small bothy.

Time: 1½hrs

Top tip

There's not only some flat ground outside the bothy, but also two picnic benches, so it's a great place to camp if you don't fancy the bothy or if it's full.

53

Alternative route

More scenic, fewer trees: It may be a longer route, but to escape the horrors of the forestry tracks you could instead start at Ballachulish to the east. Take the footpath that continues where the road ends after the school and follow it as it takes you above the River Laroch. Where the path forks take the route to the right, going past a cairn. This takes you into the woodland from the east. Keep going straight. Soon you'll join a forestry track. Continue going straight, ignoring turn-offs, until you come to a fork. Take the left fork, heading downhill. Follow it down and alongside the river. Ignore the left turn off (which goes over the river) and the right one (almost immediately after it) and continue on the track next to the river. You might spot the bothy above you – and if feeling adventurous may decide to cut up alongside the fence (many have). But for ease, continue on the path to the next turning on the right, head uphill, take the next right (you should still be heading uphill), then take the next right again and follow the track to the bothy.

Taigh Seumas à Ghlinne essentials

Maps	OS Explorer 376, 384; OS Landranger 41, 49
Grid ref	NN 022 539
Terrain	Loose stone forestry track – confusion possible during or after felling as tracks are diverted or even lost and new ones added (not shown on OS maps)
Water source	Looking at the bothy, there's a stream just to the right
Facilities	Stove; outside picnic benches; shovel
Building	Stone construction, metal roof
Inside	Going through the door you arrive in the one room. To the left is the sitting area with lots of chairs and a stove. In front is a table and chairs, then to the right are sleeping platforms that sleep six comfortably – with floor space taking a good number more.
Nearby hills	Beinn a' Bheithir, Fraochaidh

Lairig Leacach

*An abandoned homestead
on an old drove road*

Mist shrouds the hills around Lairig Leacach bothy

Sometimes it's easy to forget that roads aren't a new concept. Though the idea of tarmacking strips of thoroughfares to create a network of motorways and A-roads might be, the fact remains that since humans first existed they needed to forge routes and tracks to access food, communities and shelter in a world where everything was wild and footpath free.

To get to this small bothy south of Spean Bridge walkers trace the route of an old drove road. Thought to date back centuries, the network of drove roads includes some of the oldest of Britain's paths. They form the basis of many present-day roads, as well as the tracks and trails that walkers follow. Originally used to transport cattle by foot to market, they were a vital link between the farmers' lands and towns, villages or cities, and allowed farmers to move their animals across swathes of land in order to make a living.

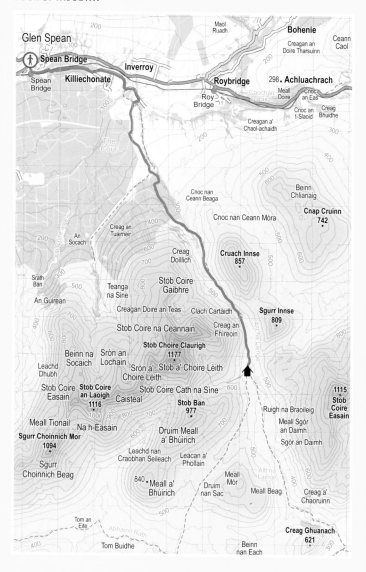

The going would, of course, have been tough. Sometimes the distances were great and herds could be in the hundreds, so the risk of losing cattle to starvation or injury, or having animals wander off into the wilds, was a definite possibility. But demand was such that a good drover would always be in work. That was until the steam train arrived in the 1800s, rendering this method of getting stock to market virtually redundant. By the early 1900s drovers, and the need for their roads, was no more.

Did you know?

On the way up the Lairig Leacach you'll no doubt meet the small wooden statue called the Wee Minister. Said to have replaced a stone version of it, destroyed in the 1970s, this has been on the track since 2010 and is said to offer good fortune to all walkers and travellers who pass by.

To get to this bothy you'll head down into the Lairig Leacach, which means 'pass of the flagstones' – a very apt description for a well-utilised trail. It would have formed part of the route that went south from the Great Glen alongside the Allt na Lairig river, ending eventually at the Kinghouse Inn in Rannoch.

To check out this shelter nowadays your journey doesn't have to be so long. And taking cattle with you is obviously optional! The house itself is curious. It looks very much as though it was formerly part of a larger dwelling that someone, at some time, for some unknown reason, decided to split in two (the other half now missing). Now it is a cosy space, complete with a fire – a great luxury compared to the makeshift shelters the drovers of old would have had to endure. So take plenty of fuel and spend the evening at the window, imagining the traffic that would have passed right by this place before the bothy even existed.

Look out for...

Flowers: Keep a lookout for some of the flowers that line the track. Among the ash trees, willow and birch you might spy the yellow 'bacon and eggs' flowers (aka bird's-foot trefoil), foxgloves or common cow-wheat.

History: Scan the hillsides as you go and you may see the remains of old buildings which would have been used by shepherds and farmers taking cattle to graze on higher ground. You can normally spot these areas because the grass around the old foundation is often a lighter shade of green.

'But what will we do if it's full?' I tried not to sound too panicked as I realised, with a growing concern, that both myself and my walking companion Peter had neglected to bring either tent or bivvy in case the little shelter of Lairig Leacach was at full capacity.

It was growing dark fast, and the rain was beginning to fall in thicker globules, faster and more intense. In the mud at our feet, the footsteps weren't dissipating, each one getting worryingly clearer. We were about one kilometre from the bothy and still the ghost-like prints continued on ahead.

'Don't worry,' reassured Peter. 'If the worst comes to the worst, and we get there and it's really full, I will simply put on my thickest Glaswegian accent. We will definitely stay.'

I could have kicked myself for not following the most basic of bothy codes - taking an alternative form of accommodation in case the building was full, but now, as its metal roof emerged in the darkness, it was too late for regrets.

'Hello,' Peter called as he pushed open the door. The wood creaked loudly on the hinges as he walked inside. 'Guess what,' he said as he turned back to face me. 'Empty...' He swung open the door so I could see inside. The chairs were empty. The bunkbeds bare. We both smiled.

Bivvy bags weren't the only things we'd forgotten to bring. As we unpacked our rucksacks, in the cold evening air of the bothy, we realised that we'd also forgotten to bring any fuel.

'Not to worry - I have this,' said Peter pulling out some kindling. We burnt it fast, and tried to warm as much as possible as it went. We made hot drinks endlessly, put on every piece of gear we had and laughed at our foolishness. We ate snacks well into the night, trying to take our minds off the cold. Then, eventually, we decided to go to sleep.

Graffiti from 1967 adorns the bothy's door

Squeaking woke me up a couple of hours later. Squeaking and tiny feet, scurrying across the floor. I knew it had to be mice, and I knew they would be near the food, but, not wanting to leave the cocoon-like warmth of my sleeping bag, I turned away and went back to sleep.

The sound of the stove firing up summoned me into the morning. I pulled on my jacket and climbed out of my sleeping bag. While waiting for a coffee I looked at the floor and spotted something. Footsteps, little tiny mouse prints going across the table, then across the floor and over to the front door. At the door, where a small arch rose up creating a tiny hole, was the remains of a Babybel cheese truckle that was just too big to fit through. I walked over and flipped it over to see the wax had been nibbled away in the corner. I couldn't help but laugh.

There were visitors here before us after all...

How to get there

Classic: The easiest place to start from is Spean Bridge, where there is parking and a train station for those coming by public transport. From the station, head over the bridge to the forest side of the tracks and turn left. Follow the track all the way to Corriechoille, where it forks. Take the right fork, then follow the well-defined track all the way up into the valley, passing forestry and dismantled railway spoils as you go. Eventually you'll reach the bothy on your right.

Time: 4hrs

Cooking beneath the skylight

Alternative route

Longer, harder: If you want more of a challenge you can instead approach the bothy from the south with a start at Corrour. From the station cross the tracks at the designated point and head north, with the railway line to your right. The route eventually cuts – via a tunnel – under the tracks, then keep following it as it bears northwest down to Loch Trieg. Continue on, past Creaguaineach Lodge and onwards in a north-north-westerly direction. The ground here can get very boggy and saturated, making the path itself hard to find. But keep funnelling down the valley and eventually the bothy will be on your left.

Top tip

The stalking season and hind culls mean access to this bothy may be restricted at certain times of the year (15 August to 20 October, and 21 October to 15 February, respectively). Before going at these times call ahead (07747 12343) to make sure it's OK. Check the phone number on the MBA website in case it changes.

Lairig Leacach essentials

Maps	OS Explorer 392; OS Landranger 41
Grid ref	NN 282 736
Terrain	Rough but straightforward forestry track, becoming rockier on approach to the bothy
Water source	Immediately outside – the Allt na Lairige
Facilities	Stove (no fuel, bring your own); shovel
Building	Stone construction, tile roof
Inside	This is a compact bothy. You enter straight into the one room. There are some sleeping platforms in bunkbed style on the left that sleep eight comfortably. There's further space on the floor that would accommodate around six more people at a push. Several chairs are present, as is a large table and some shelving containing old cooking pans, etc.
Nearby hills	The Grey Corries (Stob Coire Claurigh, Stob Coire an Laoigh, Sgurr Choinnich), Stob Coire Easain

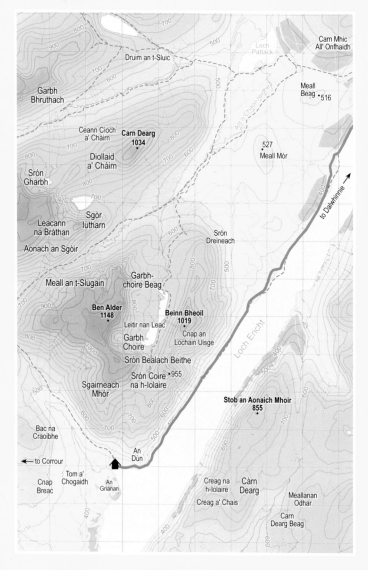

Ben Alder Cottage

*One of the most remote bothies –
and famously haunted*

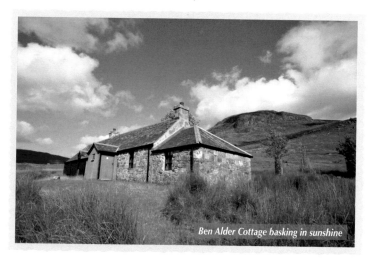

Ben Alder Cottage basking in sunshine

There are a number of reasons why Ben Alder Cottage is known in the hill-walking world. One is because it is perhaps the most remote bothy in the MBA network. No matter which direction you approach it from, you need stamina, determination and the ability to navigate in bad weather if you want to spend a night here.

But another reason is that of all the bothies, this one has the biggest reputation for being haunted. Old buildings always creak. And Hollywood and childhood fairytales have trained us to think that places that are 'wild' are also dangerous. One of the most oft-told stories, which gives us the Ben Alder ghost, is that of a deer stalker who, legend has it, hanged himself from the rafters many years ago. I've had it told to me, and search the bothy forums and you'll find stories of people hearing noises while staying there or getting bad vibes and opting to camp instead.

Like most spooky tales, this one is nothing more than the result of a badly recounted tale. It is true that a stalker and his family did live here. A man called Joseph McCook called it home for 40 years, leaving shortly after the Great War ended. But he simply left the place to retire, and eventually passed away at the age of 85 in a hospital, surrounded by his family. Nothing strange there.

Although the building gradually deteriorated due to lack of maintenance, a new stalker went to live there and did it up, but he chose not to stay long; it was too far out of the way. And so this empty cottage, as empty cottages in lonely glens have a knack of doing, became the centre of many tall tales. During the 1920s and 30s a whole host of people stayed at the building – long before it became a bothy. From dam workers (known locally as navvies) to tramps, fishermen and poachers, many people frequented the area.

And when people meet in the middle of nowhere, and have hours to while away in front of a fire, they talk. From sinister tales of a crazed woman who ate her own child to the more famous one of the aforementioned stalker hanging from the rafters, stories were perpetuated by their retelling. The latter tale was compounded by its publication in a piece by WH Murray in *Undiscovered Scotland* in the early 1950s, naming Mr McCook as the man. At that point McCook's descendants jumped on the case, pointing out that he had lived on beyond that story's end – and an apology was given in the *Scottish Mountaineering Club Journal* that same year.

Although it's thought that ghostly stories were often told to keep poachers and troublemakers away from the four walls of Ben Alder, tales continued and still seem to emerge. Although there is always a reasonable explanation for them, it seems that many of us love a good scare, no matter where we find ourselves.

Look out for...

Wildlife: Red deer are, as you would expect on an estate crowned by a multi-million-pound shooting lodge, regularly sighted on the mountains as you walk along. The dotterel use this area as an important breeding ground, and you may also see ptarmigan and grouse.

Top tip

You'll need to call the Ben Alder Estate (01540 672000) before going during stag-stalking season (15 August to 20 October) or the hind cull (21 October to 15 February).

Reflections on the long walk-in to Ben Alder Cottage from Dalwhinnie

History: Look on the OS map and you will see 'Prince Charlie's Cave' marked just to the north, uphill from the bothy. It's so called because some believe it to be the spot where Bonnie Prince Charlie (Charles Edward Stuart) hid in 1746 following his defeat at the Battle of Culloden. There is no cave here, and historians dispute that there was even a structure, but still it remains on the map.

Did you know?

Another popular way of getting to Ben Alder Cottage begins at Corrour Station. People would traditionally make this a two-day walk and combine a stay here with another MBA bothy – Culra. However, this bothy is, at the time of writing, still closed due to asbestos in the roof. It has been left open for emergency use, but the MBA recommends camping outside it only.

65

There was no getting away from it. No matter which way I turned the map, it was going to be a long walk in. I'd been to Ben Alder once before but it had been too busy for me to stay and I'd opted to camp instead. This time I was sure I could make it in time, had planned to reach it with hours to spare by darkness. Although the longer route, I thought simplicity was best so headed round to Dalwhinnie to start this epic distance.

The drive to get there took longer than I thought, the sun already hanging low when I set off. I thought that with a straight path with very little ascent it would be easy, I could get myself there in no time if I just kept my head down. Every time a cyclist went by I cursed myself for not having the foresight to bring a bicycle with me. It would have cut out so much of the relentless road.

Finally I passed the helicopter landing pad at Ben Alder Lodge. A few kilometres later the well-defined track became a rough path, often disappearing into the long grass and wild flowers. When the light began to fade purple it was time to check the map again. I realised with a sinking heart that I was still about 6km away. I was never going to make it to the cottage before it got completely dark.

It's a situation that many of us walkers have been in before, the desire to push on and reach a set goal fighting with the sensible need to stop, make camp and get warm. I've had this battle with myself plenty of times, even made the wrong decision before, stumbling into a bothy well past midnight, wishing I'd have stopped before it was too late. Now I decided to take the sensible decision.

Looking over to the beach I spied the perfect spot for a tent. As annoyed as I was to let this bothy get away from me a second time, it would wait for the next day, and I couldn't complain about my campsite.

The well-used bothy book makes a good read

With the moon reflecting in the loch, not another soul around for miles, I couldn't have asked for a better night.

The next day I ploughed on, pleased I had waited until the daylight to continue – for those last few kilometres were hard. By the time I arrived whispers of the former night's occupants lingered in the warm air, the smell of camping gas blending with the aroma of freeze-dried curries and wood smoke fused together. On the stove glowing embers still burnt, crumpled sheets on the bunkbeds still felt warm and inside the bothy book the ink was still wet.

There are some that say this place is haunted. That may be true, but no more than any other building used by many as a fleeting home. But they are nothing to fear, merely flickers of the past, reminding us why we all came here in the first place.

How to get there

Direct: By far the most straightforward route begins at Dalwhinnie. There's parking just down the road to the left of the station. From there cross the train tracks carefully and follow the long track that heads southwest, alongside the banks of Loch Ericht. You'll pass a few homesteads and then the sprawling Ben Alder Lodge, and still the path continues. Near the headland before the bothy it gets a little tricky, with rocks and overgrown scrub and a drop-off to your left, so watch your step. You soon come to a kissing gate to get through the fence. You should be able to see the bothy now. Don't be tempted to get there via the beach, but instead stick to the path on the hill, which arrives behind the bothy.

Time: 8hrs

Alternative route

Harder: For shorter distance, but a much rougher trail, you can start from Rannoch. There's a path that tracks northwest off the B846 north of Rannoch Lodge. Follow the track and it will bring you out at the southernmost end of Loch Ericht. Continue on the rougher track that can get very boggy and faint in places (especially difficult in bad weather), and you'll come to a rickety bridge at Alder Bay. Cross this, and the bothy is in front of you.

Ben Alder Cottage essentials

Maps	OS Explorer 385, 393; OS Landranger 42
Grid ref	NN 499 680
Terrain	Wide 4x4 track to start – more than suitable for a good mountain bike if you want to do a bike-hike – becoming narrow and grassy and less clear. Just before the headland is a tricky bit around the rocks, where care is needed.
Water source	Alder Burn, outside the bothy
Facilities	Stove (bring your own fuel); shovel
Building	Stone construction, tile roof
Inside	This bothy consists of three rooms. The porch features an ornate stained-glass window, then a door takes you into a small hall. On your left is the main sitting room with a large stove and a sleeping platform that takes four people; there's also enough floor space for a couple more. In front of you is a small room with bunkbeds to sleep two, and floor space for a maximum of two more. To the right is a bigger room, but there are no sleeping platforms or stove, so it's not popular. It could sleep about eight if necessary.
Nearby hills	Ben Alder, Beinn Bheoil

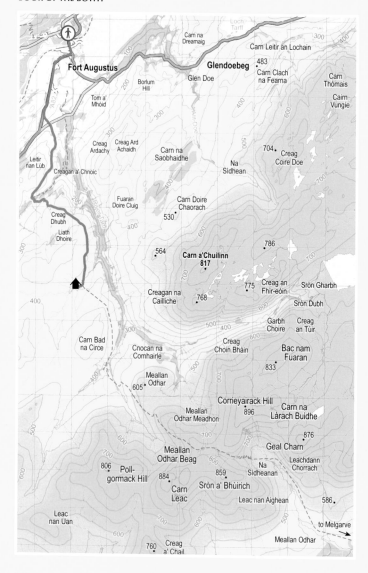

Blackburn of Corrieyairack

*A small shelter on an old military road near
the remote Monadhliath Mountains*

Blackburn of Corrieyairack bothy: small but perfectly formed

Back in the 1700s the commander-in-chief of the British military was one General Wade. While many came before and after him, his name is the one most familiar to Ordnance Survey map users. Why? Because it's he who was responsible for the construction of a vast network of roads across the Scottish Highlands in an effort to connect forts and barracks and keep control over the people. And his legacy lives on in the roads identified as 'General Wade's Military Road' on Ordnance Survey maps to this day.

Of all the roads he constructed the best preserved is the one between Fort Augustus in the north and Melgarve in the south. Rising to a high point of 770m, and running impressively up and over the hills for a total of 40km, it is the longest surviving length of General Wade's Military Road in the whole of Britain.

71

This section of road was built during his time in office, being completed in 1731. At the time, it joined together the Great Glen's fort with the soldiers' quarters over in the next valley. Significantly, it almost served as the site of one of the largest battles of the Jacobite Rising. Bonnie Prince Charlie took his men to the highest section of the road and readied for a fight. On hearing this, the commander took a squad from the south, marching up to stop the rebels. However, sensing that they were in a more vulnerable position, the British army retreated and the battle never took place.

Long after the wars the road still survived, utilised by drovers walking their cattle to market rather than by the military. After that method of moving cattle was superseded by the railway and eventually motor vehicles, the road fell into disrepair and is now only accessible to walkers and mountain bikers eager to walk an area often ignored by Munro-baggers, due to the height of the mountains.

The road is designated as an official ancient monument, and certainly worth walking for its historical credentials alone, but there is of course more to see than the track. For on the Augustus side sits a small bothy, left open for walkers to enjoy, which locals believe was originally built as a stalkers' hut.

Thankfully the only battle you may experience is one with the often boggy and mainly pathless Monadhliath hills that sit to the east of the road, but your stay at the hut should be nothing but peaceful.

Look out for...

Detour: On your way up to the bothy, consider nipping off to visit the bump of a hill called Meall a' Cholumain. Small it may be, and the 4x4 track up to its summit is not attractive, but the loch view you are rewarded with, down the Great Glen, will make you forget all its imperfections.

The open fireplace at Blackburn of Corrieyairack could probably tell a few tales!

Nearby bothy: If you opt to do the alternative route from Garva Bridge, it's worth noting that there is another bothy en route called Melgarve. It's not MBA maintained, but is a great one to link with Blackburn of Corrieyairack if you fancy a two-night adventure. It will be on your left nearly 7km after leaving Garva Bridge.

How to get there

Classic: Start in Fort Augustus, where there is limited parking. Head across the canal and shortly after take the street on your right, passing the hotel, golf course and burial ground. A footpath will cut out the road junction, and then, once you've crossed the second road (marked 'Military Road' on the map), a gate marked 'Corrieyairack Pass – Fort Augustus to Laggan' will lead you through onto the main track, known as General Wade's Military

Top tip

Outside the bothy there is a section of flat ground on which you can pitch a small tent if needed. Inside it's worth noting that the open fire on last visit didn't have a grate, which made it tricky to light – so take some firelighters with your fuel and be patient!

73

I want you to know this is completely out of character. I've never started a bothy book entry by tearing out pages of the book for a fire first, but I'm sad to report, that's exactly what I did on my first visit here, several years ago.

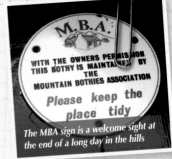

The MBA sign is a welcome sight at the end of a long day in the hills

I had found the building by mistake, while I was on my way to check out the often-neglected Corbetts that line the famous Military Road. I had intended to stay in the town of Fort Augustus or call a friend to be picked up and stay with them in Inverness. But then I spotted it. The green roof, the unmistakable round sign on the door that us walkers can't help but smile at when we see it; knowing that, for tonight, we will be able to escape from the elements and enjoy a basic manner of home comforts.

Going inside everything seemed to be in order, some candles above the fireplace, some books that had been kindly left to help pass the time, and, of course, the obligatory bothy book.

I picked it up, as I always do to read the stories of those who had been here before me. At first were the usual messages, the notes of thanks to the wonderful MBA, the tales of adventure, the scribble of delight from a walker who had happened upon this place for the first time. Then I came to it.

Not memories of a hillwalker's day. Not recounted tales of the great outdoors. No, instead were 10 pages of offensive scrawl, evidently penned by some alcohol-fuelled former resident, a delusional polemic against the world and even themselves, full of expletives and racial slurs. It made me sad. And before I knew what I was doing I had torn them out – I didn't want them to sully other visitors' views of the people who come to these places.

As I watched the pages become consumed in the flames, feeling angry and a little guilty – had I behaved just as badly as they did, destroying something that wasn't mine to destroy? – I continued to flick through the book. In it (and I counted) were over 100 more entries professing love and respect for this shelter. I'm not going to lie: sometimes the wrong kind of person finds a bothy and tries to destroy all the goodness that goes into them for everyone else. But it's up to us to not let them. Finding mess and abuse will only destroy this great community if we allow it to. For every one person like this, there are thousands who only make the bothies better places and it's up to every one of us to be one of those visitors.

Road. Follow this uphill as it passes farmers' fields and gradually climbs to cross a river. A gate leads onto open hillside as the path first zigzags and then swings round the lower flanks. Follow it until you come to another stream, called Black Burn. The bothy is on your right, a short walk from the path. Time: 3hrs

Alternative route

Longer: Blackburn of Corrieyairack sits on the outskirts of the remote and rarely visited Monadhliath Mountains, so the intrepid may want to start further northeast to begin with an ascent of those little-known tops. However, if it's just about adding distance you can take General Wade's Military Road from the other side of the hills, starting by parking at Garva Bridge (some spaces on the left before the actual bridge), near Laggan. Simply follow the road as it cleaves its way steadily uphill. At the highest point of the pass, if feeling energetic still, you can add in a climb up to Corrieyairack Hill (a Corbett for any interested list-tickers) before descending down the track for about 6km, where the bothy will be just off the track to your left.

Blackburn of Corrieyairack essentials

Maps	OS Explorer 401; OS Landranger 34
Grid ref	NH 382 029
Terrain	Minor roads to start (take care – fast-moving cars), then onto a wide but rough track to the bothy. Recent works have created a multitude of extra tracks – so take a map and the bothy grid reference to stay on the right path.
Water source	Black Burn, just outside the bothy
Facilities	Open fire (bring your own fuel); shovel
Building	Stone construction, tin roof
Inside	An internal porch is handy for leaving wet clothes. From there, go through the door to enter the only room. It's not massive, but would comfortably sleep around eight. There are a few chairs and a table but no sleeping platforms.
Nearby hills	Corrieyairack Hill

Ruigh Aiteachain

A bothy sitting in the landscape that inspired a Victorian artist

Heather-bashing en route to Ruigh Aiteachain

Some phrases can be overused when it comes to the outdoors and wild land-scapes. 'Pretty as a picture' is one. But when we're talking the East Highlands, and more specifically the trees and hills around the bothy of Ruigh Aiteachain, this may be the one case where this cliché can be used with authority.

This particular bothy has another soubriquet – Landseer's bothy. Rumour has it that this was the place from which Sir Edwin Landseer, renowned Victorian artist, studied native red deer stags – one of them becoming the model for his most famous painting, 'Monarch of the Glen'.

Painted in 1851, the picture was commissioned to form part of a set of three for the Palace of Westminster. It proved the most popular of the trio, and the often-reproduced picture became the chocolate-box image of Scotland, as well as being used in advertising and hanging in people's homes across the country.

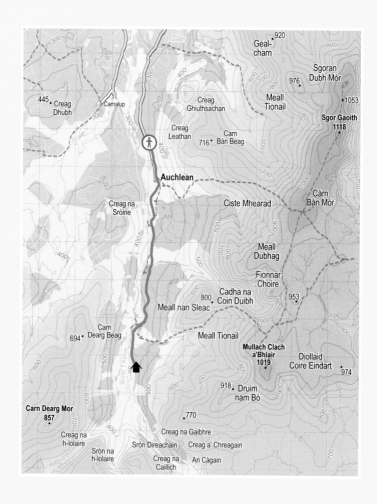

On arrival at Ruigh Aiteachain, standing amid the tall trees of the glen, with the hills rising on either side and, in autumn, the sounds of the deer in rut, you'd be forgiven for thinking this bothy was Landseer's. However – it wasn't. The place where he did his preparatory sketches for his seminal work, and where he painted an early fresco above the fireplace, wasn't actually the bothy at all – it was the adjacent building.

Sadly this house, which was at the time owned by the Duchess of Bedford, no longer stands. Instead, all that remains is the chimneystack, rising like a monument among the grass a few metres from the bothy. The legendary frescos have turned to dust in the elements – reduced to pigment by the wind. Do a search through the history books and you'll find reference to them existing as recently as the 1960s, with one describing the current bothy as the chapel for the former house. Exposed brick is all you'll spy now, standing out as it does amid the pines and juniper that rise alongside it.

Go to Ruigh Aiteachain and you'll soon forget about any quest to find the paintings, for you are standing in the living painting itself, looking at the trees and hills as they were back when Landseer himself stood here and sketched on his parchment. The painting might be famous, but really it's the landscape that is legendary.

All that remains of the Duchess of Bedford's house, near the bothy, is the chimneystack

Ruigh Aiteachain's ornate door must be one of the fanciest in the MBA network

No one but a mouse was home when I arrived at Ruigh Aiteachain in the dreich of an autumn afternoon. It audibly squealed as I opened the door and disappeared under the bunkbeds to the left.

Records that pointed to this place as a chapel ringing in my mind, I couldn't help but think they might well have been right, given the drop in temperature in this first room, the same chill you get entering a church even on a hot summer's day.

Adding further credibility to the theory is the door that separates the first room from the second. Made of two tones of wood, with rounded decoration and a glass knob in the middle, it's far too elaborate to be dismissed as just another bothy door.

I knew I should have stayed in the first room as it was one clearly made for walkers, but, I reasoned as I made my bed in the second one – the one with the stove to heat up the space – the mouse had clearly already claimed it.

The night never brought with it a clear sky, and the morning never started as I'd dreamed and hoped it might – with a deer grazing on the grass by the front door, so that I might visually recreate the Landseer picture that so famed this area. But I didn't complain; I meandered back along the water wondering just what the bunkers on either side of the path were used for many years ago.

Then – I spotted it. Deer! So red it looked pretend, and standing so still I didn't dare move. It was only after a full minute passed and it really hadn't flinched even a little that I decided to get a closer look. As I moved through the trees I began to feel foolish. This wasn't a real deer at all – it was just a decoy, a manmade outline of a doe, meant to draw out the stag in search of a mate.

I left, not failing to see the irony. Here I had come, in search of the place where an artist had mesmerised the nation with an image of a deer, and here I was, a full 164 years later not far from that same spot, now captivated by a picture of a deer.

Collecting wood for the fire

Look out for...

Wildlife: Both roe and red deer can be spotted on this walk, as well as red squirrel. During the day keep your eyes peeled for osprey, and at night listen closely as you may be able to hear one of the resident tawny owls.

Trees: On this estate, currently forested with Caledonian pine, efforts are being made to restore the native mountain woodlands with species like holly, oak and aspen.

Did you know?

There used to be another route in along the west bank of the river, but in September 2009 floods swept away the Carnachuin Bridge, so now the route on the east bank described here is the easiest and quickest way in. Do not try to cross the river as it's deep and fast flowing.

At the moment native woodland accounts for around 4700 acres here, and the estate aims to double this over the next few years.

How to get there

Easiest: Park at the public car park just north of Auchlean. Turn left as you leave it and head south on the road. At the buildings follow the signposted route to bring you to a gate and out into Glen Feshie. Follow the path all the way along the water's edge until you reach the bothy.

Time: 3hrs

Alternative route

Hard: If you want to add in some ascent, start at the same car park and, once you reach the buildings down the road, turn left and head uphill on the path to hit the summit of Carn Ban Mor. If you are after Munros you can first backtrack to tick off Sgor Gaoith, then continue south along the ridge for several kilometres until you reach Mullach

Inside the second room

Top tip

There's lots of flat ground outside the bothy suitable for pitching tents if needed. The chimney remains nearby are unstable, so don't pitch there.

Clach a' Bhlair. After that pick up the track to the north of the summit and follow it downhill alongside the Allt Coire Chaoil. Once you reach the path near the stream turn left to reach the bothy.

Ruigh Aiteachain essentials

Maps	OS Explorer 403; OS Landranger 35
Grid ref	NN 847 927
Terrain	Tarmac track gives way to a boggy section, then a clear forestry track. Several river crossings are needed; this can be tricky if river is in spate, and care is needed.
Water source	Water pipe outside the bothy on hillside before the toilet – water comes from small stream on the mountain. If there is a problem with that, head east from the bothy down to the river.
Facilities	Stove; saw and axe to be used to cut the large blocks of wood that are regularly left by the estate (do not cut live trees); shovel; outside septic toilet
Building	Stone construction, metal roof
Inside	There are two rooms in this bothy. You come into a large room with several bunkbeds to the left of the door to sleep six people. There's a fireplace, but this is not the place to light a fire. Go through the elaborately decorative door into the second room. Inside are sleeping platforms big enough to sleep three (there's floor space too), a large stove (use this for fire), some chairs and a table beneath the window into the glen.
Nearby hills	Meall Dubhag, Mullach Clach a' Bhlair, Sgor Gaoith, Sgoran Dubh Mor

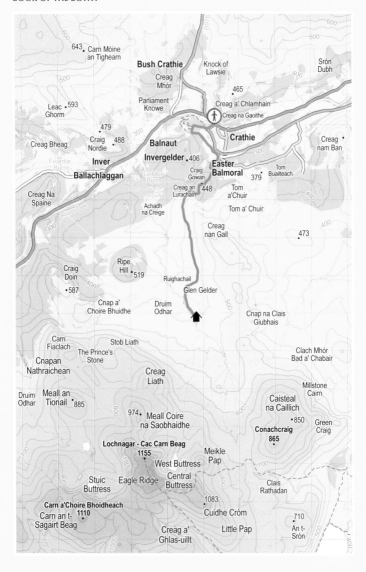

Gelder Shiel Stable

A former stable, near Lochnagar,
on the royal Balmoral Estate

Gelder Shiel Stable – a royally appointed bothy

Once upon a time, more than 30 years ago, a prince told a story about an old man who lived in a cave. Desperate to seek solitude, silence and – we understand – a hot bath, he seeks out a mountain called Lochnagar. Dragging his tub with him, he settles in a cave he finds on its flanks, and claims it as his own.

Piping up his prized possession to a spring he fills it and jumps inside, but to his dismay finds the water to be freezing cold. Frustrated, he sets about finding a way to warm it up – letting out the plug before he does. Unbeknown to him, the water drains into the underground home of Scottish pixies known as the Gorm. What follows is encounters with magical queens and kings, lessons learned from the little people, and the discovery of ways in which not only can the man heat his bathwater – but also help others in return.

The prince who told the story is none other than HRH Prince Charles – it was a fairytale he penned called *The Old Man of Lochnagar*, published in book form back in 1980, and even animated on TV and turned into a ballet performance in 2007. He chose Lochnagar – the mountain in Scotland – as it sits within the royal estate of Balmoral,

Did you know?

Balmoral has its own distillery near the start of this walk. Seeing as it's a bothy tradition to share a dram of whisky at night, why not head there first to grab a crafty bottle of malt to warm you up?

where he and his family spent many a summer holiday, and still come to stay at certain times of the year.

He's not the only one for whom the mountain inspired a creative work. Lord Byron was also sufficiently stirred by it to pen a poem call 'Dark Lochnagar', which spoke wistfully of being ruined by his relationship with the peak: 'England thy beauties are tame and domestic, to one who has roved on the mountains afar…'

If both those associations with the mountain aren't enough to pique your interest for a visit to this landscape, then you may like to know that deep inside the estate, neighbouring the fabled mountain, is a bothy for non-royals to use. Once a stable to the homestead that sits across the path from it, it's the perfect way to linger in the princely hillsides that exist here by royal appointment. Find it hard to believe that it isn't just a fairytale? There's only one way to find out…

Look out for...

Birds: The area around Lochnagar, under which this bothy sits, is the breeding ground for the dotterel, which like to nest in high mountains. Keep a lookout for their distinctive white and brown heads. It's due to their presence that the area is designated a Special Protection Area.

History: The impressive pyramid of Prince Albert's Cairn is a must-see. Built at the request of Queen Victoria to commemorate her husband, it was dedicated to 'the great and good Prince Consort by his broken-hearted widow' in August 1862. Admire it, then turn north to take in the incredible Balmoral Castle view and the surrounding hills that seem to stretch for miles.

Illustrating your bothy book entry is a great way to share your adventures

'Sorry – no right to roam today,' the policeman looked at me sternly as he stood in front of the gate, clearly blocking my way. Despite this being Scotland, with their liberal stance on a walker's right to trek around the country, I still found it hard to believe I could wander freely around the Queen's famous Balmoral Estate anyway, so wasn't surprised by his assertion.

Resigned I turned away – I needed to find another route in. Following the road I eventually saw my moment, a gap in the wall leading to a cluster of houses, where many of the families who work in the estate reside. I followed the tarmac first, then detoured into the woods, heading uphill, concealing me from view. Soon I reached a highpoint from where I could look over the whole estate, sprawling as it did over acre after acre, all the property of the royal family.

I made my way down across the network of scrub, made intricate with patterns of 4×4 tracks. Cutting a path for Lochnagar I left the main route, picked up the path by the river and followed it all the way to a pretty little lodge. Here the windows and doors were well boarded up, offering no glimpse of what lay inside. Being a mere walker I knew my place and headed to what I knew to be a bothy – the former stables for this smallholding.

As this was pre-refurb in May 2015 when a stove and insulation was added, inside, despite the warm sunlight, the temperature notably dropped. I shivered. Pulling out my insulated jacket I wandered among the bunkbeds which looked narrow and made for utility rather than comfort – very British forces standard issue. I headed back outside, bothy book in hand and began reading the entries.

Gelder Shiel Stable looks up to Lochnagar

From walkers who had stumbled upon the place by mistake after retreating from the icy wind of Lochnagar's summit to the Duke of Edinburgh Award group on their expedition who weren't allowed to sleep inside, but took shelter here nonetheless, many others had experienced the cold hall that is Gelder Shiel Stable before me.

Despite the draughty building, the resident mice and the endless hot drinks I had to make in an attempt to warm up, I spent a happy night in the depths of the Balmoral estate. By moonlight I wandered across the footpath and tried to peer into the nearby cirque of the mountain that rises crown-like from the moorland below. It appeared only as a dark outline, but here I stayed a little.

As I retreated to the bothy, the cold of a nightime air seeming to accompany me inside, I jumped into my sleeping bag and began to will myself to sleep. I felt my eyelids grow heavy, the warmth of the insulation snuggling me like an old friend. Let the Queen keep her fort-like lodge next door. For I wouldn't trade places. Here in my own castle, in this stately landscape, I felt very much like royalty.

Approaching Prince Albert's Cairn

How to get there

Classic: From the car park at Crathie turn left to go down the road towards Balmoral Castle. If conditions allow (that is, if the Queen is not home) go through the gate and follow the road round, then turn left. Continue on the road round to Easter Balmoral and turn right, then shortly after the last house you'll see a faint path leading up to a gate in the fence on your left. Go through it into the woodland. Track steadily uphill first to Princess Beatrice's Cairn and then, after a further climb, up to the pyramid that makes up Prince Albert's Cairn. From there follow the path as it descends and soon joins the main 4x4 track. Continue on it out from the cover of trees until the path forks – go right. At the next fork go left, and shortly after you'll reach the bothy.

Time: 2½hrs

Top tip

The estate prefers people not to camp outside the bothy, so unless it's full refrain from doing so. There are also restrictions on access during royal visits – in particular around the shooting season (1 September to 20 October) – so call first to check the situation during this time (01339 742534).

Alternative route

More ascent: To add some interest before you go to sleep, take the same route in but go past the bothy to take the track up to Lochnagar. Whether you stick to a visit to the water of the same name, or opt to pack in the metres with a visit to the very top, one thing's for sure – you'll deserve your shelter by the time you reach the bothy again.

Gelder Shiel Stable essentials

Maps	OS Explorer 388; OS Landranger 44
Grid ref	NO 257 900
Terrain	Mix of forestry paths and 4x4 tracks
Water source	Just next to the building opposite the bothy – Gelder Burn
Facilities	Stove – bring your own fuel; septic toilet; bucket; tap
Building	Stone construction, tiled roof
Inside	Going through the door you enter into the only room. In it you'll find a large table, lots of chairs and four bunkbeds that sleep eight people. There is plenty of floor space too. Around the back is a septic toilet, a bucket and a tap. The water is not drinkable, but should be used to fill the buckets so you can 'flush' the toilet. Don't put anything other than human waste down the toilet – there are clear instructions for use.
Nearby hills	Lochnagar

Looking south to Lochnagar from the walk-in to the bothy

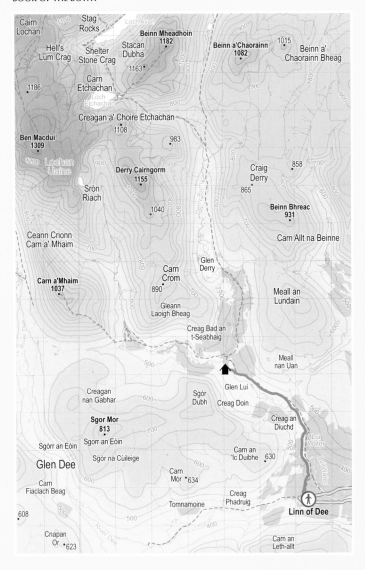

Bob Scott's

The hang-out of many a prolific Scottish climber

Bob Scott's offers not just shelter but an outside toilet too – luxury!

'Unlucky' is not the kind of descriptor you'd normally associate with a building – especially a bothy. But having been destroyed by fire – twice – and rebuilt on two separate occasions, if any bothy did deserve the adjective it's this one.

Its history may be problematic, but the man for whom this bothy was named was anything but. While a gamekeeper at Derry Lodge in 1947, Bob Scott moved into the cottage. Before his day it had been kept open by his predecessor, and walkers and climbers were allowed to stay in it. Things could have changed when Bob moved in, but they didn't – he still let people stay.

And not just any people – legendary Scottish climbers such as Tom Patey and Mac Smith were among his friends and regularly stopped in for shelter while pioneering routes and writing guidebooks. For many who walked routes from the Linn of Dee in the 1950s and 60s, a stay at Bob Scott's was

Enjoying good company in Bob Scott's – a friendly and often busy place to sleep

something of a tradition. However, he retired in 1973 and many presumed the worst would happen – the hut would be locked up and decades of hill-walking ritual would be lost, especially when the new keeper was less interested in looking after the bothy.

Fearing the estate would seize the opportunity to close the bothy to outdoor aficionados, a group was formed called Winers, Diners and Climbers, who set to work on regular maintenance. Disaster first struck in 1986, when the fabled bothy was burnt down.

Thankfully, spurred on by a love for this little shelter, a new group that still meet today, Friends of Bob Scott's, came into being that same year and somehow persuaded the landowners that the bothy could rise from the ashes. It worked, and they were given permission to rebuild it on the proviso that the new building should have a toilet and be moved to the location where it sits today. Fundraising provided the cash, and for the next 18 years – until 2003 – the new Bob Scott's was again much loved by walkers and climbers. Then, on one fateful day in December, fire destroyed it again.

Proving that you can't keep a good thing down, the Friends of Bob Scott's completed yet another rebuild – thanks to funds donated by the family and friends of a man called James Leneghan, who had sadly died in a climbing accident on Mont Blanc. They finished the work, and the bothy reopened in 2005.

Did you know?

In 2014 Bob Scott's was nearly destroyed for a third time. On 11 August the area experienced a bout of heavy rain. The river rose fast and the current was so strong that it actually ripped away Derry Burn bridge and threatened to wash away anything else in its path. Water flooded the bothy and was so fast flowing, and the current so strong, that three people who were inside had to be rescued by Braemar Mountain Rescue team. All thankfully survived.

This version 3 is the one you'll stay in today, still kindly left open by the estate so that people can use it now as they have done for the past 70 years.

Although Bob Scott's is the one bothy in this book not maintained by the MBA, it has been included because many of the MBA bothies in the Cairngorms are so well looked after and continue to remain open only because members of Friends of Bob Scott's regularly maintain these shelters for the MBA. To them, Bob Scott and the estate, which arguably initially pioneered the bothy, we salute you.

Look out for...

Wildlife: Otters, foxes, mountain hare and red squirrel can all be seen here. Golden eagle can sometimes be spotted, as well as oystercatchers, crossbill and curlew. Butterflies also abound – in spring look out for the Majestic peacock, Small tortoiseshell and the Small green hairstreak.

History: It's not just the old Victorian shooting lodge of Derry that lies unused along this track. Look carefully at the hills and landscape either side of the path on the way in and you'll notice the remains of several old settlements and townships in the glen. These date back several hundred years. People used to farm and live here until the 1700s, when they were evicted, resettled, then finally cleared for good.

How to get there

Classic: Start at the Linn of Dee pay-and-display car park and head out on the northerly track, following it down to the bridge that crosses Lui Water. Once on the other side turn left and follow the track up towards Derry Lodge. As the path rises uphill, a fenced-in copse of trees appears to your right. Look out for a faint track in the grass to your left. Follow it downhill to where the tall trees are, and you'll come to your bothy.

Time: 2hrs

A lot can change in a bothy from day to night. The first time I saw Bob Scott's was late in the morning. I was en route to Ben Macdui and stopped for an early lunch of macaroni pie and a sneaky bar of chocolate. Then it was quiet, no one else was around at all, the building was cool and silent.

My next visit happened in an early summer evening on the way over from Cairn Gorm. It had been a long day, with a mix of wind, rain and hail followed by a sudden blast of sunshine - so warm that by the time I arrived at the bothy I had started to get sunburnt.

There were already people outside and mountain bikes - lots of them. Inside I met them - a mix of cyclists who were resting before attempting to bike Ben Macdui the next morning,

Mountain-bikers make use of Bob Scott's

two brothers who had been cycling their way across the Cairngorms and, a little later, a group of three friends - none of them British, but had been living in Scotland for a while and had wanted to come and experience their first bothy.

It was that night that I first experienced a truly packed bothy. It was something I always dreaded, thought it would ruin the experience, but actually it added to it. From talking politics, to discussing trips both past and present, bike routes, walking trails, taking photographs in the dark and exactly which camping stove is best, we conversed until late into the night, with more arrivals pitching up tents just outside.

We all arrived by different means, had taken different journeys to get here, had different stories to tell and tomorrow would leave on different paths. But for that night, at that moment we were all united.

Alternative route

Hard: If you're feeling up for a challenge, try heading in to the bothy from the other side of the mountain range. Start at the ski centre below Cairn Gorm, take the path up Fiacaill a' Choire Chais then down Corie Raibeirt to Loch A'an. Take the path around the west end of the loch, past the Shelter Stone, then up and over the col into Loch Etchachan. Pass the Hutchison Memorial Hut (described in the next entry in this book) and take the path down and alongside the east bank of Derry Burn until you get to Derry Lodge. Continue past this, and the faint path to Bob Scott's hut will be on your right.

Top tip

There's lots of flat land outside the bothy that's perfect for a tent. If that area is busy (this place is very popular with mountain bikers) then head further along the river – there's many a good spot both before and after Derry Lodge.

Bob Scott's essentials

Maps	OS Explorer 403, 404; OS Landranger 43
Grid ref	NO 042 930
Terrain	Clear, well-defined rocky track, last section over grass – can be muddy/slippy after rain
Water source	Just outside – the Lui Water
Facilities	Large stove (bring your own fuel); saw; shovel; septic toilet in outhouse
Building	Timber and stone construction, corrugated iron roof
Inside	You enter into a small hallway, where there are hooks to hang coats. Go through the door and you will enter the one and only room. Here there is a raised sleeping platform that sleeps six at a push. The floor directly beneath can do the same. There's a large stove, lots of chairs and a worktop area in the corner for preparing food. Outside is an outhouse with septic toilet – make sure you don't put anything other than paper down it (such as wet wipes) as this stops it working. Flush using stream water and bucket provided.
Nearby hills	Carn Crom, Derry Cairngorm, Carn a'Mhaim

Hutchison Memorial Hut

A tiny refuge perched high in Scotland's Cairngorms

The Hutchison Memorial Hut is dedicated to Dr Arthur Gilbertson Hutchison, a geologist and outdoor enthusiast who died in 1949

High in the Cairngorm mountains, beyond the sheer cliffs of Coire Etchachan amid the boulders and beneath the slopes of Ben Macdui, sits a small hut, seemingly growing out of the side of the mountains.

Built in 1954, the Hutchison Memorial Hut was created by friends of Dr Arthur Gilbertson Hutchison, a geologist and outdoor lover, who sadly died in a climbing accident in Pembrokeshire, Wales, in 1949. Clubbing together, they sought and were granted permission from the landowners and set about making a refuge for walkers and climbers in the heart of these mountains.

Sitting at a height of around 750m, the little bothy is positioned alongside one of the main paths up Ben Macdui. It's made using local stone and was constructed by WJ Brown builders of Aberdeen. In a fittingly poignant connecting of bothy history, legend has it that many of the climbing clubs in

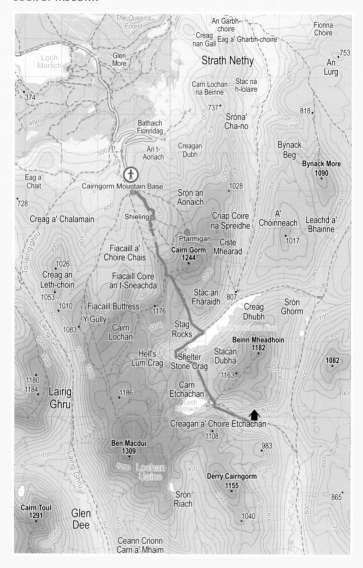

The bothy was refurbished in 2012

the area, as well one man called Bob Scott (see previous entry in this book), helped carry supplies up to the site where the bothy was built. Three weeks later the memorial was completed and became almost an obligatory stop for hillwalkers heading into these hills.

Of course, the original structure is not the more luxurious shelter you see now. When first finished it had an earth – rather than today's wooden – floor inside. Before the MBA took the bothy on after the 1980s the Etchachan Club regularly maintained it, taking out rubbish and doing any necessary DIY.

Once having a reputation for being freezing and damp – seemingly no matter what the weather outside was – courtesy of a major renovation in 2012, with internal lining and new doors added, it is now a warm shelter, boasting a bench, a large stove and even an internal porch for hanging wet gear up.

Look out for...

Wildlife: Impressively, the Cairngorms are home to 25 per cent of Britain's threatened species, including red squirrels, pine martens, capercaillie, ospreys and more. Consider taking your binoculars, as you never know what you might see.

Hail. Hard and relentless. Being blown so fast in the wind that it was difficult to even open my eyes. In fact I nearly called the whole thing off, nearly turned around and headed back for a night in the nearby Shelter Stone, where I had stayed before. It would be cold, but it would at least be dry, and I would be able to see in front of me.

But I carried on. Up the hillside, following the water, sure that any moment now I must surely top out and spy the grey tin roof of the bothy below. Until then it was a hard slog, and every footstep seemed to merely make me bob up and down rather than move onwards with any purpose.

Finally, though, I could see it. Even from here, in this gloomy mist, I could make out a tent unmistakeably pitched outside it. It was full. Feeling beaten I resigned myself to a camp further down the valley, but seeing as I had come this far it made sense to pop inside.

As I entered the porch I could hear a conversation – two men chatting away. I tried to open the door, but it was stiff. I heaved with all my might and still it wouldn't budge. On my third attempt one of them pulled it on their side and I spilled into the bothy, having to stop myself from flying across the room.

'Hell of a storm, isn't it?' one asked.

'Glad I made it here before it came in,' said the other.

I realised I was dripping on the floor, my waterproofs drenched; so I backtracked into the porch to remove them, then went back inside.

One had been out here for a couple of days, ticking off peaks using the hut as a base. He'd been cramped in here with five other people the previous night, and this time hoped he might get it to himself. Hearing this story, the other man who had visited all the way from New Zealand, had decided to sleep outside to get a little more privacy too.

In the half hour I stayed to chat and dry off two more people came to see the bothy and decide if they could stay. Seemingly the hut attracts many people no matter what the weather. I knew I could spend the night here, but decided I would go back into the rain and find my own refuge away from the potential crowds.

As I left and headed downhill I looked back to try to spy the bothy one last time, but it was already gone - lost among the boulders. I thought about those still warm at the bothy. Would they be able to see me still? I continued onwards as the mountains, like me, were enveloped by the clouds.

Writing in the visitors' book

Did you know?

The mountain of Ben Macdui (reached from this bothy), the second highest mountain in Britain, is home to sightings of the Greyman of Macdui (aka Am Fear Liath Mòr). Similar to the Sasquatch or Yeti, this human-like figure was even seen by respected climber and scientist J Norman Collie in the 1920s, who swore that a grey figure was walking behind him when he was alone on the summit. Many believe it to be a figment of an exhausted imagination or a Brocken spectre, but for now the mystery continues…

Shelter Stone: En route to the bothy you will pass a place marked on the OS map as the Shelter Stone. This is a giant granite boulder that fell thousands of years ago and is now used as an overnight shelter by adventurous walkers. You'll spot it by the mini-cairn often placed on the top, or notice it because it's by far the largest all the rocks that sit on the boulder field beneath Carn Etchachan. It's a worthwhile bothy alternative – but you'll definitely need a bivvy bag.

Top tip

This bothy fills up very quickly, but there is plenty of space around it flat enough for a tent. You might want to consider the Shelter Stone (see 'Look out for…') as an alternative, or Bob's Scott's bothy, about a 9km walk down the valley (see previous entry).

How to get there

Classic: Starting at the Ski Centre car park, take the track that goes parallel to, then under, the funicular railway. On the zig-zags look for the path that leads up to point 1141, marked by a large cairn. From there follow the faint path down to Coire Raibeirt and to the shores of Loch A'an. Turn right and follow the path along its western end then up and alongside the Allt nan Stacan Dubha. After fording the stream at Little Loch Etchachan make sure you pick up the path heading southeast downhill above the river. A couple of kilometres later the bothy appears on your right.

Time: 5hrs

Alternative route

Challenging: For a walk-in with more height after point 1141, marked by a cairn, continue southwest along the ridge, hitting Stob Coire an t'Sneachda and Cairn Lochan, then breaking south to descend and then re-ascend the 1309m summit of Ben Macdui. From there head down on its eastern path above Loch Etchachan, and then make a right at Little Loch Etchachan to descend along the burn to the bothy.

Hutchison Memorial Hut essentials

Maps	OS Explorer 403; OS Landranger 36
Grid ref	NO 023 998
Terrain	Wide track to start becomes fainter and almost indistinguishable after point 1141. Confusion certainly possible, especially in bad weather. More defined, but very steep and rocky path down to Loch A'an; very rough and rocky from then on, where again navigation can be tricky.
Water source	The nearby burn is fine for collecting water
Facilities	Stove (no fuel – take your own); shovel
Building	Stone and wood construction, metal roof
Inside	You'll enter into a tiny porch-like area, meant for leaving wet boots and jackets. The door on your left takes you into the one tiny room with a stove and bench. This will sleep two in luxury, three comfortably, and four or five at a push.
Nearby hills	Derry Cairngorm, Ben Macdui, Cairn Gorm

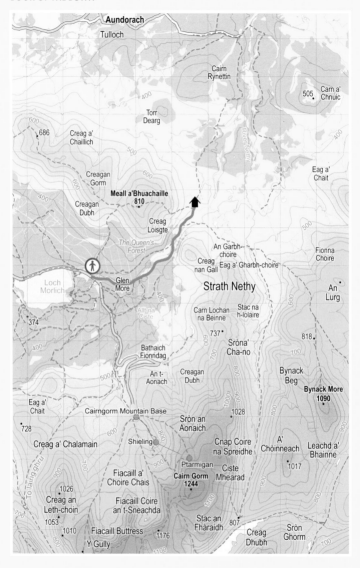

Ryvoan

A cosy hide within an RSPB bird-haven

Ryvoan bothy, once a farm, was taken over by the MBA in 1972

For those of us not lucky enough to live within easy access of the hills, the journey we take to reach them whenever we get the chance is a special one. Watching the highrises of the city give way to the naturally carved pyramids of mountains and the scooped and weathered bumps of endless highlands makes all the stresses of urban life melt away.

One person who knew all too well the sensation of leaving the city for the restorative nature of the hills was a woman called AM Lawrence. She penned a poem 'I Leave Tonight from Euston' in which she describes leaving the capital 'by the seven-thirty train, and from Perth in the early morning I shall see the hills again'. Although the poem was written in the 1950s when she lived in Cumbria, she spent a large part of her formative years at Nethy Bridge in Scotland, and the Cairngorms in particular held a special place in her heart.

View from the window at Ryvoan

Near the end of the poem she writes: 'And again in the dusk of evening I shall find once more alone, The dark water of the Green Loch, and the pass beyond Ryvoan.' You'll spot this phrase on your way into this small bothy, etched onto the bench that sits next to the Green Loch. But to read the poem in full you'll have to get to the bothy itself, where, by tradition, a copy is kept on the back of the door.

Once a farm, Ryvoan was abandoned by its occupants in 1877. It was in danger of being left to ruin, like many other farm buildings before it, until – according to locals – the Creagh Dhu Climbing Club rescued it from collapse and the MBA took over maintenance in 1967.

Sitting as it does in an RSPB reserve it's frequented by many a twitcher who watches the skies, as well as by walkers and climbers who come to explore the hills and trails so close to the legendary mountain training centre of Glenmore Lodge.

The bothy sits on the route of an old thieves' road that runs between Glen More and Nethy Bridge. Back then, those rustling cattle would make their journey below this building to escape capture. It's a great place to stop if you want to follow in their footsteps on this historic track.

So whether you're coming from Euston, or somewhere nearby, you can take comfort in the knowledge that the hidden hills and landscape that surround this bothy have been offering shelter and inspiration for hundreds of years before your visit and, with a bit of luck, will do for many years to come…

Look out for...

Wildlife: Although it's unlikely you will see any here, the Cairngorms are home to the only population of reindeer in the UK, which were reintroduced into the national park in the 1950s.

Birds: Make sure you bring your binoculars! Ryvoan belongs to the RSPB and sits in the middle of their reserve. Here they have regenerated the forest, growing pines, and the wood and moorland is home to a range of birds including an osprey pair, as well as the endangered capercaillie and Scottish crossbill.

Did you know?

The name of the loch passed en route to the bothy, An Lochan Uaine, means 'the green lochan' – so called because of its turquoise waters. Legend has it that this colour is due to the local fairies who wash their clothes here.

It felt like a dance – a two-step routine, where he was always just a little ahead of me, always looking over his shoulder to try to figure out my next move. Such was my walk in that day to Ryvoan. It's certainly not a unique dance. If ever you find yourself making your way in to a popular bothy, you may often find yourself engaged in a similar routine – every hillwalker wondering if the person they see ahead or behind them has the same shelter as their goal. Watching each other's foot placement, guessing their next move.

We continued our two-step tango for at least a kilometre. Every time he slowed, I slowed, when he quickened his pace, so did I. Until, finally, I grew tired of this ballet and overtook him.

The need for fancy footwork didn't end there. Heavy rain the days before my arrival by sleeper train had caused the river to burst its banks, transforming the path into a gushing stream. Leaping from stone to stone I made my way along, pirouetting between obstacles until, at length, I reached some higher ground and the bothy came into view on my left.

I went inside to find this – one of the most popular bothies in the Cairngorms – early evening on a Saturday night, in the summer, completely empty. I quickly grabbed a spot on the sleeping platform, began unpacking my bag and set about building a fire with the coal I'd brought in, eager to dry things out before the crowds came.

Two hours later, reading the bothy book, and no one else had arrived. I waited expectantly, any minute convinced that my silent reverie would be interrupted, but even by midnight I was still alone.

When I woke the next day, stirred by the brightening dawn glowing through the one window, the bothy was, remarkably, still absent of any other soul. It was as though I had the whole world entirely to myself.

I left that morning and mused how I never did find out where the man from last night was going. It was almost as though he had disappeared. For now, as I made my way back from the hills, the river still gushing down the trail, I began my dance once more, but this time I was all by myself.

Ryvoan bothy is situated in an RSPB reserve near Glenmore Lodge

Ryvoan bothy sits on high ground on the route of an old thieves' road

How to get there

Classic: The quickest route is also the simplest. Starting from the parking near the turn-off for Glenmore Lodge, follow the clear tarmac track to the outdoor centre. Pass the buildings, don't turn off and you'll come to a gate. Go through this and follow the grit path as it weaves first between the trees and then above An Lochan Uaine – a perfect spot to stop and contemplate the majesty of the Cairngorms. Where the path forks take the route to the left, following it as it steadily ascends. Soon the bothy will appear on your left.

Time: 1½hrs

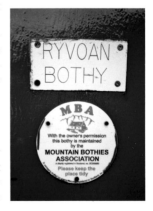

Alternative route

Added ascent: There are lots of much longer routes you can plot to get to Ryvoan, but this short one packs in a bit more of a high point. Start from the same point as the main

112

route, but rather than heading to Glenmore Lodge from the road, take the track that heads uphill through the forest. Soon you'll emerge onto the hillside. Continue on and you'll hit the summit of Meall a' Bhuachaille, then descend towards the bothy on the walkers' path down the eastern slopes – you'll see the bothy about a kilometre before you reach it, but it will make your arrival feel that much more deserved.

Top tip

There's plenty of flat space outside the bothy (where the rest of this old homestead once sat), so if the bothy is full – and it often is – then you have another option.

Ryvoan essentials

Maps	OS Explorer 403; OS Landranger 36
Grid ref	NJ 006 115
Terrain	Rough/bouldery but straightforward path right up to the bothy – last section can become particularly boggy/flooded after heavy rain
Water source	The stream outside is regularly reported as being unsafe to drink from, even after boiling – either collect water on your way up or walk back to the stream near the fork in the path.
Facilities	Stove (bring your own fuel); spade
Building	Stone construction, metal roof
Inside	This bothy is made up of just one room. You enter into a lean-to porch where you should find the bothy shovel. In an emergency the porch could sleep a couple of people, but they would probably get wet! Through the main door you enter the bothy. There's a wooden-constructed sleeping platform that takes four comfortably. The floor space would take a few more (any more than four would be a squeeze in this small bothy). There are a few chairs, a table and a stove, as well as plenty of pots and pans for cooking.
Nearby hills	Meall a' Bhuachaille, Bynack More

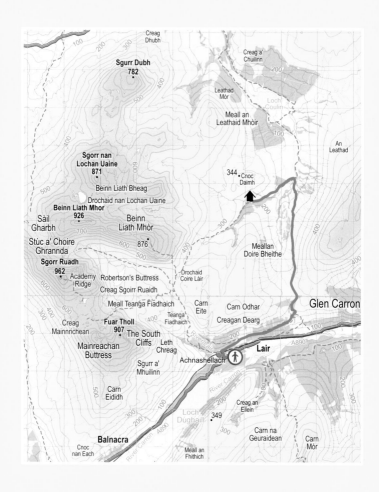

Easan Dorcha (The Teahouse)

A tiny shelter in the often-overlooked Coulin Estate – ideal for a tea-stop!

Approaching the unmissable Easan Dorcha

Hear the word 'teahouse' and the image of quaint patio furniture, tea cosies and small china cups leaps to mind. And although Easan Dorcha (aka The Teahouse) isn't quite so twee as all that, it is a charming hut in an enchanting location.

The less café-sounding name, Easan Dorcha, comes from the name of the water that runs alongside the bothy. It translates as 'dark waterfall', and the water does indeed churn a deep navy as it spills fast into the chasm below. Scots pines lines the water as you make your way to this corner of Wester Ross, offering many a spot for a camp with tent or bivvy, if you fancy an alternative.

The bothy sits on the massive Coulin Estate, and you'll notice that one route to it crosses a pass that shares the same name. The origins of the bothy's 'teahouse' appellation can be found in its former use – as a rest-stop for the estate's deer-hunting parties. In truth the bothy is small, and there are many

Looking back on the delightful Teahouse

walkers who – due to the lack of a fire-place, not to mention limited space – will only use it to grab a snack or drink and have affectionately dubbed it 'The Shed'.

Basic it may be, but the peaks around the bothy are legendary. Take Fuar Tholl, with its rocky summit and climbing routes, the Munros of Beinn Liath Mhor and the red peak of Sgurr Ruadh – all within walking distance. Whether you pass them on the way in or the way out, the first time you arrive at the valley where Easan Dorcha sits you'll be in awe. With pockets of native trees, distant mountains surrounding this high landscape and lakes reflecting the sunlight in the distance, it looks like a scene photoshopped to perfection. So don't forget to bring your flask and be sure to stop on the walk-in – there's never been a better place for a brew than this...

Did you know?

This small, unassuming bothy was visited in 2006 by Hollywood stars Michelle Pfeiffer and Robert de Niro while they were on location in the area making the film *Stardust*. Can you find their names in the bothy book?

Look out for...

Wildlife and trees: On the way in to the bothy keep a look out for the native red deer. In the water those with sharp eyes may be able to spy young salmon. When you reach the hut itself you'll be surrounded by a patch of stunning Scots pine trees, as well as some birch and rowan.

Geology: If you head in – or out – via the alternative route described above look to the peak Fuar Tholl (which translates as 'cold hole'), which is popular among climbers. It's also known as Wellington's Nose because of its shape. You'll also see some classic Torridonian geology here, with layers of sandstone and quartzite visible.

How to get there

Classic: The most straightforward route, involving least ascent, begins at the layby on the A890 opposite the driveway to Achnashellach Station. Cross the road, head up to the train line and safely cross it. Once at the other side turn right onto the forestry track and follow it uphill. The

Top tip

This is a tiny bothy that many choose to use as a shelter and tea stop rather than as an overnighter. Bring your tent/bivvy and be prepared to use it.

'It's a glorified shed surely?' I exclaimed when I first caught sight of The Teahouse. Unlike the stone shelters I'd stayed at before, this one seemed uncannily small and cabin-like. It looked like a miniature version of the huts you'd expect to find in the Alps rather than a run-of-the-mill bothy.

I'd spoken to other walkers who'd been here before and they advised me not to plan an overnighter – too cold, they'd said. But now when I arrived at the end of a summer's day, it was as though it had been storing up sunlight for the last eight hours and now felt cosy and warm.

The whole place seemed like it touched the people who visited. One kind soul had even brought wood treatment in to attempt to paint the wood – it didn't need it, the wood was meant to be left in the

Inside Easan Dorcha – a small space big enough for no more than three

elements to build up its own protection – which a note kindly informed any future do-gooders.

There were cups and containers for collecting water, and on the wall by the door was a bookshelf containing, among other things, some copies of Beatrix Potter's books about Peter Rabbit.

I hadn't read the stories about the adventurous bunny since I was a child. Now, in this pretty little valley, in the kind of shed I imagined the grumpy Scottish gardener Mr McGregor from Potter's tales would have used to house his tools, I was a child once more. Nestled away in my little den, I was no longer in Scotland, but among the potatoes and cabbages of the garden with little Peter lost in a world of imagination.

When I came to the part when Peter's mother put him to bed, I got in bed too. I made some camomile tea and, like Peter, enjoyed my brew one spoon at a time...

path breaks into three, one virtually going back on itself (don't take this one) and the others forming a fork in front of you. Take the one on your left that climbs uphill rather than down. Keep on it for several kilometres, through the forest, and eventually you'll reach a deer fence at the Coulin Pass. Go through it and head downhill on the well-maintained wide track. The views begin to open up here. Follow this track all the way down to a bridge over Easan Dorcha. Once across it turn left to take the path alongside the river. The bothy is on your right. Time: 3½hrs

Alternative route

More ascent: While the classic route exposes you to panoramic views of the Coulin Estate, this will instead take you into some wild-feeling mountain country, where it's peaks that surround you rather than expansive views. Start from the same point, but when you reach the crossroads after the station turn left to go slightly back on yourself. Follow the track through trees and shortly you'll see a fainter path on your left, marked by a cairn – take this alongside the River Lair. Go through a gate and through a brush mix of gorse and pine trees. Soon the path becomes stone, and you leave the trees and climb up into the mountains. Ignore the first turn-off on your left, then when the path forks again take the right fork, and at the final fork stick right again. Follow this path all the way to the footbridge over the Easan Dorcha, and on the other side the bothy is on your left.

Easan Dorcha essentials

Maps	OS Explorer 429; OS Landranger 25
Grid ref	NH 012 526
Terrain	Forestry tracks to the Easan Dorcha (river); from there a rougher but clear path leads to the bothy
Water source	River outside the bothy
Facilities	No fireplace/stove (fires not permitted outside either); shovel
Building	Wooden construction, metal roof
Inside	This bothy is made up of just one room. Inside is a bench and a small table as well as some shelving and books. There are no sleeping platforms – the floor will sleep two comfortably; three would be snug, four a squeeze.
Nearby hills	Fuar Tholl, Beinn Liath Mhor, Sgurr Ruadh

Shenavall

The starting point for one of the best mountain challenges – the Fisherfield Six

Shenavall marks the start for many a hillwalker undertaking the Fisherfield Six mountain challenge

An Teallach, Ruadh Stac Mor, A' Mhaighdean – mention these Munros to any hillwalker and it's like talking about Mick Jagger to a music fan. For these three peaks are the rock stars of the mountain-loving world, and ones that any hiker worth her or his salt will have heard of. Situated in the depths of the romantically named Fisherfield Forest, they present at least two serious challenges. First remoteness – the last two being officially the furthest Munros from any road, and thereby the most remote in the country. Second technicality – if An Teallach is the true A-lister, then the spires and buttresses that surround its summit are surely its bodyguards, each one requiring respect and confidence to get around.

Remote and tricky these three peaks may be, but something that makes a visit to them a little easier is the MBA bothy of Shenavall. Situated at the foot

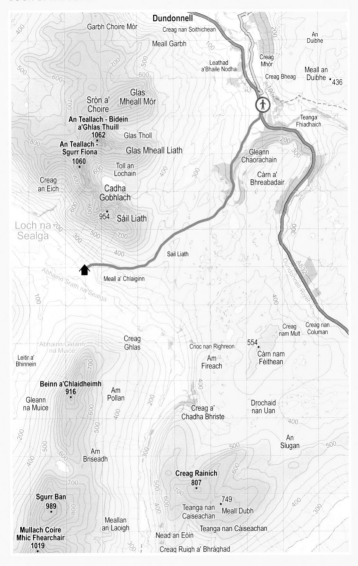

of An Teallach, and a river crossing away from starting an ascent of the other two Munros, it is – in my humble opinion – one of the most happily situated of all the bothies in the network.

But it wasn't always a place for walkers. Back in 1891 it was the family home of the MacDonalds, who lived here while their father worked as a stalker on the Dundonell Estate. Here they lived for 10 years, doing up the house with locally sourced stone, lining the walls and floors with wood, and even building a barn on the side. While in residence they grew vegetables, caught fish in the stream and used sheep's wool to make clothing – a truly self-sufficient life. However, they did rely on a twice-a-year visit by donkey from Dundonell that provided additional supplies.

Now, of course, if you need supplies you have to bring them in by foot not hoof, and the only long-term occupants of Shenavall are the resident mice – but still, get a fire going in the stove, with a hot drink in your belly and the conversation of a full bothy, and it's as homely as the day when the MacDonalds called this place home.

Top tip

There is room outside the bothy for tents and, indeed, this whole area is a wild-camper's dream. Note that this bothy is not accessible during the stag-hunting season (15 September to 20 October).

Did you know?

Shenavall is the start/finish point of a circuit of hill-bagging known as the Fisherfield Six. It's a 24hr loop made up of the six most remote Munros in Scotland – Ruadh Stac Mor, A' Mhaighdean, Beinn Tarsuinn, Mullach Coire Mhic Fhearchair, Sgurr Ban and Beinn a' Chlaidheimh (although the latter was officially demoted from Munro status after a height survey in September 2012). It's certainly a worthwhile mission, but is extremely challenging and should only be attempted by competent hillwalkers. If the rivers are in spate, crossing will be impossible and should not be attempted. If you did want to do it at a more leisurely pace, consider breaking it up into a couple of days with a wild camp in the middle.

Three days. It doesn't sound like a long time, but when it's been spent wandering through a truly wild place, with everything you need on your back, relying on finding water sources as you go and climbing the remotest Munro in Scotland, time seems to pass differently. I'd been attempting to do the Fisherfield Six, staying in bothies on the way, and after the mountains were done, Shenavall was to be my final stop.

It wasn't a long walk on that final evening - a little over six kilometres until I would arrive - but I was so tired that those kilometres couldn't be covered soon enough; each footstep a chore, every metre a challenge. By the time I saw the little tin roof of Shenavall appear, relief swept over me raising my spirits like they were cresting a wave.

I didn't even care that I saw a man was outside, meaning sharing the space; I was just relieved to have space to share. As I neared him I could see that he was taking off his boots - I'd never been so happy to see someone changing their socks in my life. I was looking forward to the company, to sharing my experience and to hearing what had brought him to this faraway glen.

A woman came out the door behind him - his daughter. I soon discovered that he was on a long distance walk, having started from Cornwall a couple of months previously. With them settled in the room upstairs, I made my bed in the downstairs room and we met together in the 'living room' to cook curries and talk walking. His daughter made a fire then we very quickly had to evacuate when the smoke began to blow back down it!

It all worked out for the best – as we ran outside the sun began to set. We chatted for a while, seemingly existing in a pocket of midge-free smog, then they both went inside to continue with their food.

But I couldn't tear myself away. As the sun slumped below the horizon it cast a tangerine glow on the mountains opposite. Every window of the bothy glowed auburn, the sky enflamed crimson and even the stream seemed to flush pink. The night ahead would bring more stories, a removal of several ticks and a couple of hours sharing whisky from a Sigg bottle. But right now I was lost in the moment, time once more seemed like a foreign concept, all that existed was me, the bothy and the most glorious sunset there has ever been.

No mistaking the name of this bothy!

Cooking and conversation by the fire in Shenavall bothy

Look out for...

Wildlife: Native red deer linger in this wild valley; keep a look out for them as you explore this area.

Famous visitor: Prince Charles famously visited Shenavall bothy back when he was a pupil at Gordonstoun School, near Elgin; he even recorded his name in the bothy book. So when you spend the night there don't forget to fill it in too – you'll be in good company.

How to get there

Classic: The quickest way in is from Corrie Hallie – the layby just outside Dundonnell. From there cross the road and take the well-defined trail that skirts alongside the Allt Gleann Chaorachain. Follow it as it begins to climb and then forks in two above Loch Coire Chaorachain. Take the path to the right – which gets rough in places – and follow this as it pulls up and over the lower reaches of An Teallach's satellite summit of Sail Liath, then descends down into the valley below. Before you reach the valley floor the bothy is on your left.

Time: 3hrs

Alternative route

Challenging: Being in one of the wildest areas of northern Scotland, there are plenty of opportunities to take a more challenging route to the bothy. Hillwalkers may want to try an ascent of An Teallach first (note that to get on top of the pinnacles requires a Grade 2 scramble – although there is a lower, less exposed path around). Those wanting a longer walk-in can begin over at Poolewe, walking in past Carnmore and down the Gleann na Muice Beag to Gleann na Muice. If it's safe to do so cross the river onto its east side, continue north to cross the Abhainn Srath na Sealga and reach Shenavall bothy.

Shenavall essentials

Maps	OS Explorer 435; OS Landranger 19
Grid ref	NH 066 810
Terrain	Well-defined track at first gives way to rougher, fainter tracing of a route over boggy and grassy terrain before becoming a more well-defined, narrow rocky path that leads to the bothy. The area demands good navigation skills and a map and compass.
Water source	Stream in front of the bothy
Facilities	Stove (bring your own fuel); shovel
Building	Stone and wood construction, corrugated metal roof
Inside	Here you'll find three rooms. Go through the small porch and emerge into something of a hallway; the stairs to your right lead up to a sleeping area that comfortably sleeps up to six people. The door to the left leads into the main sitting area, complete with a stove and several chairs. A door then leads into the back room, a secondary sleeping area that can accommodate around four or five people easily.
Nearby hills	An Teallach, Beinn a' Chlaidheimh

The Lookout

*A former coastguard's watch post with
unrivalled views of the sea*

The magnificent Lookout on the Isle of Skye

There's something special about the Isle of Skye – the constant sea views, the layer upon layer of volcanic rock scoured into other-worldly shapes and towers. The northernmost reach is arguably one of the best spots and is home to the Rubha Hunish, a headland that seeps into the water in a jagged fringe of rock. Above, the cliffs sharply rise up in dramatic fashion, the white stone seeming to glisten as brightly as the nearby lighthouses on the Isle of Lewis. At the top of this natural tower is something manmade – a small bothy.

Built in 1928, The Lookout was just that – a former watch station for the coastguard – which accounts for the superb views out over The Minch and the Isle of Lewis and Harris in the Outer Hebrides. Come the 1970s, with advances in technology, it was no longer needed and became something of a

129

The bunkbed arrangement in The Lookout's (very blue) sleeping area

The bothy-book holder inside The Lookout is made from driftwood

spot for birders and whalewatchers. Then in 2005, during a big storm, disaster struck – all the windows were blown out and, open to the elements, it wouldn't have been long before the whole building fell into disrepair.

Enter the MBA, which the landowner approached for help. They took on the building and, thanks to funds raised in memory of David JJ Brown, who died aged 72, the place was completely renovated into the perfect retreat you see today. With cedar walls, new floors, panelling and window frames, it has been money well spent.

On the wall is a memorial to the aforementioned Dave Brown, written by his friend Chris Smith in 2006. In it he is described as 'wilderness lover, anti-materialist and guerrilla bookkeeper'; he was a prolific traveller, staying with locals where he could, and when he returned to the UK he headed into the mountains. When it came to sleeping, I don't know what he would have made of the stunning Lookout, as 'Dave's view was that if you did not sleep under a hedge you were wasting money and alienating yourself from the out-doors'. But, according to his friend, he loved to disappear into the mountains and spend time in bothies, and, thanks to him, we all get a chance to disappear in the northern reaches of Skye.

Look out for...

Wildlife: At the bothy there's a chart of whales and sea mammals you might spot from the window – dolphins usually, but minke whales, orcas and even basking sharks have been spied from The Lookout. There's even a pair of binoculars for you to use. If you walk down to the headland keep an eye out for otters too.

History: On the way to the bothy you'll pass above the abandoned village of Erisco – now nothing more than a few foundation walls and piles of rocks from about eight drystone-walled buildings. It is thought to have been a crofting community established in the 1600s, but it became a victim of the clearances and was deserted by 1875.

How to get there

Classic: The easiest way is from the car park by the telephone box at the Shulista road end. From the car park cross the cattle grid and turn immediately left on a boggy path. Follow this path along the edge of the low escarpment, heading north-northwest. The path is boggy in places but fairly distinct, and continues mostly along the top of the low escarpment. The ruins of the abandoned village of Erisco come into view below to the left, while Duntulm Castle is prominent on its crag by the sea. The path eventually reaches a kissing gate in a fence. Go through it and continue to follow the faint track straight ahead. Before you reach the cliff edge, which is marked by a fence, cut up the slope to your right. Keep climbing until it levels out, once more heading to the cliff edge – the bothy is on your right.
Time: 1hr

Did you know?

Nearby Duntulm Castle is home to a local legend that explains the building's demise. It's said that it was abandoned by the family who lived there after their young son, while in the nursemaid's care, fell from the window and died on the rocks below. After that the family left and set the neglectful nurse adrift on a small boat in the sea…

Dolphins, orcas and even basking sharks have been spotted from the panoramic window in The Lookout

I didn't want to let him in. I wanted to be selfish. The thought of having to make conversation with a stranger that night, when I was being treated to 180-degree views, seemed like an unfair chore.

I'd celebrated arriving here several hours earlier to find The Lookout devoid of people. Never had a bothy been so perfectly planned; the kitchen area for making food, the bedroom complete with clothes pegs and bedside table, and then of course the living room — complete with the perfect panorama of a view out to the very tip of Skye and the islands beyond — so close I could have touched them. I was instantly sold. If the place was on the market, despite the fact there was no fireplace, I would have made an offer.

As it was I made the place very homely. I ate food, read books, wandered around outside as the sun started to set and the lighthouses on the nearby islands began to spin their light around. Using the binoculars I watched the waves for whales, kept my eye open for birds and felt so content just sitting, not really doing anything at all. Then I saw him.

The rain had started about 40 minutes earlier and I'd looked left to see his dark silhouette emerging from the gloom. He spotted me as soon as I spotted him and waved. I really didn't want to share my prized space. He walked past the building and for one

glorious minute I thought he might continue, might not even want to stay at all. Then the wind picked up, the rain morphed to hail and I found myself heading for the door, my inner bothy etiquette getting the better of me; in bad weather there is always room.

As I opened it he was about to knock and I invited him inside. He turned out to be French, alone on holiday after his girlfriend had, last minute, decided they didn't belong together. As soon as he came in he reassured me he would leave to camp, but as I saw just how much he was shivering, how little supplies he had with him, and just how heavy the rain had become. I couldn't bear it and insisted he take the floor in the room with the panoramic window.

Just as I had been helped in bothies in the past, I now felt inclined to help this lost soul. He'd mentioned how he was out of water so, in the morning, before I left, I made him my last coffee and toasted him my final brioche. I pointed out on the map where he could go to get some clean water.

We left as friends. I hadn't done anything amazing, nothing life-changing or superhuman, what I had done is show another human being kindness when they needed it the most and surely that's what staying in a bothy is all about. I looked back as I walked away and, watching the smile spread unchecked across his face, I felt mine doing the same. I was glad I had let him in after all.

Alternative route

To land's end: If you arrive with time to spare, consider taking a walk down to the most northerly point on Skye. Instead of cutting right up the hillside when you are near the fence at the cliff edge, walk right up to it then turn left, where you will see a loose path that cuts down to the Hunish. It looks fairly steep, but once you're on it the gradient is not as bad as it appears. Take walking poles to help, and take care in wet weather.

Top tip

Because it has no fire and a windswept location, this bothy can get very cold. Make sure you pack an extra layer or two, and take a camping stove for hot drinks.

The Lookout

Maps	OS Explorer 408; OS Landranger 23
Grid ref	NG 413 763
Terrain	Boggy grass track leads to the bothy; watch out for cliff edges on the ground outside the bothy
Water source	No water source at or near the bothy or anywhere around the headland, but the bothy Maintenance Officer is at the Trotternish Art Gallery, Solitote (NG 428 742), and will happily fill water bottles. Otherwise you will have to carry in all the water you will need.
Facilities	No stove, and fires are not permitted outside the bothy; shovel
Building	Western cedar and concrete
Inside	Despite no internal doors there are roughly three defined 'rooms'. On entering the bothy you arrive in a hall. On your left is a locked door, which the Maintenance Officer uses for storage. You then enter the sleeping area with bunkbeds – the bottom sleeping two and the top sleeping one; the floor area could sleep an extra one in an emergency. Go through the archway on your right and you reach the 'kitchen' area – with a metal worktop. Go through to the main sitting room, where the highlight is undoubtedly the window that offers 180-degree views. There are several chairs and a table here – the room could sleep two comfortably, three at a push.
Nearby hills	Ben Volovaig

Craig

Once the most remote hostel in the UK
– now a perfectly placed bothy

Craig bothy was formerly the most remote hostel in the SYHA network

All bothies have a history – usually as huts for estate workers or refuges for those who worked in the mines. However, Craig is different. Although it originally started life as a hut for a shepherd and his family in the 1800s, come 1935 it was adopted for a rather different purpose – a hostel.

The Scottish Youth Hostel Association (SYHA) decided to make this building into an overnight stay for backpackers. But this wasn't your usual hostel. This had the accolade of being the most remote hostel in the UK. Demanding access only by foot or bike – cars were out of the question – and with no option to have your bags carried for you, if you wanted to stay here it was a case of turning up with all you needed and hoping for the best.

Situated near the sea, alongside a river, surrounded by the birch and pine trees of its mini-copse and in front of the mountains of Torridon, it deserved

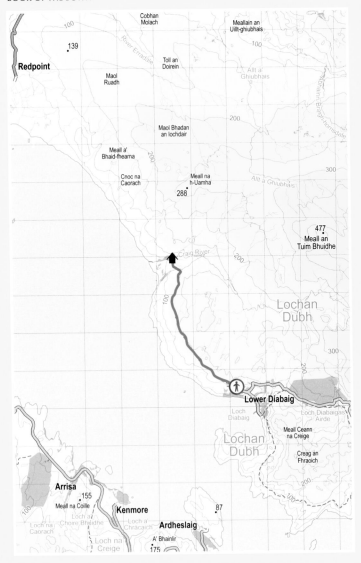

a prize for being the best-located hostel too. It's no wonder that the position of warden was one wanted by many. This unique stop-over managed to stay open for an impressive 68 years, closing its doors to guests in 2003, which is when the reliable MBA decided to look after it – with it coming into their care in 2006.

Look through the bothy book even now and you won't fail to find notes from people who fondly remember the days of the SHYA.

Take the entry from John and Vera Morrison from the Boat of Garten. His mother used to look after the hostel back when it first opened in the 1930s. She lived in one of the now derelict houses by the coast.

Then there's a note from Alistair Dickson of Paisley. He stopped at Craig in May 2012, but prior to that had been a hostel guest back in 1969, and even his mother had stayed here shortly after it was opened by SYHA in the 30s. He writes: 'Our chore in '69 was to carry coal from the beach. I remember the vicious midges.'

But it isn't just British citizens who remember this place. Jan from Germany was here 20 years previously. He talks of the warden in a long dress 'walking barefoot and picking up eggs to be served the next morning as breakfast'.

All these guest testimonials paint quite a picture of the place. But it's the fact that former wardens make a pilgrimage to Craig that makes you think what a special place this was. Among the entries I read in just one book was a note from Christopher Horton, who had been a warden here for six months in 1992 and comments: 'It's still as tranquil and beautiful as ever'.

Then in 2012 a man called David Warren, who worked there for eight months in 1982, visited with his then 11-year-old daughter to commemorate his 30-year anniversary of being at Craig.

It's incredible to think of how many memories were made in one building, and even more amazing to think that 80 years on it's still happening – all thanks to two amazing organisations.

Look out for...

Wildlife: Perfectly placed by the mountains and the coast, Craig is a great spot to look out for native wildlife. Around the bothy look for red deer and white-tailed sea eagles. If heading to the beach keep an eye on the waters – dolphins and even sperm whales have been spotted here in recent years.

Have you ever had that feeling? You know, the one when you re-enter a room where you burnt a slice of toast a while earlier and suddenly get a whiff of its scent. It's as though you've stepped back in time and are back at the moment, the smell instantly transporting you there, disorientating the brain.

That's what it's like at Craig bothy. This former hostel practically reeks of its past use and feels like, any minute, the warden is going to come down stairs and sign you in. Maybe it's the paintings on the walls, left over by a previous resident, the homely bedroom-like feel in the Warden's Room upstairs, the fact that there's a kitchen that smells like a hot meal's only just been made - I don't know. But, for certain, in a place that's seen as many visitors as Craig has, there's bound to be echoes from the past.

I was shocked to find the place empty, thought a place this big would command the crowds, but although there was no one lurking in any of the rooms when I took the Warden's Room for myself, I didn't feel alone.

I headed down to the beach and watched as a storm floated a few miles out to sea, thickening black with clouds, but never coming any closer. While I watched that, the deer at the nearby ruins watched me suspiciously, staring as he chewed the grass between his teeth.

Opening the bothy book, I spent the evening reading about visitors to the bothy, and to the hostel before that. Heated by the fire, I fell asleep

reading their tales, waiting for the morning when I would add my own to it.

At dawn I sat on the thinking stone outside and wrote my entry in the book. The briny air from the sea engulfed my senses; I could practically taste the salt on my tongue. I watched the goats move around me, unaware of my presence on this raised platform, their bleats filling my ears, the rock rough under my fingers.

Now whenever I sit by the sea, hear the sound of waves crash and smell the saline air, it is as if I took a part of that landscape with me, and I am instantly transported back to Craig...

Like the smell of burnt toast, part of me lingers there forever.

Above Loch Torridon en route to Craig

Beach: Make sure you make time to wander down to the beach in front of the bothy. There are several remains of former homesteads, which are overgrown – so a good place to spot deer. It's an ideal place to watch the sun set over the Isle of Rona, opposite, or to camp if the bothy is full or you want a night outside – just don't forget the midge repellent!

How to get there

Classic: Starting from the layby at the top of Lower Diabaig (park considerately), go through the gate signed 'Gairloch via Craig' and across the road, then through a second gate shortly after. The path takes you around and over the headland, crossing several streams as you go, until you reach Lochan Dubh. Skirt the water on the path, then descend to a flattened area of the coastline where you will immediately see Craig and the little copse of trees outside to your right.

Time: 2hrs

Top tip

Inside the Warden's Room is a shelf complete with lots of books – making this a great place to be rain-bound. Donated books are welcome, and remember – if you take one, leave another in its place.

Did you know?

Torridon is home to wild goats and, as the sky turns dusky, Craig is a great spot from which to see them. Originally descended from the domestic goat, they were protected from culling by Robert the Bruce in the 14th century. Legend has it that he did so because, before he became king, he was being pursued by soldiers and hid in a cave at Loch Lomond. Goats came to feed at the mouth of it, and when his enemies arrived they decided it would be a waste of time to search the cave because goats meant no people – and he was safe.

Alternative route

Lesser used: Most people choose to go from the Torridon side, as there are more facilities, but for something a little quieter and wild-feeling (the path this way is less trodden) start instead from Redpoint further north. There is parking just before the track starts, where the B8056 ends. Follow the track past the farm and it begins to lead you above the beach and sand dunes, becoming fainter and boggier. Continue on over the headland, fording streams as you go, and soon you reach the Craig River. The path leads round to your left, inland. Follow it to cross the river via a footbridge, and soon the bothy is on your left.

Wildlife-spotting from the comfort of Craig bothy

Craig essentials

Maps	OS Explorer 433; OS Landranger 19
Grid ref	NG 774 638
Terrain	Boggy track which can get very wet particularly after rain; faint in places
Water source	Craig River – access it by heading past the bothy towards the footbridge then cutting down to it on your right before you reach it. The ground levels off by the water here.
Facilities	Stove (bring your own fuel – don't cut from the live trees outside); 'flush' toilet with bucket; shovel
Building	Stone construction, slate roof
Inside	Craig contains a total of six rooms. On entering you arrive in a hallway. To your left is a door that leads to the main sitting area with a stove, large table and several chairs (room could sleep three or four people in emergency). Off this room to the right – covered by a curtain – is the old kitchen, which still has worktops and cupboards and is a good place to prepare food (cover anything though – mice). To the right from the main hall is the staircase leading to the upper floor and a door to a second room. Currently (as of 2014) this room is out of bounds due to holes in the floorboards, but if repaired it could comfortably sleep six people. Upstairs, as you arrive onto the main landing, is a very small room directly in front of you that has two bed frames in it and sleeps two people. To the left is a large room that would happily take six people. To the right is the old Warden's Room that has two bed frames in it and an old chest, shelves and a cupboard. It would comfortably sleep at least six. Remember, though, that permission is needed from the MBA for groups larger than six.
Nearby hills	Meall na h-Uamha, Meall an Tuim Bhuidhe

The Schoolhouse

An early 1900s classroom nestled in the highlands near Oykel Bridge

Wooden structures such as The Schoolhouse were once a familiar sight in the Scottish highlands

Remember your walk to school when you were a child? Those who used to frequent this bothy – a former schoolhouse – certainly wouldn't have forgotten theirs. For, no matter how many miles you had to traverse to reach your educational institute, in whatever kind of wind, rain or snow, you couldn't have had as bad a time of it as the pupils of the hut at Duag Bridge.

In the early 1900s, to ensure that children who lived in the remote highland areas were properly taught, local authorities built a series of buildings like this bothy to serve as a schoolhouse. School wasn't like it is today – all age groups would have been learning together in the same class and in the same classroom. The teacher usually lived on site to make it easier, so it was up to the children to find their way to the designated school. This small wooden building was no different. Made up of three rooms, it seems more than likely that the schoolteacher would have called this place home.

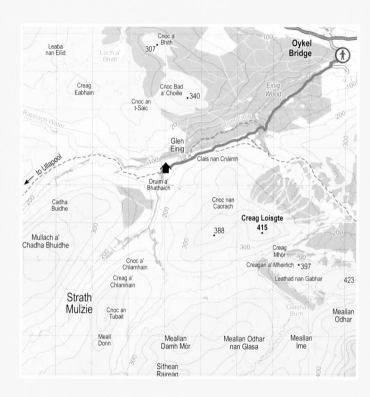

Walkers leave the comfort of The Schoolhouse and re-enter the wide open space that surrounds it

According to records obtained by the MBA, it seems that the route to education was certainly a hazardous one. Regardless of the – let's face it – extreme weather that this northern reach of Scotland can often be exposed to, it was the nearby river that presented the most problems. Some children lived on the opposite side of the River Einig. At certain times of the year, when this was in spate, children were forced to use stilts to cross it. So never mind what children say nowadays, until the 1930s – when this stopped being the local school – going to learn could, quite literally, kill you.

Since 2008 the historical schoolhouse has been in the care of the MBA and has even undergone a sympathetic renovation. Sitting among the rolling hills and forestry land near Oykel Bridge, and near the river that shares its name, the bothy is an idyllic spot to spend the night. You may well see fishermen out this way, as the stream is home to many a salmon. But the

145

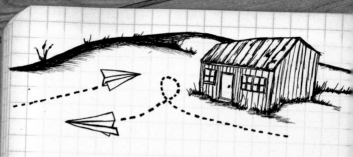

I don't know how it happened or which turn led us here, but somehow we had ended up on the high path. After tracing the river and weaving through the trees on the trail, myself and my friend Neil were deposited up on the hillside, the whole landscape undulating from beneath my feet, a patchwork of conifer and long grass.

From my position I could see two walkers near the schoolhouse lingering outside the door. I wondered whether they were heading in or out, leaving or arriving, and whether I should continue on as planned or not.

I knew they couldn't see us from our position and so we waited, loitering and watching, like the falcons that were circling overhead, trying to plot our next move.

Minutes later, they left, heading east on the track and we knew the bothy would be ours. When we reached the door I opened it expectantly, hoping that there would be no more figures in the shadow of the building. We were in luck - the bothy was ours.

Once inside Neil began to boil some water, filling the air with the hiss and spit of the stove, while I ventured into the larger room. Inside I smiled to see a couple of old school desks, along with some paper and pens, and many chairs. It was as though the class had only just been dismissed, like any minute the teacher would return to the classroom and demand to know why we were snooping before giving us a detention.

The sun still drenched in through the windows as the hours slipped by. Unlike school kids, we were happy for the time to creep on slowly, in no rush to end our session here. As we ate I made some paper airplanes from the pages of my notebook and there we sat, throwing this apparatus from our childhood years while sharing details of our favourite teachers, the class clown and the few years of our lives that seemed as distantly in the past as the children who once attended here to learn.

The bothy was once the local schoolhouse – and even now visitors can misbehave in the classroom!

watercourse itself has a much more ancient use. Historically it marked the boundary between the counties of Ross in the south and Sutherland in the north – and even the Vikings used it to split their provinces. Watch it babble and splutter as you rest at this simple shelter and learn what it is to stay in such a peaceful spot, where problems (both mathematical and in life) are relegated to the past.

Top tip

The bothy is located near to a lodge and is therefore not available to walkers during stag hunting (1 September to 20 October). There's no fire, and you shouldn't light one outside, so make sure you take plenty of layers with you.

Look out for...

Fish: The River Oykel, of which the River Einig is a tributary, is classed as a Special Area of Conservation due to the Atlantic salmon that swim in it – consequently the river alongside the bothy is home to the fish too. Note that you need a licence to fish here.

Nearby bothy: To the west of the bothy is Knockdamph, where you'll find another, more traditionally built bothy. It's a good option if you fancy a longer walk-in or if The Schoolhouse is full.

How to get there

Classic: From the parking area next to the cluster of houses just off the main road at Oykel Bridge, head out on the path going southwest until you come to a bridge on your left. Cross this and turn right following the track for a couple of kilometres. You'll come to a fork; turn right first and then

Did you know?

Some of the walkers you meet at this bothy could be doing the Cape Wrath Trail. Running from Fort William in the south to Cape Wrath in the north, it's a challenging 200-mile long-distance route (although not yet recognised as an official National Trail) – and definitely one of the toughest. It traipses through lots of unsignposted land where facilities are limited and the going is hard.

almost immediately left to continue southwest. Ignore any turn-offs, and soon you'll spy the bothy and your bed for the night.

Time: 2½hrs

Alternative route

Challenging: Any route in other than the one from Oykel Bridge will mean a very long walk over rough ground. If you're up for a challenge then by all means give it a try – one such path starts at Ullapool. You'll start on a good track through Glen Achall, but this will end and leave you to pick your own way on a network of trails and faint paths to Loch an Daimp, from where you head east to approach the bothy from the west.

The Schoolhouse essentials

Maps	OS Explorer 440; OS Landranger 15
Grid ref	NH 340 975
Terrain	Clear, wide tracks both to and from the bothy. Check maps in case forestry work has altered any paths.
Water source	Right outside the bothy, the River Einig
Facilities	Shovel; no fire/stove
Building	Wooden construction, tin roof
Inside	This bothy is made up of three rooms. You enter into a hallway. To your left is a fairly large room complete with a sleeping platform that sleeps four comfortably and some floor space, also a worktop which is good for using your stove on. In front is a small room that sleeps two comfortably on the floor. To the right is the largest room that – due to the desks and chairs present – feels like a school classroom. There's a fireplace but no fire – do not try to make one (this is, after all, a wooden building). This room would easily sleep eight people comfortably on the floor.
Nearby hills	Creag Loisgte

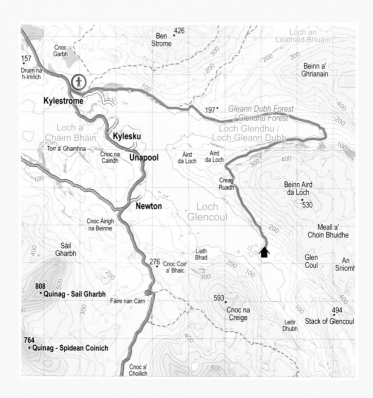

Glencoul

*A former homestead that sits near one of
the highest-drop waterfalls in Britain*

Looking down on Glencoul bothy – once a family home

There are not many people who would willingly give up their lives in a comfortable village to go and work on a Highland estate where the only way in and out was by a long boat ride or even longer walk. Yet in the late 1800s, that's just what the Elliot family did.

In common with many of the original bothy-dwellers, John and Margaret moved to this lonely house at Glencoul when John got work as a deer stalker with what is now the Reay Forest Estate. Here they lived, under the employment of the landowner (the Duke of Westminster), working the land and living off the animals that they kept on it. Margaret made cheese, butter and cream while also raising sheep, pigs and chickens to supply meat and eggs. Due to the nature of John's job, venison was also often on the menu – which could also be dried and salted to keep for times of the year when it wasn't so easy to come by.

But it wasn't just John and Margaret in Glencoul. While living there the couple had five sons – the first, William, was born in 1891, with his siblings Alistair, Matthew, John and James arriving in the years that followed up to 1901.

The bothy that walkers use now is the schoolroom that was attached to the family home. And, in it, often placed above the fireplace in the main room, or in a folder with the bothy book, are extracts of a diary by John, who recounts some of his memories from living in Glencoul. He writes about the teachers who came and went, and says that his eldest son, Will, was often the teacher and taught him to love books. But outside the classroom, he says the kids had pretty much the time of their lives. He writes: 'The Glen was a place of such freedom as my children never knew until they had grown up and travelled.'

John writes of the long trip to shops – five miles by sea and a further nine miles on the road. He jokes that Glencoul, which is Gaelic for 'the glen at the back of beyond', was a very apt appellation for the place.

Of course, somewhat ironically, visitors nowadays come to this place for exactly that reason, to escape into the wild for a night or two. So when you're enjoying your temporary fireside residence in this beautiful glen, sheltering from the elements, remember the Elliot family who called this place home. Because if it wasn't for them living here, the building which is now the bothy would never have been constructed to house their teacher and classroom. Thank you boys – we owe you in more ways than one…

Look out for...

Wildlife: The loch on which the bothy sits is home to both grey and common seals who come to feed in the safety of the sheltered bays. Keep an eye out when you're walking, and you might well see their curious faces poking up out of the waves.

Former residents: There's a small (20m) hillock in front of the bothy. If you climb up you will find a white marble cross there dedicated to William and Alistair Elliot, the two eldest brothers who grew up on the estate but sadly died in the First World War aged 25 and 24 respectively. The memorial was erected by the then

Top tip

It's stalking season on the estate from 12 August to 20 October. It is possible to visit during this time, but you'll first need to phone Reay Forest Estate (01971 502220).

Crashing a stag party is not the usual way to enter a bothy. It's certainly not how I expected my arrival to be when I set off for the remote Glencoul on a miserable and rainy afternoon, but it's exactly what I did.

To be honest I nearly didn't make it at all. I'd come in via the longer route, passing the bothy of Glendhu on my way. By that time I was already soaked to the skin, and tempted to ditch this shelter at the expense of a warm fire and an upstairs bedroom there, but stubbornness saw me continue.

The wind was howling when I topped out above the bay in which it sits and first spotted it between squinted eyes - forced to close by the hail hammering my face. I persevered, overcoming the two sections of landslip, and feeling the burning of blisters forming on my dampened feet.

By the time I descended to the river I was deliriously dreaming of casting aside my layers and defrosting my icy limbs by the roar of a fire, with a hot drink in one hand and a dehydrated meal in the other. It was only then I noticed to my utter disappointment that the footbridge marked on the OS map was missing. Nearly an hour was spent pacing the river trying to find a safe crossing point until it was make or break time and I decided to plunge through and cross it.

When I pulled myself out of the chest deep water onto the opposite bank I had never felt so cold and wet in my life.

Like the creature from the black lagoon I staggered shivering and dripping wet to the bothy door. I didn't even clock the smoke coming out

The old family homestead sits beside Glencoul bothy which was the family's old schoolhouse

of the chimney. Emerging into the room I was met with the gaze of six men, drinking beer, the fire lighting their surprised faces in an orange glow.

It could have gone either way I suppose. They could have forced me to go out and use my tent in the rainy night - they were there first after all. But instead they made me feel so welcome it was like I'd known them for years. I was immediately offered the most comfortable of the two chairs. Dry trousers and socks were offered, swiftly followed by a beer, and when I suggested I camp, they wouldn't hear of it, giving me one of the two rooms to sleep in.

The sound of them laughing and banging around lasted until easily 4am, but in my own warm room, dry and safe from the elements, knowing that in this world human kindness can come in the most unexpected of places, I slept soundly.

Another gorgeous view from Glencoul bothy

Duke of Westminster, who owned the land, so that visitors to the glen will remember the two young men who used to call this place home.

How to get there

Classic: It looks simple enough on the map, but in reality this is a long, potentially hard-going walk (especially in bad weather). From the car park at Kylestrome take the well-defined track that skirts alongside Loch Gleann Dubh all the way to another bothy – Glendhu (a possible Plan B option if the weather is bad). From there follow the path to the footbridge to cross the small stream. Here the path disappears. Don't worry; follow the shoreline around, and after crossing the outflow of two smaller streams you should begin to see a rough path heading steadily uphill as it traces west. Follow it and climb to a 205m highpoint. From here you now track southeast,

Did you know?

The Eas a' Chual Aluinn is said to be one of the highest-drop waterfalls in the Britain. With a fall of 200m, it's actually three times higher than Canada and America's Niagara Falls.

first heading slightly uphill then beginning a steady descent towards Loch Glencoul. You'll need to cross the river as the footbridge marked on the map has been washed away – do not attempt if in spate. The bothy sits beyond the outbuildings, in front of the main house.

Time: 6–7hrs

Alternative route

Challenging: Just south of Kylesku is a car park at Loch na Gainmhich. Take the track that skirts the loch then follows Allt Loch Bealach a' Bhuirich. Stick with it past the loch of the same name, then follow it above Eas a' Chual Aluinn waterfall. Do not attempt to descend here, but instead stick to your path that leads you down to Abhainn an Loch Bhig. Then it's a case of picking your own way down towards Loch Beag and the bothy at Glencoul. This is an extremely tough route, both navigationally and due to the terrain – take care if crossing rivers and watch out for peat bogs underfoot. Walking poles strongly advised.

Glencoul essentials

Maps	OS Explorer 442; OS Landranger 15
Grid ref	NC 271 305
Terrain	Clear, wide path to start that turns rockier on the approach to Glendhu. From there the path is much fainter and narrower; it gets very rocky and then boggy. A potentially dangerous river crossing to get to the bothy, so care is needed.
Water source	The river crossed to access the bothy is the best place
Facilities	Open fire (bring your own fuel); shovel
Building	Stone construction, tile roof
Inside	There are two rooms. You arrive in a small hallway. To your left the door leads to the main sitting room that has an open fire, a number of chairs, a table and a bed frame, and could sleep four comfortably and six at a push. To the right is another equally sized room with a large table. The fireplace in here has been blocked up for safety – do not attempt to use it.
Nearby hills	Beinn Aird da Loch

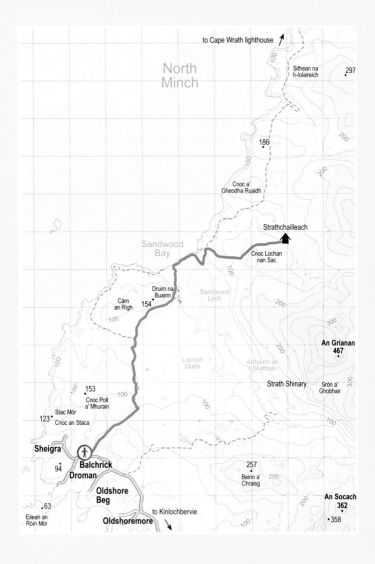

Strathchailleach (Sandy's Bothy)

A small shelter above the white beaches of Sandwood Bay

Night falls over Sandy's Bothy

The Atlantic Ocean as a neighbour; the white sand beach of Sandwood Bay as your garden; the fast-flowing river Straith Chailliach as your cold water tap. Spend a night in an idyllically placed bothy such as Strathchailleach, and there are times when many of us would be tempted to linger a little longer. But would you ever be prepared to shrug off all responsibilities, abandon the rat race and make a bothy your full-time home? Well one man once did in this very bothy.

James McRory Smith, aka Sandy, spent 32 years living in Strathchailleach. Shunning the life destined for him as a shipbuilder, like his father before him, this Dumbarton local had a life peppered with tragedy. From losing his mother at a young age to fighting in the Second World War, and losing the love of his life in a car accident and custody of his children to her parents

shortly after – it's not really any wonder that he decided to turn his back on a cruel society and took to living nomadically in the hills of Scotland.

Eventually Sandy came across this perfectly placed bothy and decided to make it his permanent home. Living off the rabbits, deer and fish he caught, salvaging furniture washed up on the shore and making the fortnightly pilgrimage to Kinlochbervie and Balcharik to collect his pension and additional supplies, his hermit life suited him well. By all accounts his evenings were spent quite happily smoking cigarettes, drinking whisky and painting on the bothy walls (many of his painting can still be seen today). That was until a storm in 1979 damaged the building and he was forced to leave it.

Short of funds in the 1980s Sandy struck a deal with the MBA – if they repaired it he would continue living there but allow walkers to use the 'spare room' to sleep in. They agreed, but reports soon came back that he wasn't always happy to share his space with strangers. From being yelled at to leave, to simply finding the door locked, many bothy-goers left disappointed, and the MBA was forced to remove it from its list. When he left in the 1990s due to ill health (he died in 1999 in Raigmore Hospital) the organisation finally managed to reinstate it, doing it up and ensuring the door has remained open to this day.

This area had been settled many years before Sandy's arrival – you only need spy several crumbling buildings on the walk-in to realise that. Originally shepherds lived here – from as early as 1840. It's thought that demand for the shelter waned in the early 1900s, and by the 1940s it was abandoned. That was until Sandy found it, and the rest, as they say, is history.

Look out for...

Wildlife: Far off the beaten track it may be, but the area teems with wildlife. Its proximity to the sea means fulmars, kittiwake, razorbill, arctic tern and even puffin can be sighted. Look carefully among the cliffs and you may also spot peregrine and buzzards. Turning your gaze inland, you may see some of the elusive red deer.

Landmarks: There are two you can spy from the beach at Sandwood and both are towers. The first is obvious and naturally formed – Am Buchaille ('the herdsman'), a dominant sea stack formed of blocks of Torridonian sandstone lying out several miles to sea. The second is Cape Wrath's lighthouse. Built in 1828, the whitewashed granite walls may require binoculars to be seen clearly from this distance, but as night falls the light's bright beam – created to be seen 22 miles out to sea – will reveal itself even to the naked eye.

Former resident: If you want to go and pay your respects to Strathchailleach's former keeper then, after your bothy stay, head to the tiny hamlet of Sheigra and the cemetery – his final resting place. Facing out to sea, you're sure to agree that there couldn't be a better spot for an eternal sleep.

How to get there

Classic: The shortest way is to drive to Blairmore near Balchrick, where you'll find the John Muir Trust car park complete with drinking water tap, rubbish bins, toilets and information leaflets. From there follow the sign across the road to the start of the 7km walk to Sandwood Bay on a rough but fairly obvious path. From the beach it's a case of choosing your own route across the sand and up the cliffs, then walking the extra 2.5km to

Top tip

If the bothy is full, or if the weather is particularly good, then the sand dunes above the beach at Sandwood Bay offer a great alternative for a night's sleep. There is no more soothing sound to fall asleep to than that of the waves.

Did you know?

Sandwood Bay cottage, the shell of an old homestead without a roof that sits above the bay, is said to be visited by the ghost of a sailor from one of the many shipwrecks that took place in the nearby Atlantic. It's said that he peers through the windows and doors, checking to see if anyone is home…

161

When I first arrived I was convinced someone was already was home. Wisps of smoke unfurled from the chimney stack as a dim yellow light flickered in the window. Part of me was frustrated that I would have to share my bothy experience, but another part of me was relieved to have someone to share the evening with - someone who understood the challenge faced in finding Strathchailleach in the first place...

It was very late and very late when I had set out to get here. Very late and very wet. I did it purposely so that I wouldn't be tempted back to the beach of Sandwood Bay, to sleep among the sand dunes - something I had done before on a previous visit. This time I would stay the whole night. I left Blairmore at 2.30pm and, seeing as it was nearly winter, it would be getting dark soon. Add to that the rain pelting down on my hood, and it had barely gotten light at all that day.

The walk in from Blairmore follows a path that cleaves through fields and alongside tarns for 7km until it finally reaches the sea. On that particular day an icy wind was blowing, chilling my fingertips. I kept my head down and continued on my mission. The ground began to get tough, rippling up and down with more rocks scattered across it. Finally I reached the shell of the old cottage at Sandwood - now a roofless wreck. I turned to look out at the bay.

Cliffs framed it on either side, creating a perfect slice of the wild ocean. The sand was smooth and seemed to glow a pale white in the dusk. A little further out, waves crashing against it, was the sea stack of Am Buachaille, a splinter of stone that stands almost at the height of the cliffs but sticks into the water. Its Gaelic name means 'the herdsman' and from where it was positioned, it did resemble a shepherd's

crook and was
doing a fine job
of driving the
sea into the
inlet where I
stood. Here,
more stacks
of rock acted
like a natural

breakwater as the sea crashed against
them, frothing as it made contact with the stone.

I followed footsteps across the sand. They looked
fresh so I began to wonder then if the bothy might be
occupied when I finally made it. Crossing the chute of
water that connects the briny sea to the freshwater
loch I felt the water permeate my gaiters and begin
to soak into my socks. It would all be alright, I told
myself, the fire at the bothy would dry them out.

Minutes later I was scrambling up through the
sandstone ledges of the crumbling cliff, traipsing
between the boggy plateau that awaits walkers at the
top, before stopping to watch the fluffy tails of three
red deer disappear into the darkening horizon. Tracing
the water of a small loch I continued on, just as the
sky was deepening to a pink tinged grey. I reached a
fence; then I saw the bothy. Still a good few minutes'
walk away, but distinctly occupied. I made my way
towards it, filled with the anticipation always felt
before entering a bothy.

I reached for the door handle and stepped into
a little hallway. I made a right turn first, into the
room where the fireplace is and I had seen the light
in the window. Surprisingly, it was empty. 'Hello,' I
called out expecting a reply to come from the small

room to the left, but my words just hung in the air - an unanswered question. I looked to the window to see a bottle, which someone had wedged a candle into, but it wasn't lit. I peered into the 'kitchen' - empty. I took off my backpack then wandered back to the entry corridor and into the second room - no one. I had surely been mistaken. I was alone.

I knew all about Sandy, the previous resident of this small shelter, and set about making myself a warm drink while looking at a photo of him someone had placed on the wall. Underneath it was a shelf filled with books. The ramshackle furniture made it look shabby chic and Sandy's paintings, which he'd laboured over in the evenings, made this feel like I was sitting in the home of an old relative. As I poured hot water on my camping meal and waited for it to cook I set about lighting the fire. The room smelt of old smoke and peat from the many flames lit before mine. Using the bellows I pumped air onto the flames and watched as the peat glowed red. Near the fireplace was a painting of a woman playing a harp and I studied the brush strokes intently, trying to imagine Sandy setting about penning this portrait.

As the night drew on and the fire warmed the room it was easy for me to see how Sandy would have whiled away his evenings. For many hours I sat reading the entries in the bothy book - each story brought to life in this atmospheric setting, - and flicking through pages of the walking guides looking at the pictures of Scotland's dramatic landscapes. I watched the rain tap on the window and wondered again why I had been so convinced there was someone there before me.

Finally, when the hot drink and fire began making my eyes heavy I decided, as this was Sandy's home, it was only right for me to sleep in the guest bedroom - no matter how easy it would be to curl up on the floor by the fire. I retired to bed. Although I knew that I was, in fact, here alone, I felt like there was company with me. And unlike the reports of Sandy turning walkers away I felt distinctly welcome.

Sandy famously said in an interview in the 90s that he could live in Strathchailleach forever. I never really thought that sentiment would be one I would share. But, as the dim morning light woke me the next morning, and I left the warmth of my sleeping bag to peer outside the front door, I suddenly got it. With the landscape turned peach, and the warm memories of the night before still as fresh in my mind as the morning dew on the grass at my feet, it was clear: for wilderness lovers like me, a place like this will always feel like home.

Strathchailleach. It's best to use the lochs and streams to help navigate, but make sure you take an OS map and compass – and know how to use them.
Time: 3½hrs

Alternative route

Hard: A tough but rewarding alternative walk starts from the Cape Wrath lighthouse. There is no path, and the ground is boggy for just over 10km. You will be crossing land used by the military, so you need to check in advance that there's no activity on your chosen day(s) (call range control on 0800 833300 or 01971 511242). You will also have to cross some barbed wire before reaching the bothy at Strathchailleach, so take a foam sit-mat to help you get across it.

Strathchailleach essentials

Maps	OS Explorer 446; OS Landranger 9
Grid ref	NC 249 657
Terrain	Rough but straightforward path to Sandwood Bay; from there pathless beach followed by loose ground up to boggy, fairly featureless terrain. Very difficult to navigate in bad weather.
Water source	Right outside the bothy, the Strath Chailleach river
Facilities	Peat fire, which is regularly topped up by wardens; shovel
Building	Stone construction, corrugated iron roof
Inside	There are three rooms in the bothy. On entering the bothy you immediately come into a corridor with a door to the left and one to the right. The one to your left leads into a single room complete with a window and sleeping platform that comfortably sleeps two, but at a push could take four. The door on the right leads into the 'sitting room' where there are some chairs, shelves, books, photographs of its famous former resident and a fireplace (on which you burn peat). There is floor space in here to sleep on if necessary. At the back of the room a doorway leads to a type of kitchen area, which could take a couple of extra people sleeping on the floor if needed.
Nearby hills	Creag Riabhach, Beinn Dearg

WALES

Dulyn bothy looks tiny among the rolling hills of the Carneddau

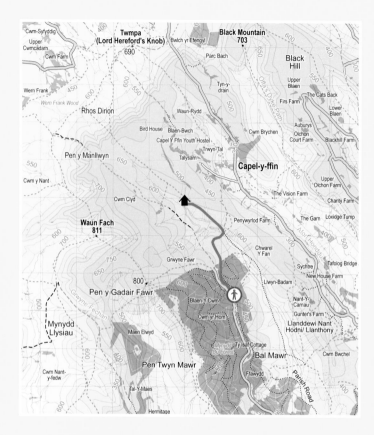

Grwyne Fawr

This tiny bothy sits at the head of the Grwyne Fawr Reservoir

Grwyne Fawr bothy – a former water pumping house

Bothy books can teach you more about a building than any historical account ever could. Take the one in this, the smallest of the MBA bothies in Wales's Brecon Beacons. Here the pages are full of tales – from the 70-year-old man who came up here on Christmas Day 2013 and impressively made a full roast meal (I'm guessing a lot of it will have been pre-cooked) to Kara, aged five, who arrived here with her mum and dad on a spring adventure. Flicking through its pages reveals the bothy's past in meticulous detail. Some tales tell the story of adventurous middle-aged skinny dippers, others of family outings where first peaks were climbed, and more still of would-be chefs who foraged here in the autumn for wild mushrooms for supper. If you want to understand the surrounding area, a primary place to go to is the beloved line-ruled leaves of a well-used bothy book.

There was a chair outside the bothy. Nothing could make my heart sink so fast as that. Seeing such an innocuous piece of furniture in any other context would likely not bring with it such devastating feelings to my stomach. But here, and in the rain of a heavy springtime shower, it would only mean one thing - someone had beaten me to the bothy.

I moved closer to it and watched as my fear was confirmed - a man emerged from it. Seeing me he waved and was soon joined by two more men. I felt like crying. I had raced to get here to experience this place, battled wind and rain all the way determined to claim it, and now I would have to bivvy instead. It felt rude to just walk on, dejected, so instead I carried on to my intended destination and did the best I could to smile.

'Don't worry I have a tent,' I exclaimed as I approached the aforementioned chair. 'You don't have to we're going,' said one of them. I felt a grin uncontrollably spreading across my face as they explained how they were part of a work party, one was the Maintenance Officer, and they had just that minute finished the brand new sleeping platform that sits in the rafters of this tiny bothy.

I felt like the luckiest person in the world. In a matter of minutes I'd lost the bothy then gained it again in spectacular fashion. After they

C.LL.M.

CEDWIR Y LLOCHES HON GAN Y
GYMDEITHAS LLOCHESAU MYNYDD
AR RAN EI PERCHENNOG

Gwnewch bob ymdrech
i'w chadw'n daclus

In Wales the MBA
is known as the CLLM

left, taking with them broken chairs and what rubbish they could, I set about making this place my home for the night. I swept the floor, set out the furniture, had a coffee and settled down in front of the fire to read the bothy book and tales of adventures from hundreds of people I will be unlikely ever to meet.

All evening I thought someone else would arrive. I watched the door expecting it to fling open, I watched the mist come in so thick with thin shards of rain that suddenly nothing existed save for the doorstep and little bothy I stood in.

When my eyelids started to become heavy I retired upstairs and discovered to my delight that heat from the stove had warmed it. No one ever did arrive that night, and I soon fell asleep to the scent of new wood and lingering spices from my curry, cocooned by mist in this perfect little hide.

The work party celebrate installing the new sleeping platform

This bothy sits in the depths of the Grwyne Fawr valley, and the name may originate from the word 'gweryn' (meaning 'large river at the wet place'). If true it's certainly a particularly apt moniker. For this building sits at the head of the reservoir of the same name, at the point where a river enters the reservoir before flowing on to reach the massive dam, then trickling down into the valley to continue on its river journey.

Believed to be a relic from the dam's construction – an old water pumping house – the small building makes for a cosy night in the heart of the Black Mountains. With a simple layout large enough for two or three, once you get the stove going this utilitarian little stone square quickly warms to become a toasty shelter, with the upstairs sleeping platform benefiting from unintentional underfloor heating.

The peaks and landscape that surround the bothy are as unique in Wales as this small building itself. Geologists believe that this section of the national park escaped the big freeze of the last Ice Age that carved and gnarled the nearby ranges into more dramatic formations. Because of this, rather than sharp shapely pyramids, the hills majestically roll like a tidal wave of sandstone and rock, cresting at summits dotted with limestone and sediment. In autumn and spring they are particularly beautiful, blending like a watercolour palette of orange and burnt amber with brown hues.

The valley is famous in Welsh history for being the site of a murder in 1136, when the first Earl of Hertford was killed by Iorweth ab Owain, kickstarting a conflict between the English and Welsh. Nowadays, while sitting in the peace and tranquillity of the bothy, with the stream gently stirring outside, it's hard to believe that this could be the site of anything so brutal…

Look out for…

Landmark: En route to the bothy, take a minute to walk along the dam and peer over the edge. It was here in 1998 that Princes William and Harry controversially abseiled – without wearing helmets.

Birds: The Black Mountains, where this bothy sits, are home to breeding birds such as red grouse and golden plover. They tend to stick to the

Top tip

If the bothy is full head past it and up the river a little. There are a few flatter spots that will neatly take a small tent and still offer easy access to the river.

ground, nesting among the long grass, rather than taking flight.

Hang gliders: This area is very popular with hang gliders, and many a time you'll hear the whoosh of their wings before you see them ride the thermals above.

How to get there

Classic: From the car park at Blaen-y-Cwm join the road and turn right, then pick up the path as it slowly cuts uphill and then levels out above the

Did you know?

The Grwyne Fawr Reservoir opened in 1932 to supply water to Abercarn. It took 20 years to build, and scattered around the shores are the foundations of the houses that the workers here used to call home.

river where you reach the Grwyne Fawr Reservoir dam. Continue past it, and just near the far end of the reservoir, as the path begins to steadily rise, look beyond the fence down to your left. You should see this small bothy that sits just above the weir. Carefully go through a small gap in the fence and follow the path down to the building. It's quite steep so watch your step.

Time: 2hrs

Looking down on the bothy and river

Alternative route

Hard: If you really want to feel you've earned a night in this cosy bothy, then start from the same car park, but instead of taking the path uphill take the bridge over the river. Follow the path that climbs up alongside forestry land to the summit of Pen y Gadair Fawr. Then follow the ridge along first to Waun Fach, then Pen y Manllwyn, then head downhill on the path that sits above the Grwyne Fawr river. You'll approach the bothy from the northwest – it will be on your right.

Grwyne Fawr essentials

Maps	OS Explorer 13; OS Landranger 161
Grid ref	SO 227 312
Terrain	Clear path with obvious landmarks to look for. Short track down to bothy is steep and very slippy after rain, especially for those carrying a big rucksack – care is needed.
Water source	Right outside the bothy, the Grwyne Fawr river
Facilities	Stove (bring your own fuel); shovel
Building	Brick construction, tile roof
Inside	It's a very small building, made up of a single room – perfect for two but do-able for up to four at a push. There are a few chairs, a table and then a ladder takes you up to a small sleeping platform.
Nearby hills	Waun Fach, Rhos Dirion, Twmpa (Lord Hereford's Knob)

Nant Syddion

A huge former country house flanked by Welsh woodlands

Nant Syddion bothy sits beside thick forest

Looking through the 'Wales' section in this book you may be thinking that most Welsh bothies are fairly small affairs – so just to prove otherwise I introduce you to Nant Syddion. Thought to have been built in the 1930s, this massive house is the antithesis to petite Grwyne Fawr-type bothies. Sitting within Forestry Commission land, on a sloping field, it is surrounded by trees on all sides. With a total of four rooms upstairs and two sitting rooms downstairs, a similar property, if transported to southern England, would be worth close to a million pounds – if not more. As it is, this old farmstead is completely free for walkers and mountain bikers to use, proving the true value of such a fantastic network.

Although the house that you see today is relatively new, this site has been home to people since around the early 1500s. It was farmed and habited by local families, many of them miners. The area itself was important for lead

Upstairs in Nant Syddion

mining, particularly in the 1700 and 1800s. Indeed, to this day there are ruins of old buildings and concealed shaft entrances within the surrounding forest and on the hillside, with one entrance going under the forestry track not far from the bothy itself. However, by the early 1900s there was much less demand for home-mined lead, and many of the mines closed. It's thought that families continued to live at Nant Syddion for a while afterwards, mainly farmers, but the last people left the house in the 1940s. And now, since the late 1990s, this bothy has been in the MBA's care.

As with many bothies, stories of former residents abound. But of all the stories about this particular shelter, by far the most heartbreaking is that of the ill-fated Hughes family who lived here in 1856. In that year, at Nant Syddion, one Margaret Hughes, who already had a young son and daughter, was celebrating with her husband Isaac after giving birth to quadruplets – believed to have been the first ones in Wales ever recorded. The celebrations did not last, however. It seems that two died that same day, another four days later, and the final one the following day. Tragic as that story is, it doesn't end there. A week later her son died, five days after that her husband passed away, then four days later her last child, a daughter, died too. Historical records indicate infection, and some sources suggest smallpox or a form of flu. Either way, the loss must have been devastating for Margaret. Some historians say she moved

' I'm telling you it's this way.'
' No – you're wrong – give me the map...'
' I'm navigating, leave it to me!'

So went the discourse of the Duke of Edinburgh group who were training for their expedition when I arrived in the woods above Nant Syddion. Packed as though prepared for a crossing of a continent, their mammoth rucksacks were a giveaway as I strode up to them and overheard their minor tantrum.

I never did my D of E. When I was their age I had far more important things to occupy my time – mainly dreaming of the day I would be a rock star. For those still curious I'll confess, that never actually happened, and so now I wistfully watch them learning the ropes of the outdoors – although am secretly pleased I don't have to travel in groups arguing over who holds the map and compass.

Room with a view: Nant Syddion overlooks the little-explored mid-Wales valley of the same name

Knowing I couldn't help them in any way – they fail instantly if they ask a person for assistance – I continued past them content that younger people were hopefully getting a taste for the wilder places and happy that over the years my backpack had been fine-tuned into a much more lightweight and manageable load.

The bothy came not long after and for a minute I had to pinch myself – this was a proper country house – it even had an outside loo (with a view) and a nearby pipe from which fresh water trickled. For a minute I was worried that I would be spoilt by this stay and any other bothy would seem like a downgrade, then I thought to hell with it and set about choosing a bedroom. I decided I'd sleep in the main room with the fire then, if more people arrived, I'd claim the smallest bedroom near the back.

A mist crept into the valley before sunset and I kept the door open to freshen the smell of old firewood, moving my chair in front of it to watch the sky change colours. Looking through the bothy book I knew that no D of E group is allowed to stay inside a bothy like this and, besides, I'd already seen their tents back at the start.

As the light dimmed and the flames from my fire seemed to glow brighter in the darkening room, I did what I often do when alone in such a large space – I started to sing. I may not have made it as rock star, life may have had other plans, but to be in a secluded valley like this, and for one night have a four-bedroomed house all to myself, made me feel like a VIP.

One of the storerooms

away, while others have it that she killed herself, but no one knows for sure. If after your stay you have time, call in to the churchyard at St John's in nearby Ysbyty Cynfyn, where the Hughes' graves can be found.

Look out for...

Birds: The forest around the bothy – Bwlch Nant yr Arian – has been home to the red kite feeding station since 1999. They get as many as 150 kites coming to grab some of the beef they give them – including one rare 'white kite', so called because of its pale colouring, caused by a genetic fault. Even if you don't stop in at the centre you have a high chance of seeing one of these birds in the skies over the woodland, so keep a lookout.

Top tip

Remember to keep the wicket gate on the front door closed at all times to stop sheep coming inside the building. If the bothy is full (fairly unlikely given the size) there is plenty of land outside suitable for pitching a tent.

History: The remains of Nant Syddion mine can still be spied. Just south of the bothy is the hidden entrance, cutting below the forestry track and passing underneath it; it's usually flooded with water.

How to get there

Classic: The fastest route comes up from the campsite at Tymawr farm. There is limited parking here for a small fee – otherwise there are a few more spaces in the hamlet of Ysbyty Cynfyn. Follow the wide track up to and past the farm buildings (remember to shut the gates). Then climb steadily along the 4x4 track until you reach a kissing gate, which gives access into the forest. Go left and follow the track downhill. Where it forks, turn right and continue downhill. At the next

Did you know?

The nearby village of Devil's Bridge is so named after a legend about a local old woman outwitting the devil. The fable tells of the Devil building a bridge on the promise of having the soul of the first living thing to cross it. Thinking he would get the old lady when she crossed, he was mortified to find that she sent her dog over instead. It's said that out of embarrassment he left and has never been seen in Wales since…

fork turn right to go almost back on yourself, and shortly you'll come to this large bothy.
Time: 1½hrs

Alternative route

Longer: If you want to discover more of the forest then consider coming in from Devil's Bridge (Pontarfynach). From there you can take the footpath that follows the north bank of the Mynach river and then the Afon Merin. You'll approach the bothy from the southwest.

Nant Syddion essentials

Maps	OS Explorer 213; OS Landranger 135
Grid ref	SN 773 790
Terrain	Easy-to-follow farm track, then forestry tracks to the bothy through woodland
Water source	Stream right outside the bothy
Facilities	Two multi-fuel stoves (bring your own fuel – if you use wood there, replace it before you leave from the dead wood left by the MO); saws; shovel; bike lock-up; separate outside earth toilet (bring your own paper)
Building	Stone construction, slate roof
Inside	Inside there are an impressive six rooms plus two storerooms. Downstairs on entering there are stairs immediately in front of you. The main sitting area is through the door to the left, a large room with a table, chairs and stove. To the right is a kind of kitchen area, with sinks and worktops as well as chairs and a bed frame – there is also a stove and access to the two storerooms. Upstairs are four 'bedrooms'. One had a bed frame on last visit, but this is not guaranteed. The two front rooms are the largest, easily sleeping six or more in each. The smaller back rooms are suitable for two each. If extra space is needed the two downstairs rooms would sleep perhaps as many as 10 between them.
Nearby hills	Pen y Garn

Arenig Fawr

A bothy perched high above Llyn Celyn
Reservoir – the site of a flooded village

The small but perfectly formed Arenig Fawr bothy

Beyond the town of Bala sits a silent valley of Tryweryn, to which few bother to venture. At its centre sits Llyn Celyn, a massive reservoir that glistens and sparkles in the sunlight. On either side rise up two related peaks, the Arenigs – Fawr and Fach. They are by no means small, but their proximity to Snowdonia's high mountains means they are rarely climbed – certainly not in the numbers their neighbours attract. Go there now and the lack of sound can be deafening. So it's strange to think that this was a bustling village as recently as the 1950s.

Capel Celyn was the name of the village that once sat where this water does now. A bastion not only of Welsh culture but of the language itself, the village was controversially flooded in 1960 to build the reservoir that would – wait for it, because this really does add insult to injury – provide the city

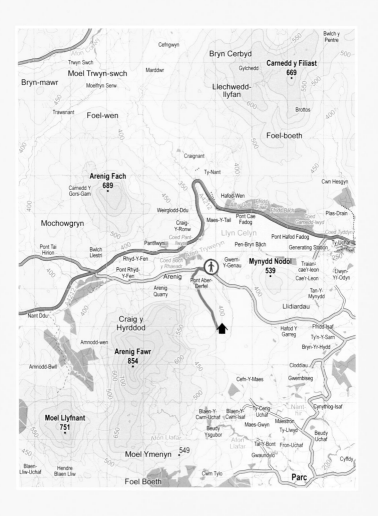

of Liverpool with water. Despite lobbying from locals and the fact that 35 of a possible 36 Welsh MPs voted against it in parliament (the 36th, in case you're wondering, abstained from voting), it was allowed to happen. A total of 67 people were forcibly cleared from the area, and the following five years saw the fields and farms decimated as it was built. To make things worse, it also led to the flooding of the Bala to Blaenau Ffestiniog railway line – which was being considered for closure (as were many smaller lines across the UK). Although a promise of a diverted route was made initially, this, sadly, was the final nail in the coffin and the track was closed, never to reopen.

Nowadays a road is the only way in and out of the valley, and the train no longer ferries people in by the carriage-load, making this a quiet and perhaps even lonely place to venture. Although that was a while ago now, and Liverpool City Council formally apologised for it in 2005, memories somehow linger here. Whether in the form of old graffiti that reads 'Corfiwch Dryweryn' ('remember Tryweryn'), or simply in the silent whispers of the wind, it's a hard event to forget.

Across the road (literally) from this controversial water site another reservoir, Llyn Arenig fawr, sits. Older (dammed and piped in 1830) and much less controversial – this one provides water to the nearby town of Bala – it acts almost as a perfect mirror to the peak that shares its name. Along its banks sits a small old building (probably used by those who built this dam or maintained it), which is now an open shelter for walkers who decide to venture off the beaten mountain tracks. It's the perfect place to spend a night and contemplate the fate of this now lonely valley.

Look out for...

History: If you take the alternative route and head up to the summit of Arenig Fawr you'll notice a memorial on the summit to eight airmen who died when their Flying Fortress bomber crashed on the mountain back in August 1943. Indeed, some of the wreckage can still be found lying a few hundred metres below it.

Did you know?

Back in the early 1900s two artists were so smitten with this area that they decided to paint it, and the mountain under which the bothy sits appears in a lot of their work as a backdrop. The artists were James Dickson Innes and Augustus John, and you can see Innes's painting 'Arenig, Sunny Evening' in the Tate's online gallery (www.tate.org.uk).

It smelt like burnt plastic. Someone had obviously tried to burn something here in the open-grate fire and things had clearly gotten out of hand. I had a packet of wet wipes in my backpack and began to clean the black smudges of smoke off the walls and windows.

Outside the sun shone brightly. I'd arrived thinking that a t-shirt would be enough for the walk-in but the wind had forced me to layer up, the cold wind made freezing as it blasted over the reservoir. Now inside scrubbing away at the glass I began to defrost. It annoyed me to think someone had come and caused this kind of mess and then left without even taking their rubbish out.

Cleaning felt good and as I did it I began to lose some anger. The black soot revealed a PVC noticeboard with an extract from a book called 'Lakes of Eryri' by Geraint Roberts pinned up.

I scanned it as the words appeared before me. It said how this area is rife with legends of the Tylwyth Teg - more commonly known as fairies. Apparently they left a bull calf here that was taken by a farmer. He couldn't believe his luck and managed to spawn from it a herd of cattle. But, years later, a man returned to this very spot and played a flute to summon all of them to join him and they disappeared into the lake.

The musical theme didn't end there. It also stated that certain conditions up here can mimic the

sounds of piano keys.
That description made
me pause and listen.
I put down my cloth
and headed outside.
Climbing the little bank
I peered out over the
homely refuge, past
the water and up
to the mountain. I
noted two people walking on
the path. Expecting them to come over to see the
bothy I prepared myself for pleasantries, but they
never came. The walkers were oblivious to my, and
the building's presence, too engrossed in their own
conversation to take in what lay a little off the
path. Beginning to feel a little magical myself, I
watched as another set of three mooched up the
path and never once glanced over to where I sat.
    When I finally went back to the building I
cleared out the fire and swept the floor. I was
lost to my thoughts once more. Someone may have
done something foolish in the valley below, losing
a whole community in a single act, but hopefully,
I mused, maybe lessons had been learned from it.
In a same way that someone nearly destroyed this
beautiful building through stupidity, hopefully by
cleaning up their mess it will mean that the next
visitor after me will want to keep this place in the
same way they found it. If every one of us took
the time to be a more responsible bothy user –
every time we visit – then hopefully these shelters
will last and these secluded valleys will never be
truly devoid of people, remembering the past.

Arenig Fawr bothy sits beside the llyn (lake) and hill of the same name

Nearby peak: If lingering beneath the flanks of Arenig Fawr has piqued your curiosity about this little-visited range, then after your night in the bothy head north to check out the other major hill – Arenig Fach. Standing at 689m it certainly deserves its moniker (Arenig Fach means 'small high ground'). To check it out head to its north face, which looks the most dramatic, before making your way up to its summit.

Top tip

The land near the reservoir offers many flat sections perfect for pitching a tent.

How to get there

Classic: By far the quickest and most direct way to access the bothy is via the path that leaves the minor road (itself just off the A4212) above Llyn Celyn. There's room for parking just off the road on the grass (watch for stones), as long as you park considerately. Then take the wide gravelly track uphill to Llyn Arenig fawr. Once there follow the rougher track above the water until you come to the signs and brickwork of the reservoir. The bothy is just off the path to your left.

Time: 1½hrs

Sleeping platforms don't come much cosier than this!

Alternative route

Hard: If you have never explored the often-overlooked Arenigs you're well placed to remedy that by bypassing the bothy on arrival and making your way, via the shoulder of Y Castell, to the summit of Arenig Fawr. From there you can enjoy commanding views over Snowdonia, the Berwyns and beyond. Retrace your steps back to the bothy and enjoy a well-deserved fireside night.

Arenig Fawr essentials

Maps	OS Explorer 18; OS Landranger 124
Grid ref	SH 850 379
Terrain	Easy wide track up to Llyn Arenig Fawr, then rougher path to bothy
Water source	The adjacent Arenig Fawr Reservoir can be used – with care. Do not collect water by the stone walls, but go further down to where the grass meets the water. Otherwise the nearby Nant Aberderfel is convenient too.
Facilities	Open fire (bring your own fuel – do not burn anything except coal or smokeless fuel); shovel; two sleeping platforms
Building	Stone construction, concrete roof
Inside	There is just one room. As soon as you step inside you will see it all. It's a cosy affair with a beautiful large window that allows in a lot of light, a fireplace and two sleeping platforms (although the floor can be used to sleep an extra person in an emergency). Large enough to sleep two in luxury, three in comfort and four at a tight squeeze.
Nearby hills	Arenig Fawr, Moel Llyfnant, Arenig Fach

Dulyn

*An old shepherd's hut hidden in
Snowdonia's uncrowded corner*

Arriving at Dulyn bothy in the Carneddau

Standing stones, hut circles, hill forts – ever since the Stone Age humans have descended on the valleys and mountains of the Carneddau, attempting to tame it. With the sea visible from its northern flanks and the higher Snowdonian peaks poking out at its southern end, the range is a perfectly placed vantage point from which to admire the surrounding landscape.

Not that the Carneddau don't offer height themselves. Here sit seven of the highest hills in Wales, their banks a rolling mass of splintered rock, left behind from retreating ice over 400 million years ago. Carving through the grass and soil, in the valleys below the giants, are winding rivers, babbling and sputtering as they descend the hillsides or spill out from the reservoirs that sit beneath the amphitheatre of sheer cliffs.

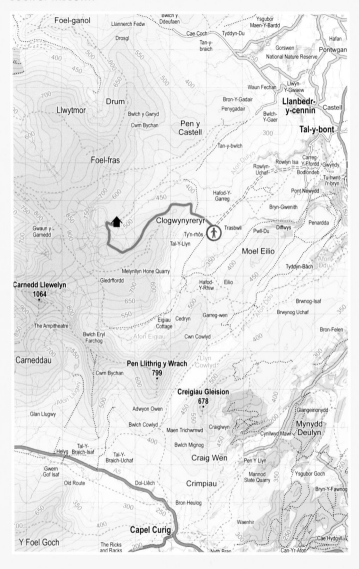

One such patch of water is Llyn Dulyn, which pools below the craggy corners of Craig y Dulyn before rising up to the summits of Foel Grach and Carnedd Gwenllian (formerly known as Carnedd Uchaf). Its name translates as 'black lake', and a visit to this particular part of the Carneddau will reveal why. Sinking to an estimated depth of around 60m, its waters appear dark and mysterious. Dig a little deeper and you'll discover it's been the site of several light-aircraft crashes due to the sudden height gain after a lower valley and the mist that such a place so often attracts. Llyn Dulyn is an eye-catching landmark to visit in its own right, but what makes it even more attractive to walkers is that a few hundred metres from its edge sits an old hut, now known as Dulyn bothy.

Thought to be a shepherd's hut, or remnants of workers' quarters built when they were damming the lake (which supplies water to the nearby town of Conwy), it is a cosy two-roomed affair that sits in arguably one of the wildest-feeling areas in the northern end of the national park.

Your walk-in alone will tell you that this is not the first homestead to sit among these mountains. En route you'll be able to make out the old boundary walls of earlier farms. Look over to the peak of Drum and you'll spy standing stones and circles, and if you head out along the river moss-covered remains of old settlements and sheepfolds will litter your route.

At the bothy itself, though, the presence of human neighbours feels a whole world away. You don't get the crowds here that you will at the adjacent Ogwen valley, or the summer tourists that flock to Llanberis and Snowdon. No, here you can often find yourself quite alone…and it's simply wonderful.

Did you know?

For at least 500 years the Carneddau has been home to a unique population of wild ponies, which the Carneddau Mountain Pony Association is working to have protected as a rare breed. They belong to no one, but each year are rounded up by the local community to be counted. Although a very difficult winter in 2013 saw at least 50 die, the last count showed healthy numvbers. And although you are by no means guaranteed to see them on a visit here, they are worth keeping an eye out for.

Half-light. That odd time of the evening when your eyes can play tricks on you - bushes become sheep, metres seem like miles and that shape of a building you're peering down the valley hoping to spy keeps morphing into nothing more than another cluster of boulders.

It was this time of evening that I set off from the car to pay another visit to Dulyn bothy. The first time I saw it was several years before. I had been hoping to find it for an overnight sleep, arrived from Carnedd Dafydd too late, and instead wild camped next to Melynllyn. It was only the next morning when I walked out to the car that I spied the bothy and realised just how close I had been to it. I made myself a promise to return.

Now I walked, straining my eyes against the deepening purple sky, trying to spot it once more. My boots crunched on the gravel as I paced the ground, the moon above now beginning to offer more glow than the dying rays of daylight. Then, deep in the valley below I saw it, its stone walls visible against the rock-covered grass it sat on. I quickened my pace, eager to reach it before dark.

Every step I took felt like I was merely bobbing up and down rather than striding forwards. Soon I became impatient, and despite the clumps of heather I struck right, heading directly towards it. The sodden hillsides tugged at my boots as I descended the heather rising around me, up to my waist and occasionally my cheek, but still I continued, the bothy now sharpening into focus. Summoning up my strength I leapt across the river on a series of protruding rocks then stumbled up the slopes and made a left - I was going to make it.

The rhythmic sound of snoring alerted me to the fact that I was not going to get this place to myself. Outside the door a tent was pitched on the flattened grass, the occupant already sound asleep. I crept on by, knocked on the door and opened it to a group of ruddy-faced bothy-dwellers, their skin made red from the glow of the fire and the plates of pasta they were eating.

'Come on in,' the one over the camping stove welcomed, and I was presented almost immediately with a plate of hot food and offered a seat by the fire. The smell of the pasta blended with the scent of a damp building being made warm in a summer evening, and I felt instantly at home.

Conversation began, and it transpired that one of them was the Maintenance Officer from the MBA. As we talked and I peered around the building I realised with a sinking heart that once more a stay in the bothy would elude me - it was full.

I went outside and admired my surroundings from the doorstep, which had now become drained of colour in the pallid tones of pre-darkness. I knew I could have squeezed in that night but I made my excuses and left, deciding to camp instead.

As my headtorch lit the way ahead I glanced back over my shoulder to my hosts. It was amazing how four simple walls could transform into a cosy shelter in an isolated valley and become instantly alive with the banter that comes from the gathering of strangers in a wild place. Despite a chill in the evening I felt a warmth running through my body.

Look out for...

Vegetation: The hardy plants that call these hills home range from Welsh poppies to bilberry, twisted hawthorn, holly and rowan – there's lots to take in if you keep your eyes peeled.

History: What you can't fail to see in the Carneddau are relics from the Stone, Bronze and Iron Ages, whose people littered these peaks with a mix of standing stones, circular stone huts and cairns. Although many are now just impressions of what used to stand there, or stones scattered on the ground, they are a testament to the fortitude of the people who used to live and farm these Welsh highlands.

How to get there

Classic: The shortest way is from the car park near Llyn Eigiau. Finding the car park can be tricky – but it's via the small lane heading uphill next to the bridge in Tal-y-bont. Once you've left your vehicle simply follow the well-maintained track around the bump of Clogwynyreryr and along to the

Top tip

Directly outside is some flatter ground (in front of the building) that you could feasibly pitch a two-man tent on. Otherwise, the flat ground next to Melynllyn is perfect for a wild camp.

The main sleeping room

Candles and stoves provide light and heat in bothies such as Dulyn

water at Melynllyn. Here you veer north to pick up the path over to the Dulyn Reservoir, cross the river, and the bothy is about 300m east of it.
Time: 1½hrs

Alternative route

Hard: Those wanting to maximise their hills could approach the bothy from the A5 in the Ogwen valley. A track opposite Gwern Gof Isaf leads up to Pen yr Helgi Du and on to Carnedd Llewelyn and Foel Grach, from where you can take the path down towards Melynllyn, go off-piste towards the water and then pick up the path to Dulyn Reservoir and the bothy. Harder still – and really packing in the ascent and mountain peaks – would be to pick up the path further west down the A5, opposite Ogwen Cottage, and start by ascending Pen yr Ole Wen and Carnedd Dafydd, then go on to Carnedd Llewelyn and continue as per above.

Dulyn essentials

Maps	OS Explorer 17; OS Landranger 115
Grid ref	SH 705 664
Terrain	Wide and well-defined track towards Melynllyn, then rougher, boggy ground to get to the bothy. A river crossing is involved, but this is usually straightforward.
Water source	The nearby Afon Dulyn flows below the bothy
Facilities	Coal fire (bring your own fuel); shovel
Building	Stone construction; metal roof
Inside	There are two rooms. After coming through a small porch you enter the main room. This is large and offers tables, chairs, a fire, an array of pots and pans left by other bothy users and candleholders on shelves. On your right is a door leading into the sleeping area. There are no raised platforms here, just a large space that could easily sleep 10 comfortably on the floor (more if you were prepared to snuggle!).
Nearby hills	Foel Fras, Carnedd Gwenllian, Foel Grach, Carnedd Llewelyn, Yr Elen

ENGLAND

The million-dollar view from Warnscale Head, in the Lake District, that won't cost you a penny…

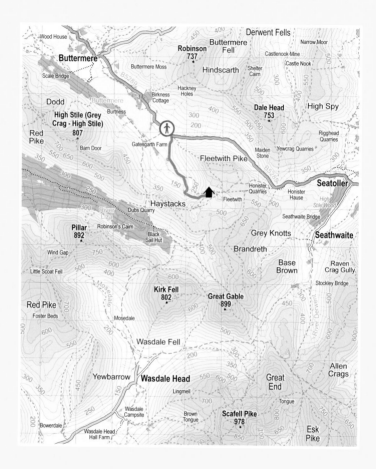

Warnscale Head

*This simple slate-built building offers
amazing views over Buttermere*

Warnscale Head bothy blends into the landscape in this slate-mining area

If the theme for bothy locations in Wales is reservoirs, then the theme for England is undoubtedly mining, and this perfectly placed Lake District shelter is no exception. Almost moulded into the mountainside from the slate that's smattered across the slopes, Warnscale Head bothy sits above the glorious Buttermere valley and boasts a window with a money-can't-buy view down over it.

Running parallel to Fleetwith Pike, the bothy is located near to Honister Slate Mine, where the search for high-quality green slate has taken place since the 1750s. Although the industry has slowed down significantly since then, and the need for all the old paraphernalia such as tramways, excavation wheels and workers' lodges high in the hills is no more, the slate mine still

201

Heading up to the bothy from Gatesgarth

makes a trade – although, granted, nowadays it's more about people coming to try the mine's via ferrata (fixed ladders and ropes on the quarry walls that a climber safely attaches themselves to) and new rope bridges.

Thankfully those old miners' shelters remain in small numbers, and this little bothy happens to be one of them. The MBA advises that its size and construction make it a more suitable temporary shelter or lunch stop than an overnight stay, but as long as there's only one or two of you there shouldn't be any problems – and, as there's a flat space outside perfect for tents, it can be a great wild camp spot too.

Its location is perfect for fans of eminent guidebook author Alfred Wainwright. This flat-cap-wearing, pipe-smoking writer and illustrator was so smitten with the nearby peak of Haystacks that when he died in 1991 his friends and family were instructed to scatter his ashes up at its summit near Innominate Tarn – a fitting resting place for a man who helped so many people to fall in love with the Lakes. Be careful when visiting, as a trip to this spectacular valley, bothy and summit will see you leaving a little part of yourself here with it too…

Look out for...

Innominate Tarn: Beneath the heights of Haystacks is this so-called nameless patch of water. It was here where the legendary fellwalker Alfred Wainwright's ashes were scattered on his death in 1991. It's certainly a serene place to stop and think. If you're intrigued further, once you've visited the summit and bothy make your way to Buttermere and pop into the church. There on the window at the rear, on your right as you enter, is an etching commemorating the man that perfectly frames the mountain where he remains.

Nearby peak: If the weather is good and you want to vary your descent route you could try making your way over to the small hill of Fleetwith Pike. The views from the summit are spectacular. On the way down keep a lookout for

Did you know?

There is another MBA bothy, owned by the Honister Slate Mine, not far from Warnscale Head called Dubs Hut, which many people mistakenly believe is this one. It's much larger and even marked on the map; however, it's not very warm and there is no fireplace, so you'll need to take plenty of warm layers with you if you go.

I love setting off for a walk near the end of a day. The looks of concern from other walkers at seeing you heading up when everyone else is heading down; the confusion caused when they watch you going off-piste away from the crowd, and the curiosity in their eyes when they wonder just what sort of person you are and just where you are going...

I'd enjoyed many such glances on my way up to Warnscale Head. Being my first visit here I couldn't watch them watching me for too long, though, as I had a bothy to find and knew this one had the potential to be tricky. I'd done my research before I came, knew it seemingly morphed out of the slate that sat around it, and had read how several people had set off to find it and resorted to camping when they couldn't. But I was determined.

I had a plan to keep my eyes peeled for the window — because surely the window would reflect the tiny bit of sunlight. Making my way up the rocky slopes I had never felt so alert. Getting closer to the col I felt eyes burning on me, and looked to the left to see a group of five staring at me across the river that by now cut so deep into the valley it was practically a gorge between us. Yet still I carried on.

Soon a faint tracing of years of footfall gave itself away. I took a chance and followed it and

Warm and cosy inside Warnscale Head

soon emerged onto a flat grassy protrusion. The bothy was in front of me. I disappeared from view into the slate room. It may have been dark, but I was instantly drawn to the window from where I could gaze down at Buttermere's expansive water and – if I squinted – even make out the pub that sits at the end.

Once the crowds had gone from the opposite path, and the sun began to set, I sat outside the structure and watched as one by one tiny lights flickered in the houses in the valley. It began to rain and I pulled my jacket closer. They may have the warmth of their houses, the modern conveniences of a kitchen and a comfy mattress, but I wouldn't have traded places for the world.

the white cross (that you'll have spotted from the road when you arrived). It marks the death of Fanny Mercer here back in 1887.

How to get there

Classic: Park in the pay-and-display area around Gatesgarth. Take the path that heads around the lower slopes of Fleetwith Pike. Where it forks alongside the river that feeds Buttermere, take the path on the right to head steeply uphill. The path crosses a stream, which is straightforward enough as long as there's not been too much rain. Continue on and before the path levels out at a col you'll see the bothy disguised by the surrounding slate to your right. Look at the grass and you'll be able to make out a faint path leading to it.

Time: 2hrs

Top tip

Outside the bothy is a lot of soft grass suitable for pitching a tent. However, if it's full you may want to take the path and make your way to Blackbeck Tarn – this is a perfect secluded spot for a wild camp, with water right outside and a short walk for great views not just down to Buttermere but over to Ennerdale too.

Remember to duck when you enter through the tiny door

Alternative route

Hard: There are a number of other routes in that you could take. For one with altitude start instead in Buttermere and head up onto the ridge taking either the path to Red Pike or High Stile. From there continue along it southeast to take in Seat and Haystacks. Contour round past Blackbeck Tarn and then follow the path that curves downhill – you'll very soon reach the bothy on your left.

Warnscale Head essentials

Maps	OS Explorer 4; OS Landranger 89, 90
Grid ref	NY 205 133
Terrain	Rough but obvious path from Gatesgarth. Becomes faint around Warnscale Bottom, but then presents itself once more. Stick to the zig-zags to get yourself over the wet and loose slate and stones. Higher up, confusion is possible at the river crossing, but follow your nose and you should pick up the path again. It's easy to miss the bothy in bad weather – it's easier to see on the way down than the way up, so if all else fails continue on to the col and then retrace your steps, keeping a lookout for it on the left.
Water source	Small stream fairly near the bothy – NOT the river below. Head uphill a little to access it – take a couple of containers to avoid several trips in the dark.
Facilities	Open fire grate (no fuel – bring your own); two sleeping platforms; shovel
Building	Stone construction, slate and stone roof; shell of two rooms before you reach the door; slate bench outside
Inside	The bothy has just one room. You will need to duck to get inside – and probably remove your pack too! It's certainly cosy. There's an L-shaped stone/slate sleeping platform that will comfortably sleep two – any more would be a squeeze. The floor could take an additional two if needed. There's one window with a million-dollar view down to Buttermere.
Nearby hills	Fleetwith Pike, Haystacks, Seat, Brandreth, Grey Knotts

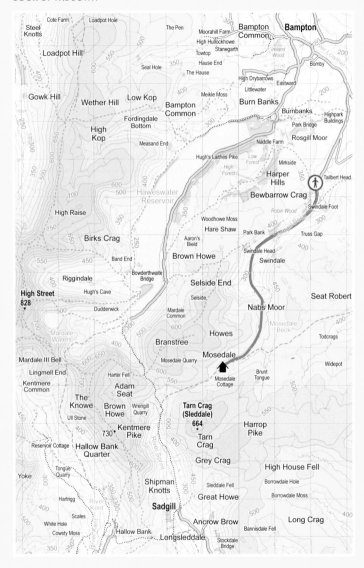

Mosedale Cottage

*A whitewashed cottage that sits in a
secluded corner of Lakeland*

Mosedale Cottage – a homely bothy in a far-removed location

Perhaps the least visited valley in Lakeland, Mosedale not only lacks the crowds but also has a different feel to the other areas of the national park. It's not only because it lacks the gear shops and cafés, not to mention the National Trust motifs that you find elsewhere, but it feels both geographically and culturally cut off from it too.

Walking here, you can almost guarantee to have the path to yourself for the majority of your kilometres. The peaks lack the big names and heights, facilities are non-existent, and access to it even takes dedication – and that's even before you've so much as pulled on your walking boots. But, as they say, nothing worth having ever comes easy, and that sentiment certainly applies to this grand old bothy.

The silence was almost deafening. Sometimes, I find, when a place is too quiet the lack of noise can make you hear things that aren't actually there. Before I went to Mosedale, on researching its location I found many a tale of hauntings and spooky goings-on in this building. One man told of how his dog refused to go inside, another said he heard scratching and banging in the night although he was alone. I chalked these tales up to overactive imagination and, of course, the ubiquitous bothy mice who often wake the bothy-dweller with their chewing and scurrying antics.

On arrival I looked into the book. I'd already experienced that familiar sensation that I was following another walker on my way here – the footprints were there, every time I placed my boot into the mud, and a few hundred metres from the building I began to find (and pick up) pieces of firewood someone had obviously dropped on their way here. Yet when I entered there was no one there but me.

Somewhat serendipitously the page the bothy book opened on told of ghosts in the night and a group of girls so scared they almost left. It was only when I turned the page and read the next entry from a mature man and his wife that the story became clear – a small group of boys had also stayed and spooked the girls through the window, forcing them to ask to sleep in the other bedroom with this older couple. I felt immediately at ease.

The thing about Mosedale is that it's just really quiet. So quiet, in fact, that the quiet itself seems loud. It was only when I heard a noise and headed outside to investigate, thinking it had come from the abandoned quarry, and quickly realised it was actually a passing plane coming from the Manchester direction, that I realised how quickly we can scare ourselves unnecessarily.

Mosedale Cottage bothy-book holder

Above all it was when I read the entry from the two descendents of one of the children who was born in this house in the early 1900s that I could begin to relax. A place

En route to little-visited Mosedale

that clearly held such happy memories for the Richardson family could only ever be good. I vowed to actually enjoy the silence - to embrace this brief pause I had allowed myself in a world normally deafening from the sounds of phones beeping and TVs and radios. Bothy stays force you to do this, to embrace the gaps rather than trying to fill them with sound. To make you see that life is often what happens in between all the chaos.

I slept soundly that night, woken only by the sunlight, and left with as much love for the place as the Richardson boys had.

Inside the bothy

Mosedale Cottage sits deep in this sequestered corner, amidst boggy ground and adjacent to a quarry – now disused. Some believe it was a classic workers' shelter or store for the quarrymen's equipment (it was active until around the 1920s). However, looking in the bothy book here, I found an entry from a descendant of a former resident. It read:

'John Walter (Jock) Richardson and Thomas Jackson Richardson, two of the still surviving eight grandchildren of Thomas and Martha Jackson, visited this place on 31 May 2013. Thomas Jackson and Martha Jackson lived here at the end of the nineteenth and beginning of the twentieth centuries with several of their nine children. Our mother, Jessie Jackson, was born here on 7 July 1906. It has taken us a long time to get here, but it was worth the trouble.'

So, as you can see, this was a family home for several years. Other entries confirm that workers did come here for food, which was made by the mother described above – offering them a proper taste of homemade grub while they toiled in such an inaccessible location.

212

Now it still does look very much like a home. With an outside toilet, comfy armchairs round a fire and what seem like proper bedrooms, all placed around a courtyard, if Jessie ever came back she might feel as though she had never really left.

Although no longer a family dwelling, these whitewashed walls are now visited by hillwalkers and even local shepherds, who have a separate section of the property.

Look out for...

Wildlife: Deer can sometimes be spotted in this part of Lakeland, and ring ouzels and peregrines are frequent visitors too – keep your eyes peeled on your walk-in and as the sun sets.

Landmark: Not far from here, to the east, is the valley of Wet Sleddale – it's here, high on the fell, that an abandoned building called Sleddale Hall sits – the location for the filming of cult classic *Withnail and I*. It is privately owned, so certainly not the place for an overnighter, but if you wanted to see it you could combine an amble up the valley with a stay at Mosedale.

How to get there

Classic: The most straightforward route begins at Swindale Foot. The road continues on, but there is nowhere to park beyond it, so you have to suffer a couple of kilometres on undulating tarmac. After passing the last building at Swindale Head, emerge into the valley and skirt the beck. Climbing up from the valley on the faint muddy track arrive on Nabs Moor and then follow Mosedale Beck below you further into the valley. At last the path begins to widen and become more clear, and alongside a tiny copse of trees you will spy your shelter.
Time: 4hrs

Alternative route

Hard: There are several options, but the most interesting starts from Haweswater Reservoir at the car park at the end of the road. Take the

Top tip

The courtyard outside is perfect for pitching a tent, with the stone walls offering shelter if you find yourself here in high winds. Don't cut wood from the neighbouring trees – you need to bring your own fuel. Equally, don't be tempted to light a fire outside as others clearly have done – it's not good bothy etiquette.

bridleway up to Gatescarth Pass. The more adventurous may want to combine it with an ascent of the lesser-trodden peaks of Harter Fell, Adam Seat or Branstree. Otherwise descend to the beck and then pick up the path that tracks northeast, uphill, then descends into Mosedale, this time approaching the bothy from the southwest.

Mosedale Cottage essentials

Maps	OS Explorer 5, 7; OS Landranger 90
Grid ref	NY 494 095
Terrain	Tarmac road at start gives way to defined grassy track that becomes fainter on the climb out of the valley onto Nabs Moor. Boggy and muddy going from there, but nearer the bothy a more defined wide track leads right to the door.
Water source	Stream to the right of the bothy as you approach it
Facilities	Stove; shovel; outside toilet
Building	Stone construction, tiled roof
Inside	There are five rooms in the bothy. The main door to access the bothy is in the right-hand corner when you access the courtyard. To your left, diagonally opposite, is the toilet. The other doors lead to locked storerooms and shepherds' private quarters. For the bothy you enter into a porch and then go through another door to the main room. Here there's a fire and a number of old leather sitting-room chairs. There are two small rooms in front of you – each sleeping no more than three at a push. To your left is a door that leads to a small corridor and two further bedrooms. The one on the right sleeps around six comfortably – all on the floor. The one on the left has a large sleeping platform that also sleeps six, with room for more on the floor.
Nearby hills	Selside Pike, Branstree, Harter Fell, Kentmere Pike

Greg's Hut

*A former mineworker's hostel and the
highest bothy in the MBA network*

Greg's Hut bothy sits high in the Pennines

Much has been written about the Pennines. Stretching up like a spine through northern England, separating the North West from the North East and continuing all the way up to the Anglo-Scottish borders, they are a range of mountains many will have experienced in one location or another. Those who walk the Pennine Way (the oldest long-distance path in the country) in its entirety cannot fail to notice the region's ever-changing scenery – from the gritstone edges at Stanage in the Peak District to the limestone pavements of Malham and the glacier-scooped High Cup near Dufton.

But as much as there are some beautiful and striking sections, anyone who's walked that trail will also tell you that some stretches are just a seemingly endless slog over peat hags, quivering quagmires and desolate

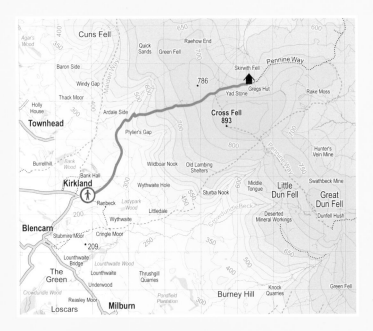

Greg's Hut was saved from dilapidation by friends of John Gregory, who died in a climbing accident in Switzerland

moorland. One of those places exists a little further north of the aforementioned High Cup – the expansive land over Cross Fell. Up here the weather can change fast from blazing sunshine to flurries of snow, or from overcast humidity to gale-force winds, making a trip up here feel properly wild in the weather sense of the word.

Handy, then, that nearby is a bothy – one that has even, on occasion, been a life-saver for walkers on the hills. It sits at 700m above sea level and, as such, is the highest bothy in the entire MBA network. A former lead-mining lodge, it was a weekday-worker's bunkhouse for those at Katelock lead mine and nearly wasn't a bothy at all. When the industry declined in the late 1800s, the building fell into disrepair. Sitting where it does, it was exposed and battered by the elements for about 50 years and was nearly left to crumble away, as were many others in this area – you'll see the remains of some when you walk in.

It was, however, saved in 1968 when the MBA managed to get permission to include it in their renovation programme. Almost by coincidence, at this same time the Mercian Mountaineering Club heard about it and wanted to renovate it in memory of John Gregory, a member who sadly died in a climbing accident in Switzerland. They teamed up to create this memorial to their friend, and finally, on 6 May 1972, it was finished and ready to receive walkers. Now the Greg's Hut Association (still made up of his friends) estimate they get around 600 people visiting each year – from UK walkers to overseas

An unusually yellow door welcomes walkers

Tears were streaming down my face when Neil walked into the bothy. He's a photographer and we'd come up to finally visit Greg's Hut together after both our individual previous attempts had seen us forced to turn back – his by driving rain, soaking all his equipment, and mine by a snowstorm that fast become a blizzard. Finally we'd made it and he'd set to work photographing the exterior, while I ventured inside to get a feel for the place. Nepalese prayer flags hung from the rafters, and behind them I spied the smiling face of the building's namesake – John Gregory. I'd read about John before I'd come, had known that he'd tragically perished during a climbing trip with his friend. But it wasn't until I walked over to the noticeboard on the other side of the room, my footsteps on the flagstone floor echoing in the emptiness, that I learned of the full story and a second one that made my eyes well up.

When John Gregory (aka Greg) fell he was climbing with a man called Bob (Robert Richard Broxap). It was Bob who held Greg on the rope when he fell, it was he who raised the alarm, and it was he who sat and tended his friend, freezing cold and injured, while he waited for that help to arrive. Sadly Greg died before the helicopter came, but Bob accompanied his body both to hospital and back to the UK overland. It wasn't until 25 years after this event that Bob felt able to tell people exactly what happened. He got a group of friends together in 1993 and revealed all. Then, just months later in 1994, he too lost his life. In an all too similar tale, he was canoeing with a friend called Mark when they had a terrible accident. Despite Mark's efforts to save him, Bob died on 2 April.

Prayer flags usually hang above John Gregory's picture

The heroics and loyalty of friends in the outdoors, and the love for those friends that raised money and created shelters such as this was overwhelming, and I couldn't help but weep unashamedly.

The night passed in much happier spirits, a night by the fire with warm food and hot drinks and shared tales of our own adventures. As we left the next day, though, the weather turned again, a grey, lingering cloud damp and cold. I stole a glance back to the bothy, thinking how apt the weather was for the melancholy past behind such a place, but then gave a quiet 'thank you' to both the men. It's people such as these who enable us to experience these wild places in comfort, and for them, and the friends they leave behind, we will be eternally grateful.

guests, local shepherds and even the Penrith Mountain Rescue Team.

The group carry out maintenance each year and even bring up fuel so that visitors can have a fire – but do bring your own and always make sure you leave some for the next guest. Being so key to many rescues, it's worth noting the donation collection boxes – do give generously to keep this shelter and the memory of John Gregory alive.

Did you know?

The nearby summit of Cross Fell is the place where the Helm Wind blows – the only named wind in Britain. This happens when a very strong northeasterly blows down the hill's southwest slope creating a sound reminiscent of a freight train. You can tell when it's blowing as a cloud known as the Helm Bar forms above Cross Fell. It can last for a few hours or even a few days.

Look out for...

Vegetation: The top of Cross Fell is unique outside Scotland in terms of its vegetation. Made up of some rare alpine plants – including Mountain forget-me-nots and Starry saxifrage – the fell is designated a Special Area of Conservation.

Landmarks: Given its mining past, it's not surprising that remains of old huts and buildings litter the slopes. On the way up you'll spot some corrugated iron shelters in varying states of disrepair – some are even marked on the OS map. Although interesting to look at, they are certainly not suitable shelters for a night's sleep, but can make a good windbreak if you want to stop for a snack.

How to get there

Classic: A start from Kirkland will get you to the bothy the quickest. Park either near the church or in one of the limited spaces near the hall, then follow the farm track through fields. Skirt around the flanks of the knobble called High Cap before heading further uphill. Where the path swings round sharply to the left at a cairn, continue on and up heading northeast. It is easy to lose the path here, as the ground is boggy and the path

Top tip

If the bothy is full there are many patches of flat ground outside where you could pitch a tent. Be careful, though, as the area was mined extensively and there are sections of subsidence. At the time of writing the area about 500m to the east of the hut had fallen away, so watch your step.

faint, but continue to pick your way and soon the Pennine Way intersects with your trail. Continue straight on, and in a little under 1km you will reach the bothy on your left.

Time: 3hrs

Alternative route

Hard: As the bothy sits on the Pennine Way, there are a number of options for increasing the distance and difficulty of getting here. If you want to add in some summits you can start at Dufton and take the Pennine Way to tick off Little Dun Fell, Great Dun Fell and Cross Fell before arriving at the bothy. It's a long day, but certainly a rewarding walk – providing you are competent at navigating (mist descends quickly and often up here). Otherwise you might decide to start at Garrigill to the east and take the longer route along the Pennine Way up to Greg's Hut.

Greg's Hut essentials

Maps	OS Explorer 19, 31; OS Landranger 91
Grid ref	NY 691 355
Terrain	Clear farm track followed by faint and boggy section over fairly featureless high moorland, then a better-defined, although rough and rocky, path to the bothy
Water source	Outside the bothy – a pipe has been constructed to funnel the water conveniently
Facilities	Stove (bring your own fuel); sleeping platform; shovel
Building	Stone construction, slate roof
Inside	There are two rooms. You enter into a small porch where you'll find the shovel. A door takes you into the main room, which contains a painting of John Gregory, the man to whom this building is dedicated. You'll also find a plaque detailing the story of his friend who died several years ago. There's an array of chairs in here and a table for preparing food – there always seem to be prayer flags hanging. A door in the far corner of the room leads into the second room. Here is a raised sleeping area that sleeps six comfortably; eight or even ten at a push. There is a small table in here as well as a stove.
Nearby hills	Cross Fell, Great Dun Fell

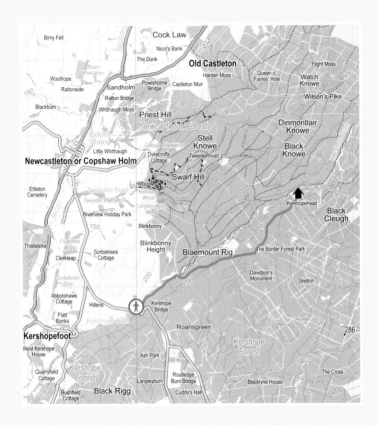

Kershopehead

An old farmstead surrounded by the trees of Kielder Forest Park

Kershopehead bothy

Murder and bothies are natural bedfellows. Not in the sense that murders happen in bothies, you understand, but in the sense that people often attach horror stories and tales of strange happenings to the wildest places in the UK, which are, of course, where bothies tend to be situated. Among all these macabre tales, however, the one of the murder of a gamekeeper near Kershopehead bothy is actually true…

It all happened back in November 1849, and although I'm connecting it with this bothy, the actual site of the foul play was in fact 2km away from the structure that you will sleep in – but nonetheless… Thomas Davidson, a gamekeeper for Sir James Graham for over 20 years, set out to do his rounds of the land a couple miles from his home. When he didn't return that evening his wife raised the alarm and a search began. His body was finally discovered

Looking out from the main room

two days later. He was found lying face down in blood, strangled by his own neck scarf. Three people suspected of the murder were taken in by police. They were a poacher called James Hogg (who had been fined not long before for his illegal shooting activities based on evidence that none other than one Thomas Davidson had given), his cousin known as John Nichol and a third man called Andrew Turnbull.

Accused and imprisoned to await trail, Turnbull always protested his innocence and was found hung in his prison cell. He left a note once again stating his innocence and firmly pointing the finger at the other two. Perhaps shockingly, when the case went to trial the other two were found not guilty and no one was ever charged. Hogg and Nichols, shortly after being released, mysteriously left the country. Now, to commemorate the loyal Davidson for his service, a stone pillar stands at the very spot where he was found.

It may sound like an unhappy tale, but the actual bothy itself has no strange atmosphere or gloomy undertones. Lovingly kept by the local Maintenance Officer it's full of quirky nick-nacks, including an old kettle and comfy furniture, and even relics from the past – an old wagon wheel adorns the wall, and bed frames upstairs and down make sleep that much more comfortable.

So the lesson is don't let a grisly story put you off a place – judging a bothy by its cover, in this case, would mean you'd miss out on one of the best places to sleep in northern England. So go forth and have your own adventures, form your own memories and tell your own stories.

Look out for...

History: As mentioned in the alternative route description, it's certainly worth the diversion (around 2km extra) to check out the weathered stone memorial cairn to the gamekeeper Thomas Davidson who was murdered in this forest while protecting the land back on 8 November 1848.

Landmark: Further north up the river, on the opposite bank, is the Three Counties Meeting Point, a place

Did you know?

The Kershope Burn that flows a little way downhill beneath the bothy runs along the border between England and Scotland. A little before the bothy it's actually known as Hobb's Flow, but it changes its name once it reaches the bothy area.

When I was a child there was a small public woodland behind my house. In the summer me and my friends would spend hours exploring it, making dens among the tree trunks, hanging rope swings from the branches and wishing we could spend the night amongst the old oak trees. But around teatime we always heard our mums calling us back home and our forest adventures were relegated to distant dreams of what could have been.

Now, as a grown up (in age although not in spirit), I get to live out the missions I planned all those years ago. Packing up my sleeping bag and camping stove – and some candles to make a place homely – I spend my weekends escaping back to childhood by heading into the wild and sleeping out under the stars or in abandoned buildings – running away from the mundane responsibilities that daily life brings with it.

That's why I was particularly excited to stay at Kershopehead. It had all the ingredients for a proper expedition – a gruesome back-story, a house in the middle of the forest and effort to reach it. As I walked underneath the conifer canopy I felt

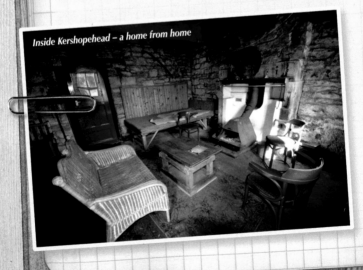

Inside Kershopehead – a home from home

the anticipation growing as I imagined what lay ahead.
The confusion at some of the path junctions, made
so by work on the forest that had forged new tracks
where they shouldn't be, only served to add to the sense
of adventure.

Arriving at the house I felt adrenaline surge through
me as I realised that half the building was a shell of a
structure and a crow circled above the hole where the
window should be. I nervously opened the door, unsure
of what I might find, then the familiar scent of wood
smoke filled my nostrils, and the aroma of aged paper
from old books added to it and I felt as though I was
coming home.

The personal touches made me forget the murder
and the foreboding crow, and instead I settled down for
what can only be akin to a stay in a holiday home, with
a warm fire a comfy chair and plenty of reading material.

As I left the following day I felt as refreshed as
if I'd been sleeping in my own bed. I followed the path
to pay my respects to the murdered gamekeeper and took
my time meandering through the trees as a mountain
biker whizzed by on the tracks. The sun began to burn
even warmer and I didn't want the journey here to end.

Once I reached the long straight track to the car I
spied three young boys coming along it on their bikes. As
they got closer I realised that they were watching me
nervously. I bade them hello and they started to look
less concerned - they had spotted my larger rucksack.
When they rode away I looked back and realised that
strapped to the back of their bicycle racks were
pillows, sleeping bags and camping mats. I couldn't help
but feel contented.

A new generation were discovering bothies, having
their own adventures in the great outdoors, rather than
rushing back home to play on their computer games or
update their Facebook status. They are the reason we
all need to work together to retain these shelters, for
they are tomorrow's intrepid explorers attempting to
find their way in Britain's beautiful wild spaces.

The monument commemorating Thomas Davidson, the murdered gamekeeper

where the Scottish Borders, Cumbria and Northumberland all meet. If you've decided to come along on your mountain bike, you'd certainly have time to explore more of this huge patch of woodland.

How to get there

Quickest: The most obvious route starts from Kershope Bridge. Follow the forestry track alongside the burn until you finally get to head into the trees just after the bridge. Where the path forks make sure you head on the route that bears uphill slightly, and continue on this to the crossroads at English Kershope. To get to the bothy fast go straight on. At the next fork, head left, then at the final one straight on. Soon you'll begin to descend downhill a little and the bothy will be on your left.

Time: 2hrs

Alternative route

Added history: Follow the route above but when you reach the English Kershope crossroads head right, rather than straight on. Continue on the main path, ignoring any turn-offs. On the map it looks die straight but in reality it does curve – follow it and soon it straightens out once more, heading north-east. Follow it for a little under half a kilometre and, on your left, you'll spot the monument to the gamekeeper who was murdered on this very spot all those years ago. To reach the bothy from here carry on the path to the cross-roads, turn left, then at the next path junction turn right. You're now on the main path again described above. At the next fork keep straight on and the bothy will shortly be on your left.

Kershopehead essentials

Maps	OS Explorer 324; OS Landranger 79, 80
Grid ref	NY 544 863
Terrain	Forestry tracks – well defined, but can be muddy and wet after rain and sustained vehicle use. Confusion possible after felling, as new paths frequently appear – keep your map to hand and don't be afraid to backtrack if needed.
Water source	There used to be a spring here, but not any more. It's best to bring in enough water for your stay. If you get desperate head downhill to Kershope Burn, but care is needed.
Facilities	Stove (bring your own fuel; if using wood left in bothy remember to replace it – with dead wood only); saw; shovel
Building	Stone construction, corrugated metal roof
Inside	There are three rooms. On entering the bothy you are faced with a flight of stairs. These take you up to the main sleeping area, where there is an old bed frame and lots of floor space – would sleep 10 comfortably (although remember that groups of more than six must seek permission from the landowner/MBA first). The door to your right leads into the main sitting area, where there is also a bed frame. There are several chairs, tables and benches, and it is kept immaculately, with historical points of interest on the wall. Another door leads to a small kitchen area and even a mini-library of outdoor books and magazines (if you take one, replace it – or better yet bring one to donate). The far left of the building is left empty/for storage and is unsuitable for a stay.
Nearby hills	Glendhu Hill, Black Knowe, Wilson's Pike

APPENDIX A
Further information and reading

A long walk to Ben Alder Cottage is well worth the effort

General

Mountain Bothies Association
www.mountainbothies.org.uk

RSPB www.rspb.org.uk

The National Trust
www.nationaltrust.org.uk

Scotland

Tunskeen

'Tunskeen 1965', by Bernard Heath
(www.mountainbothies.org.uk/cust_
images/documents/Tunskeen.pdf)
An account of the rebuilding of the
bothy from its ruined state

Mountain Bothies: Celebrating 50 years
of the MBA (MBA, 2015)

Forestry Commission Scotland
www.scotland.forestry.gov.uk
Use the site's search facility to access
information about Galloway Forest Park
and its 'Dark Sky' status

Kettleton Byre

Roman Britain Organisation
www.roman-britain.org
Search for 'Durisdeer' to find details of
a nearby fortlet and marching camps

Scotland movie location guide
www.scotlandthemovie.com

Includes information about the 1959 filming of *The Thirty-Nine Steps*

Taigh Seumas a' Ghlinne

Kidnapped Robert Louis Stevenson (Puffin, 1983)

Walking With Murder: On The Kidnapped Trail Ian Nimmo (Birlinn Ltd, 2005)

Lairig Leacach

Heritage Path Project
www.heritagepaths.co.uk
Enter the bothy name in the site's search engine to learn about the local drove road

Undiscovered Scotland
www.undiscoveredscotland.co.uk
Find information about Spean Bridge using the site's A–Z Index

Ben Alder Cottage

'Strange happenings at Ben Alder Cottage', *Scottish Mountaineering Club Journal* Paddy Buckley (2011)
www.smc.org.uk/downloads/LitPrize2011a.pdf

Kidnapped Robert Louis Stevenson (Puffin, 1983)

Undiscovered Scotland WH Murray (Dent, 1951)

Blackburn of Corrieyairack

Undiscovered Scotland
www.undiscoveredscotland.co.uk
Search using 'General George Wade' to find out about the man who created a network of Highland roads – including the Corrieyairack Pass

Old Roads of Scotland
www.oldroadsofscotland.com/military_roads.htm
More information about the region's network of military roads

Speyside Trust www.badaguish.org
Find out how to enter the Corrieyairack Challenge

Ruigh Aiteachain

Edwin Henry Landseer
www.bbc.co.uk/arts/yourpaintings/
Enter his name to see the work of this acclaimed artist, who once stayed next to the bothy to sketch pictures of the Highlands

Heritage Path Project
www.heritagepaths.co.uk
Enter 'Glen Feshie' into the keyword search box to find information about the old drove road

Visit Scotland www.visitscotland.com
Local attractions, information and facilities

Gelder Shiel Stable

The Old Man of Lochnagar
HRH The Prince of Wales (Puffin, 1991)

Balmoral www.balmoralcastle.com
Website of the Scottish home of the Royal Family

Bob Scott's

'Bothying before the MBA' by Ashie Brebner, in *Mountain Bothies: Celebrating 50 Years of the MBA* (Mountain Bothies Association, 2015)

One Man's Mountain Tom Patey (Canongate Books, 2007)

Hutchison Memorial Hut

The Cairngorm Club
www.cairngormclub.org.uk
See 'Past meets', 23–24 June 2012 for
an account of an overnighter at the
Shelter Stone

Video about the hut restoration
www.bbc.co.uk
Search using the bothy name, then
select 'Bothy restoration project begins'

Ryvoan

Forestry Commission Scotland
www.scotland.forestry.gov.uk
Enter 'Ryvoan' for information about the
forest and related activities

Cairngorms National Park
www.cairngorms.co.uk
All manner of information about the
area

Glenmore Lodge
www.glenmorelodge.org.uk
Details of courses and events at the
National Outdoor Training Centre

Easan Dorcha

Forestry Commission Scotland
www.scotland.forestry.gov.uk
Enter 'Achnashellach' for information
about the forest and related activities

National Rail Enquiries
www.nationalrail.co.uk
Plan your rail journey to and from
Achnashellach Station

Shenavall

'Shenavall: a brief history',
Alex Sutherland *Mountain Bothies
Association Journal* (1990)

www.mountainbothies.org.uk/
Cust_images/documents/shenavall1.pdf
An account written by the bothy's
former Maintenance Organiser

Fisherfield Six information:
*Great Mountain Days in Scotland:
50 Classic Hillwalking Challenges*
Dan Bailey (Cicerone, 2012)

The Lookout

Isle of Skye www.skye.co.uk
Plan your visit to the island using this
comprehensive resource

Royal Commission on the Ancient and
Historical Monuments of Scotland
www. rcahms.gov.uk
Enter 'Duntulm Castle' to access
detailed information about this historic
landmark

Craig

Visit Torridon www.visittorridon.co.uk
Website catering for the needs of
visitors to the area

Scottish Youth Hostelling Association
www.syha.org.uk
Browse and book a place at a local
youth hostel – of which Craig used to
be one

The Schoolhouse

Kyle of Sutherland Fisheries
www.kylefisheries.org/Oykel
Get the lowdown on the River Oykel
and its riches

Discover Assynt
www.discoverassynt.co.uk
Plan a trip to the area using this website

The focal point for every bothy night – a roaring fire

Mountain Bothies Association
www.mountainbothies.org.uk
Use the site's Location Map to navigate
to a history of The Schoolhouse

Glencoul

Journal of John Elliot (1844–1928)
inside Glencoul bothy

The Daily Record
www.dailyrecord.co.uk
See 'Scotland's most remote war
memorial' (4 Nov 2012) for an article
about the Elliot memorial

Strathchailleach

John Muir Trust
www.jmt.org/sandwood-estate.asp
Information about this beautiful area
and the Trust's work on it

Visit Cape Wrath
www.visitcapewrath.com
Visitor resource about the area –
including the famous lighthouse

Mysterious Britain
www.mysteriousbritain.co.uk
Search using 'Sandwood Bay' to read
about its strange phenomena

*Highland Hermit – The Remarkable Life
of James McRory Smith* James Carron
(Kindle eBook)

Wales

Grwyne Fawr

Dictionary of the Place-names of Wales
Hywel Wyn Owen and Richard Morgan
(Gomer Press, 2007)

Medieval Wales David Walker
(Cambridge University Press, 1990)

'Prince orders abseil investigation'
www.bbc.co.uk/news
News story, published 10 Aug 1998,
about the young princes' escapades at
the Grwyne Fawr dam

Nant Syddion

Welsh Mines Preservation Trust
www.welshminestrust.org
Details of past and present mining
projects

Welsh Mines Society
www.welshmines.org
More information about local mining
activity

Natural Resources Wales
www.naturalresources.wales
Use the search box at the top of the

web page to find information about the
red kite feeding station at Bwlch Nant
yr Arian

Devil's Bridge Falls
www.devilsbridgefalls.co.uk
Visitor information, including opening
times and walk directions

Arenig Fawr

Capel Celyn, Ten Years of Destruction: 1955–1965 Einion Thomas
(Cyhoeddiadau Barddas & Gwynedd
Council, 2007)

'Tryweryn: 50 years since bombing of
reservoir dam' www.bbc.co.uk/news
News story from 10 Feb 2013

'The Mountain that had to be Painted',
BBC Four Documentary (2011)

Lakes of Eryri Geraint Roberts
(Gwasg Carreg Gwalch, 1995)

Dulyn

'Carneddau ponies annual round-up shows population in recovery'
www.bbc.co.uk/news
News story published 11 Nov 2013

'Watch: Stunning drone footage captures Carneddau Ponies being gathered for annual check up'
www.dailypost.co.uk
Article published 26 Nov 2014

Snowdonia National Park
www.eryri-npa.gov.uk
A wealth of resources for visitors to the area

England

Warnscale Head

A Pictorial Guide to the Lakeland Fells: The Western Fells Alfred Wainwright (Frances Lincoln, 2013)

Honister Mine www.honister.com
Includes details of the UK's first via ferrata

Mosedale Cottage

Sleddale Hall
www.rawes.co.uk
To discover more about the history of the hall select 'Rawes' on the homepage, then look under 'Some Rawes Houses'

Greg's Hut

Dufton Village website
www.dufton.org.uk
Find out about the area's very own weather system – the Helm Wind

The Pennine Way Association
www.penninewayassociation.co.uk
Information about Britain's first long-distance path

Joint Nature Conservation Committee
www.jncc.defra.gov.uk
Enter 'Moor House' into the search box to find out about the Special Area of Conservation

Greg's Hut Association
www.culgaith.org.uk/Ghut.html
Read about the organisation that helps to maintain the bothy

Kershopehead

'Notes on the history of, and a sad story from Kershopehead', Margaret Rich
www.mountainbothies.org.uk/cust_images/documents/Kershopehead.pdf

Forestry Commission Scotland
www.scotland.forestry.gov.uk
Using the site's regional search facility, select 'Scottish Borders' to find information about local forests

LISTING OF CICERONE GUIDES

C000025495

Newnes Computer Engineer's
Pocket Book

Newnes

Computer Engineer's Pocket Book

Third edition

Michael Tooley

BNEWNES

Newnes
An imprint of Butterworth-Heinemann Ltd
Linacre House, Jordan Hill, Oxford OX2 8DP

 A member of the Reed Elsevier group

OXFORD   LONDON   BOSTON
MUNICH   NEW DELHI   SINGAPORE   SYDNEY
TOKYO   TORONTO   WELLINGTON

First published 1987
Second edition published by Heinemann Newnes 1989
Third edition published by Butterworth-Heinemann 1991
Reprinted 1993

British Library Cataloguing in Publication Data
Tooley, Michael
  Newnes computer engineer's pocket book. – 3rd ed.
  I. Title
  621.39

ISBN 0 7506 0372 0

Typeset by Vision Typesetting, Manchester
Printed and bound in Great Britain by
Clays Ltd, St Ives plc

Contents

Preface

With the advent of the information technology revolution we are witnessing the convergence of three disciplines: computing, electronics and telecommunications. For us to be able fully to exploit the potential of microprocessors and microcomputers in what remains of the twentieth century, it will become increasingly necessary to abandon the old, and somewhat rigid, boundaries which have until now existed between 'hardware' and 'software'.

Within the computing and information technology industry this trend has already manifested itself in the shape of a growing demand for a new type of engineer, able to specify, install, maintain and integrate hardware and software in fully functional and fully optimized systems.

The precise skills required are hard to define in just a few words but essentially they centre on an awareness of and familiarity with electronic and microelectronic circuitry, coupled with a detailed knowledge of programming in either assembly language or an appropriate high level language. In addition, some knowledge of computer interfacing and communications is highly desirable.

This book aims to provide the sort of everyday information required by such individuals, but it should also be of value to hardware and software specialists. Indeed, anyone engaged in regular use of a computer or microcomputer system at more than just the applications level should find something of value contained herein.

This book cannot replace standard texts or detailed specifications. It does, however, cover a vast range of subjects at a practical level with, where appropriate, some explanatory text. It has also not been designed with readability in mind; rather the aim has been that of presenting information in the most concise manner and in a form which can be readily accessed.

Finally, one brief word of advice to the reader. Don't be content to leave this book on the shelf—it should form part of your everyday 'toolkit'. If you use it in much the same manner as your trusty pocket calculator then it will have achieved its aim!

Michael Tooley

Abbreviations (general)

a.c.	Alternating current
A	Ampere
A/D	Analogue to digital
ACC	Accumulator
ACIA	Asynchronous communications interface adaptor
ACK	Acknowledge
ACU	Automatic calling unit
ADC	Analogue to digital converter
ADCCP	Advanced data communication control procedure
AES	Application environment services
AFIPS	American Federation of Information Processing Societies
ALU	Arithmetic logic unit
AM	Amplitude modulation
ANSI	American National Standards Institution
APPC	Advanced program-to-program communications
APPS	Automatic parts programming system
APT	Automatically programmed tools
APU	Arithmetic processor unit
AQL	Acceptable quality level
ARLL	Advanced run length limited
ARQ	Automatic repeat request
ARU	Audio response unit
ASCII	American Standard Code for Information Interchange
ASM	Assembler
ASR	Automatic send/receive
ATE	Automatic test equipment
ATG	Automatic test generation
AUX	Auxiliary
B	Battery
BABT	British Approvals Board for Telecommunications
BBD	Bucket brigade device
BBS	Bulletin board service
BBT	Bit block transfer
BCCD	Buried channel charge-coupled device
BCD	Binary coded decimal
BCS	British Computer Society
BDOS	Basic disk operating system
BIOS	Basic input/output system
BIU	Bus interface unit
BOS	Business operating system
BPS	Bits per second
BS	Backing store
BSC	Binary synchronous communication
BSI	British Standards Institution
BTAM	Basic telecommunications access method
BV	Bus vectored
c	Centi ($\times 10^{-2}$)
C	Capacitor
CAD	Computer aided design
CAI	Computer aided instruction
CAL	Computer aided learning
CAM	Computer aided manufacture
CCD	Charge-coupled device
CCITT	International Telegraph and Telephone Consultative Committee

CCP	Console command processor
CCR	Condition code register
CERDIP	Ceramic dual-in-line package
CLK	Clock
CML	Current mode logic
CMOS	Complementary metal oxide semiconductor
CSMA	Carrier sense multiple access
CNC	Computer numerical control
CODASYL	Conference on Data Systems Languages
CODEC	Coder/decoder
COM	Computer output to microfilm
CP/M	Control Program for Microcomputers
CPE	Central processing element
CPM	Cards per minute
CPS	Characters per second
CPU	Central processing unit
CR	Card reader
CR	Carriage return
CRC	Cyclic redundancy check
CROM	Control read only memory
CRT	Cathode ray tube
CRTC	Cathode ray tube controller
CU	Control unit
CWP	Communicating word processor
d.c.	Direct current
D	Diode
D/A	Digital to analogue
DAC	Digital to analogue converter
DAC	Data acquisition and control
DAL	Data access line
DAR	Data access register
DART	Dual asynchronous receiver/transmitter
DASM	Direct access storage medium
DASS	Digital access signalling system
DBMS	Database management system
DC	Don't care
DCE	Data circuit-terminating equipment (RS-232D)
DCS	Data carrier system
DCTE	Data circuit terminating equipment
DCTL	Direct coupled transistor logic
DDL	Data description language
DEMUX	Demultiplexer
DES	Data encryption standard
DIB	Data input bus
DIL	Dual-in-line
DIN	German Standards Institute
DIP	Dual-in-line package
DL	Diode logic
DMA	Direct memory access
DMAC	Direct memory access controller
DMM	Digital multimeter
DMOS	Double diffused metal oxide semiconductor
DMS	Data management system
DNC	Direct numerical control
DOB	Data output bus
DOS	Disk operating system
DP	Data processing
DPM	Digital panel meter
DPMA	Data Processing Management Association

DPNSS	Digital private network signalling system
DPU	Display processing unit
DRAM	Dynamic random access memory
DSDD	Double-sided double-density
DSSD	Double-sided single-density
DSW	Device status word
DTE	Data terminal equipment
DTL	Diode transistor logic
DTMF	Dual tone multi-frequency
DUV	Data under voice
DVM	Digital voltmeter
E	Earth
E^2ROM	Electrically erasable read only memory
E^2PROM	Electrically erasable programmable read only memory
EAN	European article number
EAM	Electrical accounting machine
EAROM	Electrically alterable read only memory
EBCD	Extended binary coded decimal
EBCDIC	Extended binary coded decimal interchange code
EBL	Extended batch language
ECD	Electrochromeric display
ECL	Emitter coupled logic
ECMA	European Computer Manufacturers' Association
EDC	Error detection and correction
EDP	Electronic data processing
EDS	Exchangeable disk storage
EEROM	Electrically erasable read only memory
EEPROM	Electrically erasable programmable read only memory
EFL	Emitter follower logic
EFTS	Electronic funds transfer system
EIA	Electronic Industries Association
EITB	Engineering Industries Training Board
EMI	Electromagnetic interference
EO	Erasable optical
EOC	End of conversion
EOD	End of data
EOF	End of file
EOM	End of message
EOT	End of text or end of transmission
EPROM	Erasable programmable read only memory
EPU	Extended processing unit
EROM	Erasable read only memory
ESDI	Enhanced small device interface
EXEC	Executive system
F	Farad
FAMOS	Floating gate avalanche metal oxide semiconductor
FAT	File access table
FAX	Facsimile
FCB	File control block
FCS	Frame check sequence
FDC	Floppy disk controller
FDM	Frequency division multiplexing
FET	Field effect transistor
FIFO	First-in first-out
FM	Frequency modulation
FOT	Fibre optic transmission
FPGA	Field programmable gate array

FPLA	Field programmable logic array
FP	Floating point
FPU	Floating point unit
FSK	Frequency shift keying
FSM	Frequency shift modulation
G	Giga (× 10⁹)
GDP	Graphic display processor
GIGO	Garbage-in garbage-out
GP	General purpose
GPI	General purpose interface
GPIB	General purpose interface bus
GUI	Graphic user interface
H	Henry
Hex	Hexadecimal
Hz	Hertz
HDLC	High level data link control
HMOS	High-density metal oxide semiconductor
HPIB	Hewlett-Packard interface bus
i.c.	Integrated circuit
i/p	Input
I/O	Input/output
I²L	Integrated injection logic
IAS	Immediate access storage
IBG	Inter-block gap
IBM	International Business Machines
ICE	In-circuit emulation
ICL	International Computers Limited
IDPM	Institute of Data Processing Management
IDX	Integrated digital exchange
IEE	Institution of Electrical Engineers
IEEE	Institution of Electrical and Electronics Engineers
IERE	Institution of Electronic and Radio Engineers
IGFET	Insulated gate field effect transistor
IIL	Integrated injection logic
IOP	Input/output processor
IP	Instruction pointer
IPL	Initial program loader
IPSE	Integrated project software environment
IR	Instruction register
IR	Index register
ISAM	Indexed sequential access method
ISDN	Integrated services digital network
ISDT	Integrated services digital terminal
ISDX	Integrated services digital exchange
ISL	Integrated Schottky logic
ISO	International Standards Organization
ISPBX	Integrated services private branch exchange
ITeC	Information Technology Centre
JAN	Joint Army/Navy
JCL	Job control language
JFET	Junction gate field effect transistor
JUGFET	Junction gate field effect transistor
k	Kilo (× 10³)
K	Binary kilo (2¹⁰ = 1024)
KSR	Keyboard send/receive
KWIC	Keyword-in-context
L	Inductor
LAN	Local area network
LCD	Liquid crystal display

LED	Light-emitting diode
LF	Line feed
LIFO	Last-in first-out
LOC	Loop on-line control
LP	Line printer
LPM	Lines per minute
LPS	Low-power Schottky
LRC	Longitudinal redundancy check
LRL	Logical record length
LRU	Last recently used
LS	Low-power Schottky
LSB	Least significant bit
LSD	Least significant digit
LSI	Large scale integration
m	Milli ($\times 10^{-3}$)
M	Mega ($\times 10^{6}$)
MAP	Macro-arithmetic processor
MAP	Manufacturing automation protocol
MAP	Microprocessor Applications Project
MAPCON	Microprocessor Applications Project Consultants
MAR	Memory address register
MBR	Master boot record
MBR	Memory buffer register
MCP	Message control program
MCU	Microcomputer unit
MFM	Modified frequency modulation
MICR	Magnetic ink character recognition
MIDI	Musical instrument digital interface
MIS	Metal insulator silicon
MIS	Management information system
MMU	Memory management unit
MNOS	Metal nitride oxide semiconductor
MODEM	Modulator/demodulator
MON	Monitor
MOS	Metal oxide semiconductor
MOSFET	Metal oxide semiconductor field effect transistor
MPU	Microprocessor unit
MPX	Multiplex
MROM	Mask programmed read only memory
MSB	Most significant bit
MSD	Most significant digit
MSI	Medium scale integration
MTBF	Mean time between failure
MTF	Mean time to failure
MTTF	Mean time to failure
MUX	Multiplexer
n	Nano ($\times 10^{-9}$)
NaN	Not a number
NBV	Non-bus vectored
NC	Numerical control
NCC	National Computing Centre
NDP	Numerical data processor
NDRO	Non-destructive readout
NLQ	Near-letter quality
NMOS	N-channel metal oxide semiconductor
NOP	No operation
NRZ	Non return to zero
NRZI	Non return zero invert
NTSC	National Television Systems Committee

NUA	Network user address
NUI	Network user identification
NVM	Non-volatile memory
o/p	Output
OCR	Optical character reader
OCR	Optical character recognition
OEM	Original equipment manufacturer
OIS	Office information systems
OMR	Optical mark recognition
OP	Operation
OPCODE	Operation code
OSI	Open systems interconnection
p	Pico ($\times 10^{-12}$)
p.c.	Printed circuit
p.c.b.	Printed circuit board
PABX	Private automatic branch exchange
PAD	Packet assembler/disassembler
PAL	Programmed array logic
PAM	Pulse amplitude modulation
PBX	Private branch exchange
PC	Personal computer
PC	Program counter
PCIO	Program controlled input/output
PCM	Pulse code modulation
PCS	Process control system
PDN	Private data network
PERT	Program evaluation and review technique
PFR	Power failure restart
PIA	Peripheral interface adaptor
PIC	Position independent code
PIC	Program interrupt control
PID	Process identification number
PIO	Programmable input/output
PIPO	Parallel input/parallel output
PISO	Parallel input/serial output
PIT	Programmable interval timer
PLA	Programmable logic array
PLL	Phase-locked loop
PM	Phase modulation
PMOS	P-channel metal oxide semiconductor
POS	Point of sale
POST	Point of sale terminal
PPI	Programmable parallel interface
PPM	Pulse position modulation
PRF	Pulse repetition frequency
PROM	Programmable read only memory
PRT	Program reference table
PSE	Packet switch exchange
PSI	Programmable serial interface
PSN	Packet switched network
PSS	Packet switch stream
PSTN	Public subscriber telephone network
PSU	Power supply unit
PSW	Processor status word
PTP	Paper tape punch
PTP	Point-to-point
PTR	Program tape reader
PTT	Post, telegraph and telephone
PWB	Printed wiring board

PWM	Pulse width modulation
Q	Transistor
QAM	Quadrature amplitude modulation
QISAM	Queued indexed sequential access method
QUIP	Quad in-line package
R	Resistor
R/W	Read/write
RALU	Register arithmetic logic unit
RAM	Random access memory
RB	Return to bias
RCTL	Resistor capacitor transistor logic
RDSR	Receiver data service request
REC	Rectifier
RJE	Remote job entry
RLL	Run length limited
RND	Random
ROM	Read only memory
RPG	Report program generator
RPROM	Reprogrammable read only memory
RSA	Real sector access
RTBM	Real-time bit mapping
RTC	Real-time clock
RTE	Real-time executive
RTL	Resistor transistor logic
RX	Receiver
RZ	Return to zero
S/H	Sample and hold
S/N	Signal-to-noise
SA	Signature analysis
SAR	Successive approximation register
SBC	Single-board computer
SC	Short-circuit
SC	Start conversion
SCCD	Surface channel charge-coupled device
SCRN	Screen
SCSI	Small computer systems interface
SDLC	Synchronous data link control
SDR	Statistical data recorder
SEQ	Sequential
SI	International System
SID	Serial interface device
SID	Symbolic interactive debugger
SIO	Serial input/output
SIPO	Serial input/parallel output
SISO	Serial input/serial output
SLIC	Subscriber line interface circuit
SMC	Surface mounting component
SMD	Storage module device
SMD	Storage module disk
SMD	Surface mounting device
SME	Society of Manufacturing Engineers
SMT	Surface mounting technology
SMT	Systems management terminal
SNA	Systems network architecture
SOC	Start of conversion
SOI	Silicon on insulator
SOS	Silicon on sapphire
SP	Stack pointer
SQL	Structured query language

SR	Service request
SRAM	Static random access memory
SSDA	Synchronous serial data adaptor
SSDD	Single-sided double-density
SSI	Small scale integration
SSSD	Single-sided single-density
SUB	Subroutine
SYN	Synchronizing
SYGEN	System generation
SYS	System
SYSGEN	System generation
SYSLOG	System log
SYSOP	System operator
TC	Terminal controller
TD	Transmitter distributor
TDM	Time division multiplexing
TDSR	Transmitter data service request
TP	Test point
TPA	Transient program area
TR	Track
TR	Transistor
TRL	Transistor resistor logic
TSL	Tri-state logic
TSS	Time-shared system
TTL	Transistor-transistor logic
TTY	Teletype
TV	Television
TX	Transmitter
UART	Universal asynchronous receiver/transmitter
UBC	Universal block channel
ULA	Uncommitted logic array
UPC	Universal peripheral controller
UPC	Universal product code
UPS	Uninterruptible power supply
USACII	United States standard code for information interchange
USART	Universal asynchronous receiver/transmitter
USRT	Universal synchronous receiver/transmitter
V	Volt
VAB	Voice answer back
VDE	Voice data entry
VDG	Video display generator
VDI	Virtual device interface
VDP	Video display processor
VDT	Video display terminal
VDU	Visual display unit
VIA	Versatile interface adaptor
VIC	Video interface chip
VIP	Visual information processor
VLSI	Very large scale integration
VM	Virtual memory
VMA	Valid memory address
VMOS	V-groove (vertical) metal oxide semiconductor
VMPU	Virtual memory processing unit
VPA	Valid peripheral address
VRAM	Video random access memory
VRC	Vertical redundancy check
VRC	Visual record computer
VS	Virtual storage

W	Watt
WAN	Wide area network
WATS	Wide area telephone service
WCC	Wild card character
WCS	Writable control store
WIMP	Window icon mouse pull-down
WORM	Write once, read many
WP	Word processor
WPC	Write precompensation
WPM	Words per minute
WS	Working store
X	Crystal
XTAL	Crystal
Y	Crystal
Z	Impedance
μ	Micro ($\times 10^{-6}$)
μC	Microcontroller
μP	Microprocessor
Ω	Ohm

Abbreviations commonly used in pin connection data, etc.

a	Anode (diode)
A	General data input (binary weight = 1)
An	Address bus (binary weight = 2^n)
ADn	Multiplexed address/data bus (binary weight = 2^n)
ADRn	Address lines (Intel Multibus)
ALE	Address latch enable (output from CPU)
ARDY	Peripheral port A ready (output from PIO)
ASTB	Strobe pulse for port A (input to PIO)
ATN	Attention (IEEE-488)
b	Base (bipolar transistor)
B	General data input (binary weight = 2)
B	Blue (output to RGB monitor)
BCLK	Bus clock (Intel Multibus)
BCRDY	Ready (IBM PC expansion bus)
BERR	Bus error (input to CPU)
BG	Bus grant (output from CPU)
BGACK	Bus grant acknowledge (input to CPU)
BHEN	Byte high enable (Intel Multibus)
BPRN	Bus priority input (Intel Multibus)
BPRO	Bus priority output (Intel Multibus)
BR	Bus request (input to CPU)
BRDY	Peripheral port B ready (output from PIO)
BREQ	Bus request (Intel Multibus)
BSTB	Strobe pulse for port B (input to PIO)
BUSEN	Bus enable (control input to bus transceiver)
c	Collector (bipolar transistor)
C	General data input (binary weight = 4)
C	Carry (output from hardware adder)
Cin	Carry input
Cout	Carry output
Com.	Common (0V)
C/D	Control/data select input

CAn	Peripheral control line (port A)
CAS	Column address strobe (dynamic RAM)
CBn	Peripheral control line (port B)
CBRQ	Common bus request (Intel Multibus)
CCLK	Constant clock (Intel Multibus)
CE	Chip enable
CHCK	Channel check (IBM PC expansion bus)
CI	Carry input
CK	Clock input
CLK	Clock input
CLR	Clear input
CO	Carry output
CS	Chip select
CTS	Clear to send (RS-232C)
CY	Carry output
d	Drain (FET)
D	Data input for bistable latch
D	General data input (binary weight = 8)
Di	Data input (RAM)
Din	Data input (RAM)
Dn	Data bus (binary weight = 2^n)
Do	Data output (RAM)
Dout	Data output (RAM)
DACKn	DMA acknowledge (IBM PC expansion bus)
DATn	Data line (Intel Multibus)
DAV	Data valid (IEEE-488)
DCD	Data carrier detect (RS-232C)
DIS	Disable input for tri-state devices
DTR	Data terminal ready (RS-232C)
DRQn	DMA request (IBM PC expansion bus)
e	Emitter (bipolar transistor)
E	Earth
EN	Enable input
EOI	End or identify (IEEE-488)
FCn	Function code (output from CPU)
FG	Frame ground (RS-232C)
g	Gate (FET)
G	Enable input for tri-state devices
G	Green (output to RGB monitor)
Gnd	Ground, common, 0 V
GND	Ground, common, 0 V
I/O	Input/output mode control
I/On	Input/output (RAM, binary weight = 2^n)
IEI	Interrupt enable input (PIO)
IEO	Interrupt enable output (PIO)
IFC	Interface clear (IEEE-488)
IIOR	I/O read (IBM PC expansion bus)
IIOW	I/O write (IBM PC expansion bus)
IMW	Memory write (IBM PC expansion bus)
IMR	Memory read (IBM PC expansion bus)
INH	Inhibit
INHn	Inhibit (Intel Multibus)
INIT	Initialize (Centronics printer bus, Intel Multibus)
INT	Interrupt request (input to CPU)
INTn	Interrupt request (Intel Multibus)
INTA	Interrupt acknowledge (output from CPU)
INTR	Maskable interrupt (input to CPU)
IOn	Input/output (RAM, binary weight = 2^n)
IORC	Input/output read (Intel Multibus)
IORQ	Input/output request (output from CPU)

IOWC	Input/output write (Intel Multibus)
IPLn	Interrupt priority level (n denotes bit significance, e.g. 0 = LSB)
IRQ	Interrupt request (input to CPU)
J	Data input for J-K bistable
k	Cathode (diode)
K	Data input for J-K bistable
LDS	Lower data strobe output
LE	Latch enable input
LSB	Least significant bit
LT	Lamp test input for display driver
M1	First machine cycle (output from Z80-type CPU)
MR	Master reset input
MRDC	Memory read (Intel Multibus)
MREQ	Memory request (output from CPU)
MRQ	Memory request (output from CPU)
MSB	Most significant bit
MWTC	Memory write (Intel Multibus)
n.c.	Not connected
N.C.	Not connected
NDAC	Not data accepted (IEEE-488)
NMI	Non-maskable interrupt input
NRFD	Not ready for data (IEEE-488)
o.c.	Open circuit or open collector
O/C	Open circuit
On	Output (ROM, binary weight = 2^n)
OE	Output enable (input to support/memory device)
OEN	Output enable (input to support/memory device)
OV	Overflow
OVF	Overflow
P/S	Parallel/serial shift register mode control
PAn	Peripheral data line (port A)
PBn	Peripheral data line (port B)
PE	Paper end (Centronics printer bus)
PG	Protective ground (RS-232C)
PGM	Program control input (EPROM)
PH	Phase input for LCD display
PR	Preset input
Q	General output for bistable, latch, counter, and shift register
Qn	Output from latch, counter, or shift register (binary weight = 2^n)
R	Red (output to RGB monitor)
R	Reset input for R-S bistable
R/B	Ready/not busy (EEPROM program control output)
R/W	Read/write select output
RxD	Receive data (RS-232C)
RC	Receive clock (RS-232C)
RD	Receive data (RS-232C) or read (output from CPU)
REN	Remote enable (IEEE-488)
RES	Reset (input to CPU and support devices)
RFSH	Refresh (output from CPU)
RSn	Register select (n denotes register)
RTS	Request to send (RS-232C)
s	Source (FET)
s.c.	Short circuit
S/C	Short circuit
S	Set input for R-S bistable or sum (output of hardware adder)
Sin	Serial input of shift register

Sout	Serial output of shift register
SDL	Serial data input (left shift)
SDR	Serial data input (right shift)
SEL	Select input for multiplexer/demultiplexer
SG	Signal ground (RS-232C)
SLCT	Select (Centronics printer bus)
ST	Strobe input
SR	Synchronous reset input/output
T	Trigger input
TxD	Transmit data (RS-232C)
TC	Transmit clock (RS-232C)
TC	Terminal count (IBM PC expansion bus)
TD	Transmit data (RS-232C)
U/D	Up/down select input for counter
UDS	Upper data strobe output
Vbb	Negative supply for RAM device (usually -5 V)
Vcc	TTL positive supply (usually $+5$ V)
Vdd	CMOS positive supply (often $+5$ V)
Vee	ECL negative supply (usually -5 V)
Vi	Analogue input voltage (A to D converter)
Vin	Analogue input voltage (A to D converter)
Vo	Analogue output voltage (D to A converter)
Vout	Analogue output voltage (D to A converter)
Vpp	Programming voltage (EPROM)
Vss	Voltage source-source (CMOS common 0 V)
VID	Video
VMA	Valid memory address (output from CPU)
VPA	Valid peripheral address (output from CPU)
W	Write output
WE	Write enable
WR	Write output
X	General output for logic gate arrangement
X	Data (input to data selector)
XACK	Transfer acknowledge (Intel Multibus)
Y	General output for logic gate arrangement
Y	Data (input to data selector)
Y	Luminance (output to PAL encoder)
Z	General output for logic gate arrangement
Z	Data (input to data selector)
0 V	Common, ground
—	Active low
ϕ	Clock (input to CPU)
ϕn	Clock input/output (n denotes phase)
⎍	Schmitt device
Σ	Sum output of hardware adder

Note: n = 0, 1, 2, 3, etc.

Manufacturers' prefixes for semiconductor devices

AD	Analog Devices
AD	Intersil
AH	National Semiconductor
AM	AMD
AY	General Instrument
C	Intel
CD, CDP	RCA
CP	General Instrument

D	Intel
DG	Siliconix
DM	National Semiconductor
DMPAL	National Semiconductor
DS	National Semiconductor
DS	Signetics
DS	Texas Instruments
DP	AMD
DP	National Semiconductor
EF	Thomson/EFCIS
F	Fairchild
F	Ferranti
G	GTE
H	SGS
HCMP	Hughes
HD	Hitachi
HEF	Mullard
HEF	Signetics
HM	Hitachi
HN	Hitachi
I	Intel
ICL	Intersil
ICM	Intersil
IM	Intersil
INS	National Semiconductor
KMM	Texas Instruments
LF	National Semiconductor
LM	National Semiconductor
LM	Signetics
LM	Texas Instruments
LS	Texas Instruments
NM	National Semiconductor
M	Mitsubishi
MAB	Mullard
MBL	Fujitsu
MC	Motorola
MC	Signetics
MC	Texas Instruments
MJ	Plessey
MK	Mostek
ML	Plessey
MM	National Semiconductor
MN	Plessey
MP	MPS
MSM	OKI
MV	Plessey
N	Signetics
NE	Signetics
NJ	Plessey
NS	National Semiconductor
NSC	National Semiconductor
P	AMD
P	Intel
PC	Signetics
PCF	Signetics
PIC	Plessey
R	Rockwell
R	Raytheon
RAY	Raytheon
RC	Raytheon
S	American Microsystems

SAA	Signetics
SCB	Signetics
SCN	Signetics
SCP	Solid State Scientific
SE	Signetics
SL	Plessey
SN	Texas Instruments
SP	Plessey
SY	Synertek
TAB	Plessey
TBP	Texas Instruments
TC	Toshiba
TCA	Signetics
TCM	Texas Instruments
TDA	Signetics
TEA	Signetics
TIC	Texas Instruments
TIL	Texas Instruments
TIM	Texas Instruments
TIP	Texas Instruments
TL	Texas Instruments
TLC	Texas Instruments
TMM	Toshiba
TMP	Texas Instruments
TMS	Texas Instruments
UA	Signetics
UA	Texas Instruments
UCN	Sprague
UDN	Sprague
UDN	Texas Instruments
UGN	Sprague
ULN	Signetics
ULN	Sprague
ULN	Texas Instruments
UPB	NEC
UPD	NEC
X	Xicor
Z	Zilog
Z	SGS
ZN	Ferranti
μPD	NEC

Integrated circuit technologies

A variety of different semiconductor technologies are currently
employed in the manufacture of integrated circuits. These
technologies are instrumental in governing the operational
characteristics of devices and an awareness of their essential
differences can be useful in selecting devices for use in a particular
hardware configuration.

P-channel metal oxide semiconductor (PMOS)
PMOS devices use enhancement-mode p-channel MOS transistors
to form gates. PMOS devices employ positive charge carriers which
are known as 'holes'. All of the first generation of microprocessors
were based upon PMOS technology (the process was originally
employed in preference to NMOS by virtue of its relative freedom
from contamination).

  PMOS devices have typical densities of around 20 000 devices per chip but are relatively slow in operation (a typical PMOS microprocessor is capable of executing around 500 000 instructions per second).

N-channel metal oxide semiconductor (NMOS)

NMOS devices use n-channel MOS transistors, in which electrons rather than holes are employed as charge carriers. NMOS devices provide excellent densities (over 100 000 devices per chip) and operate at acceptably high speeds (a typical NMOS microprocessor is capable of executing 1 million instructions per second).

A number of variants of NMOS are in common use. These include:

(a) Double diffused metal oxide semiconductor (DMOS)
(b) High-density metal oxide semiconductor (HMOS)
(c) V-groove metal oxide semiconductor (VMOS)

Complementary metal oxide semiconductor (CMOS)

CMOS employs both n-channel and p-channel devices and its performance is therefore something of a compromise between the two technologies. CMOS provides densities of typically around 50 000 devices per chip but is inherently slower than NMOS.

Despite its speed and density limitations, CMOS offers several important advantages over its rival technologies. It requires very little power and operates over a very wide range of supply voltages. It also offers excellent noise immunity.

Readers should note that the power consumption of a CMOS device is directly related to the speed at which the device is operating. Furthermore, in a 'standby' condition, such devices consume negligible power.

Bipolar

Bipolar technology is based on conventional NPN junction devices and exists in several forms of which the most common are:

(a) transistor-transistor logic (TTL)
(b) low-power Schottky transistor-transistor logic (LS-TTL)
(c) emitter-coupled logic (ECL)
(d) integrated injection logic (I^2L)

TTL devices are extremely fast in operation (equivalent to 10 million instructions per second) but consume appreciable power. This makes them unsuitable for high-density applications (such as complete microprocessors).

ECL devices offer the highest switching speed of all but they demand so much power that only small scale integration is possible. For this reason ECL devices are reserved for such specialized applications as HF and VHF measuring equipment and the synthesis of VHF signals.

Integrated injection logic (I^2L) provides moderately high speed operation coupled with low power consumption. I^2L devices provide moderately good packing densities and have thus proved popular in the implementation of 'bit-slice' devices. I^2L devices are also popularly used in pocket calculators.

Charge-coupled devices (CCD)

As the name implies, charge-coupled devices rely upon charge rather than current carriers for their operation. CCD comprise a large matrix of individual capacitors formed by deposition of aluminium on silicon oxide. In order to replace the charge that must eventually leak away from an elementary cell, cells are periodically refreshed by the regular shifting of charges from one cell to the next in a constant circulating manner. Densities are excellent but the technology is still relatively new and its cost-effectiveness has yet to be proved.

Scale of integration

The density of integration of a device is popularly expressed in terms of its relative scale of operation. The following terms are commonly used but their meaning (in terms of the number of equivalent logic gates) is open to some variation:

(a) Small scale integration (SSI)
Logic gate equivalent: 1 to 10
Typical examples: TTL logic gates
(b) Medium scale integration (MSI)
Logic gate equivalent: 10 to 100
Typical examples: Bipolar memories
(c) Large scale integration (LSI)
Logic gate equivalent: 100 to 1000
Typical examples: Programmed logic arrays
(d) Very large scale integration (VLSI)
Logic gate equivalent: 1000 to 10 000
Typical examples: Most common microprocessors
(e) Super large scale integration (SLSI)
Logic gate equivalent: 10 000 to 100 000
Typical examples: NMOS dynamic RAM

Basic logic gates

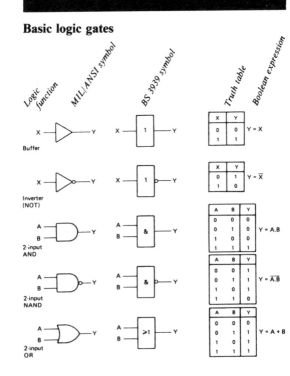

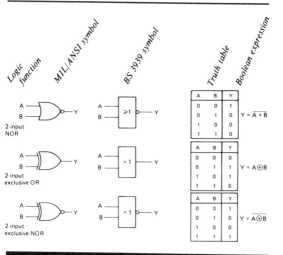

Logic function	MIL/ANSI symbol	BS 3939 symbol	Truth table	Boolean expression

2-input NOR

A	B	Y
0	0	1
0	1	0
1	0	0
1	1	0

$Y = \overline{A + B}$

2-input exclusive-OR

A	B	Y
0	0	0
0	1	1
1	0	1
1	1	0

$Y = A \oplus B$

2-input exclusive-NOR

A	B	Y
0	0	1
0	1	0
1	0	0
1	1	1

$Y = \overline{A \oplus B}$

Logic circuit equivalents

The following logic circuit equivalents are useful when it is necessary to minimize the number of logic gates in a given arrangement or when a restriction is placed on the types of gate available. It should be noted that, while the logical functions will be identical, the electrical performance may be different. This is particularly true in the case of propagation delay.

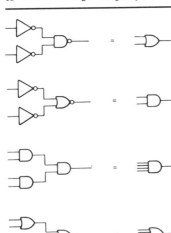

Positive and negative logic equivalents

Positive Logic		Negative Logic
AND	=	OR
OR	=	AND
NAND	=	NOR
NOR	=	NAND

Positive Logic: Logic 1 = High, Logic 0 = Low
Negative Logic: Logic 1 = Low, Logic 0 = High

Mixed logic equivalents

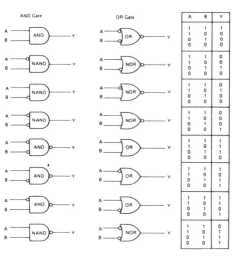

A	B	Y
1	1	1
1	0	0
0	1	0
0	0	0
1	1	0
1	0	1
0	1	0
0	0	0
1	1	0
1	0	0
0	1	1
0	0	0
1	1	0
1	0	0
0	1	0
0	0	1
1	1	1
1	0	1
0	1	1
0	0	0
1	1	1
1	0	0
0	1	1
0	0	1
1	1	1
1	0	1
0	1	0
0	0	1
1	1	0
1	0	1
0	1	1
0	0	1

Typical CMOS and TTL gate circuits

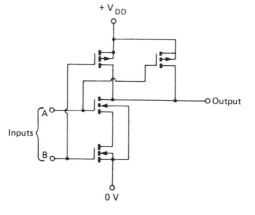

CMOS 2-input NAND

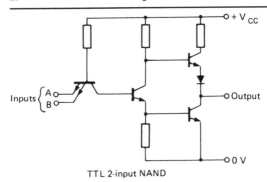

TTL 2-input NAND

TTL and CMOS device coding

TTL

The most common family of TTL devices is the 74-series, in which the device code is prefixed by the number 74. In addition, manufacturers may introduce their own identifying prefix letters. Common examples are:

N	=	Signetics
CD	=	RCA
DM	=	National Semiconductor
MC	=	Motorola
MM	=	National Semiconductor
PC	=	Signetics
SN	=	Texas Instruments

Additional letters may be inserted within the device coding to indicate the sub-family to which the device belongs:

C	=	CMOS version of the TTL device
F	=	fast
H	=	high speed
L	=	low power
S	=	Schottky
HC	=	high speed CMOS version (with CMOS-compatible inputs)
HCT	=	high speed CMOS version (with TTL-compatible inputs)
LS	=	low power Schottky
ALS	=	advanced low power Schottky

A suffix letter may also be added to denote the type of package. The most common is N, which describes the conventional plastic dual-in-line (DIL) package.

Examples 1. SN7400N   is a quad 2-input NAND gate manufactured by Texas Instruments and supplied in a plastic DIL package.

2. MM74HC32N   is a quad 2-input NOR gate using high speed CMOS technology which is speed, function, and pinout compatible with 74LS-series logic. The device is supplied in a

3. N74LS373N   plastic DIL package and is manufactured by National Semiconductor.
is a low power Schottky octal tri-state latch. The device is manufactured by Signetics and supplied in a plastic DIL package.

CMOS

The most common CMOS families are the 4000 and 4500 series of devices. Devices are usually coded with a suffix letter which indicates the series to which the device belongs. The original A-series is now largely obsolete and has been replaced by the pin and function compatible B-series. These devices feature buffered outputs. Unbuffered B-series devices are also available and these are coded with the suffix letters UB.

As with TTL devices, a manufacturer's prefix may be added. Common examples are:

CD   =   National Semiconductor
CD   =   RCA
HEF   =   Signetics
MC1   =   Motorola

A final suffix letter may also be added in order to specify the type of package. Manufacturers' literature should be consulted for further information.

Examples 1. CD4002BF   is a quad 4-input NOR gate manufactured by RCA. The device is a buffered B-series device and supplied in a ceramic DIL package.
2. HEF4069UBP   is a hex inverter produced by Signetics. The device features an unbuffered output and is supplied in a plastic DIL package.

Abbreviations

The following abbreviations are used in the list of TTL and CMOS devices:

h.v.	=	high voltage
nv.	=	inverting
o.c.	=	open collector
o.d.	=	open drain
str.	=	strobed
ALU	=	arithmetic logic unit
BCD	=	binary coded decimal
FIFO	=	first-in first-out
GPIB	=	general purpose instrument bus
PIPO	=	parallel-input parallel-output
PISO	=	parallel-input serial-output
SIPO	=	serial-input parallel-output
SISO	=	serial-input serial-output

74 series

00   Quad 2-input NAND
01   Quad 2-input o.c. NOR
02   Quad 2-input NOR
03   Quad 2-input o.c. NAND

04	Hex inverter
05	Hex o.c. inverter
06	Hex o.c. h.v. inverter
07	Hex o.c. h.v. buffer
08	Quad 2-input AND
09	Quad 2-input o.c. AND
10	Triple 3-input NAND
11	Triple 3-input AND
12	Triple 3-input o.c. NAND
13	Dual 4-input Sch. NAND
14	Hex Sch. inverter
15	Triple 3-input o.c. AND
16	Hex o.c. h.v. inverter
17	Hex o.c. h.v. buffer
20	Dual 4-input NAND
21	Dual 4-input AND
22	Dual 4-input o.c. NAND
23	Dual 4-input str. NOR
25	Dual 4-input str. NOR
26	Quad 2-input o.c. NAND
27	Triple 3-input NOR
28	Quad 2-input NOR buffer
30	Single 8-input NAND
32	Quad 2-input OR
33	Quad 2-input o.c. NOR buffer
37	Quad 2-input NAND buffer
38	Quad 2-input o.c. NAND buffer
40	Dual 4-input NAND buffer
42	BCD to decimal decoder
43	Excess 3 to decimal decoder
44	Gray to decimal decoder
45	BCD to decimal o.c. h.v. decoder
46	BCD to 7-segment o.c. h.v. decoder
47	BCD to 7-segment o.c. h.v. decoder
48	BCD to 7-segment decoder
49	BCD to 7-segment decoder
50	Dual AND/OR/invert
51	Dual AND/OR/invert
52	Single AND/OR
53	Single AND/OR/invert
54	Single AND/OR/invert
55	Single AND/OR/invert
60	Dual 4-input expander
61	Triple 3-input expander
62	Single AND/OR expander
63	Hex current-sensing interface
64	Single AND/OR/invert
65	Single AND/OR/invert
70	Single J-K bistable
71	Single J-K bistable
72	Single J-K bistable
73	Dual J-K bistable
74	Dual D-type bistable
75	Quad bistable latch
76	Dual J-K bistable
77	4-bit bistable latch
78	Dual J-K bistable
80	2-bit full adder
81	16-bit RAM

82 2-bit full adder
83 4-bit full adder
84 16-bit RAM
85 4-bit comparator
86 Quad 2-input exclusive-OR
87 4-bit complementor
88 256-bit ROM
89 64-bit RAM
90 Decade counter
91 8-bit shift register
92 Divide-by-twelve counter
93 4-bit binary counter
94 4-bit shift register
95 4-bit shift register
96 5-bit shift register
97 6-bit binary rate multiplier
98 4-bit data selector
99 4-bit bi-directional shift register
100 Dual 4-bit latch
101 Single J-K bistable
102 Single J-K bistable
103 Dual J-K bistable
104 Single J-K bistable
105 Single J-K bistable
106 Dual J-K bistable
107 Dual J-K bistable
108 Dual J-K bistable
109 Dual J-K bistable
110 Single J-K bistable
111 Dual J-K bistable
112 Dual J-K bistable
113 Dual J-K bistable
114 Dual J-K bistable
116 Dual 4-bit latch
118 Hex R-S bistable latch
119 Hex R-S latch
120 Dual pulse synchronizer
121 Monostable
122 Retriggerable monostable
123 Dual retriggerable monostable
124 Dual voltage controlled oscillator
125 Quad tri-state buffer
126 Quad tri-state buffer
128 Quad 2-input NOR line driver
132 Quad 2-input Sch. NAND
133 Single 13-input NAND
134 Single 12-input tri-state NAND
135 Quad exclusive-OR/NOR
136 Quad 2-input exclusive-OR
137 3 to 8-line decoder
138 3 to 8-line decoder
139 Dual 2 to 4-line decoder
140 Dual 4-input NAND
141 BCD to decimal decoder
142 4-bit counter/latch/decoder/driver
143 4-bit counter/latch/decoder/driver
144 4-bit counter/latch/decoder/driver
145 BCD to decimal converter
147 Decimal to 4-bit BCD encoder

148	8 to 3-line octal encoder
150	1-of-16 data selector/multiplexer
151	1-of-8 data selector/multiplexer
152	1-of-8 data selector/multiplexer
153	Dual 4 to 1-line data selector/multiplexer
154	4 to 16-line decoder
155	Dual 2 to 4-line decoder
156	Dual 2 to 4-line o.c. decoder
157	Quad 2 to 1-line data selector
158	Quad 2 to 1-line data selector
159	4 to 16-line o.c. decoder
160	4-bit counter
161	4-bit counter
162	4-bit counter
163	4-bit counter
164	8-bit SIPO shift register
165	8-bit PISO shift register
166	8-bit PISO/SISO shift reg.
167	Decade synchronous rate multiplier
168	4-bit up/down synchronous decade counter
169	4-bit up/down synchronous binary counter
170	4-by-4 o.c. register file
172	16-bit tri-state register file
173	4-bit D-type tri-state register
174	Hex D-type bistable
175	Quad D-type bistable
176	Presettable decade counter/latch
177	Presettable binary counter/latch
178	4-bit universal shift register
179	4-bit universal shift register
180	9-bit parity generator/checker
181	ALU
182	Look-ahead carry generator
183	Dual full adder
184	BCD to binary code converter
185	Binary to BCD code converter
186	512-bit o.c. PROM
187	1K-bit o.c. ROM
188	256-bit o.c. PROM
189	64-bit RAM
190	BCD synchronous up/down counter
191	Binary synchronous up/down counter
192	BCD synchronous dual clock up/down counter
193	Binary synchronous dual clock up/down counter
194	4-bit bidirectional universal shift register
195	4-bit parallel-access shift register
196	Presettable decade counter/latch
197	Presettable binary counter/latch
198	8-bit bidirectional universal shift register
199	8-bit bidirectional universal shift register
200	256-bit tri-state RAM
201	256-bit tri-state RAM
202	256-bit tri-state RAM
207	1K-bit RAM
208	1K-bit tri-state RAM
214	1K-bit tri-state RAM
215	1K-bit tri-state RAM
221	Dual monostable
225	Asynchronous FIFO memory

226	4-bit parallel latched bus transceiver
240	Octal tri-state inv. buffer/line driver/receiver
241	Octal tri-state non-inv. buffer/line driver/receiver
242	Quad tri-state inv. bus transceiver
243	Quad tri-state non-inv. bus transceiver
244	Octal tri-state non-inv. buffer/line driver/receiver
245	Octal tri-state non-inv. bus transceiver
246	BCD to 7-segment o.c. h.v. decoder
247	BCD to 7-segment o.c. h.v. decoder
248	BCD to 7-segment decoder
249	BCD to 7-segment o.c. decoder
251	8 to 1-line tri-state data selector
253	Dual 4 to 1-line tri-state data selector
256	Dual 4-bit latch
257	Quad 2-input tri-state non-inv. multiplexer
258	Quad 2-input tri-state inv. multiplexer
259	8-bit addressable latch
260	Dual 5-input NOR
261	2 by 4-bit parallel binary multiplier
265	Quad complementary output generator
266	Quad 2-input o.c. exclusive-NOR
270	2K-bit ROM
271	2K-bit ROM
273	Octal D-type bistable
274	4 by 4-bit tri-state binary multiplier
275	7-bit-slice Wallace tree
276	Quad J-K bistable
278	4-bit cascadable priority register
279	Quad R-S latch
280	9-bit parity generator/checker
281	4-bit parallel binary accumulator
283	4-bit binary full adder
284	4 by 4-bit parallel binary multiplier
285	4 by 4-bit parallel binary multiplier
287	1K-bit tri-state PROM
288	256-bit tri-state PROM
289	64-bit o.c. RAM
290	Decade counter
293	4-bit binary counter
295	4-bit bi-directional universal shift register
298	Quad 2-input multiplexer
299	8-bit bidirectional universal shift register
300	256-bit o.c. RAM
301	256-bit o.c. RAM
302	256-bit o.c. RAM
314	1K-bit o.c. RAM
315	1K-bit o.c. RAM
320	Crystal controlled oscillator
321	Crystal controlled oscillator
323	8-bit bidirectional universal shift register
324	Voltage controlled oscillator
325	Dual voltage controlled oscillator
326	Dual voltage controlled oscillator
327	Dual voltage controlled oscillator
348	8 to 3-line tri-state priority encoder
351	Dual 8 to 1-line tri-state data selector
352	Dual 4 to 1-line inv. data selector
353	Dual 4 to 1-line tri-state inv. data selector
354	8 to 1-line data selector

356	8 to 1-line data selector
362	Four-phase clock generator
363	Octal tri-state D-type latch
364	Octal tri-state D-type latch
365	Hex tri-state non-inv. buffer
366	Hex tri-state inv. buffer
367	Hex tri-state non-inv. buffer
368	Hex tri-state inv. buffer
370	2K-bit tri-state ROM
371	2K-bit tri-state ROM
373	Octal tri-state D-type latch
374	Octal tri-state D-type bistable
375	4-bit bistable latch
376	Quad J-K bistable
377	Octal D-type bistable
378	Hex D-type bistable
379	Quad D-type bistable
381	4-bit ALU
386	Quad 2-input exclusive-OR
387	1K-bit o.c. PROM
390	Dual decade counter
393	Dual 4-bit binary counter
395	4-bit tri-state universal shift register
398	Quad 2-input multiplexer
399	Quad 2-input multiplexer
412	8-bit tri-state buffered latch
423	Dual monostable
424	Two-phase clock generator
425	Quad tri-state buffer
426	Quad tri-state buffer
428	Bidirectional system controller
438	Bidirectional system controller
442	Quad tri-state bus transceiver
443	Quad tri-state bus transceiver
444	Quad tri-state bus transceiver
446	Quad bus transceiver
449	Quad bus transceiver
470	256 by 8-bit o.c. PROM
471	256 by 8-bit tri-state PROM
472	512 × 8-bit tri-state PROM
473	512 × 8-bit o.c. PROM
474	512 × 8-bit tri-state PROM
475	512 × 8-bit o.c. PROM
476	1K × 4-bit tri-state PROM
477	1K × 4-bit o.c. PROM
481	4-bit slice processor
482	4-bit slice controller
490	Dual decade counter
500	6-bit analogue to digital converter
505	8-bit analogue to digital converter
521	Octal comparator
524	8-bit register comparator
533	Octal tri-state latch
534	Octal tri-state latch
537	1 of 10 tri-state decoder
538	1 of 8 tri-state decoder
539	Dual 1 of 4 tri-state decoder
540	Octal tri-state inv. buffer
541	Octal tri-state non-inv. buffer

543	Octal bidirectional latch
544	Octal bidirectional latch
545	Octal bus transceiver
547	3 to 8-line decoder
548	3 to 8-line decoder
550	Register transceiver
551	Register transceiver
552	8-bit register
557	8 × 8 multiplier
558	8 × 8 multiplier
563	Octal tri-state latch
564	Octal inv. tri-state latch
568	Decade tri-state up/down counter
569	Binary tri-state up/down counter
573	Octal tri-state latch
574	Octal tri-state non-inv. D-type bistable
576	Octal tri-state inv. D-type bistable
579	8-bit up/down counter
580	Octal tri-state inv. latch
582	4-bit BCD ALU
583	4-bit BCD adder
588	Octal transceiver (GPIB compatible)
589	8-bit shift register
590	8-bit binary counter
592	8-bit binary counter
593	8-bit binary counter
594	8-bit shift register
595	8-bit shift register
597	8-bit shift register
598	8-bit shift register
604	Dual octal tri-state latch
605	Dual octal tri-state latch
606	Dual octal tri-state latch
610	Tri-state memory mapper
612	Tri-state memory mapper
620	Octal tri-state inv. bus transceiver
621	Octal o.c. non-inv. bus transceiver
622	Octal o.c. inv. bus transceiver
623	Octal tri-state non-inv. bus transceiver
624	Voltage controlled oscillator
625	Dual voltage controlled oscillator
626	Dual voltage controlled oscillator
627	Dual voltage controlled oscillator
628	Dual two-phase voltage controlled oscillator
629	Dual oscillator
638	Octal tri-state inverting o.c. bus transceiver
639	Octal tri-state inverting o.c. bus transceiver
640	Octal tri-state inv. bus transceiver
641	Octal o.c. non-inv. bus transceiver
642	Octal o.c. inv. bus transceiver
643	Octal tri-state inv. bus transceiver
644	Octal o.c. non-inv. bus transceiver
645	Octal tri-state non-inv. bus transceiver
646	Octal tri-state bus transceiver
647	Octal o.c. bus transceiver
648	Octal tri-state bus transceiver
649	Octal o.c. bus transceiver
651	Octal bus transceiver
652	Octal bus transceiver

668	Synchronous decade up/down counter
669	Synchronous binary up/down counter
670	4 × 4-bit tri-state register file
673	16-bit SISO shift register
674	16-bit PISO shift register
675	16-bit SIPO shift register
676	16-bit PISO shift register
681	ALU
682	8-bit comparator
683	8-bit o.c. comparator
684	8-bit comparator
685	8-bit o.c. comparator
686	8-bit comparator
687	8-bit o.c. comparator
688	8-bit comparator
689	8-bit o.c. comparator
690	8-bit tri-state decade counter
691	4-bit tri-state binary counter
692	4-bit tri-state decade counter
693	4-bit tri-state binary counter
696	4-bit tri-state decade up/down counter
697	4-bit tri-state binary up/down counter
698	4-bit tri-state decade up/down counter
699	4-bit tri-state binary up/down counter
740	Octal tri-state inv. buffer/driver
741	Octal tri-state non-inv. buffer/driver
744	Octal tri-state non-inv. buffer/driver
748	8 to 3-line encoder
779	8-bit up/down counter
784	8-bit serial multiplier
795	Octal tri-state buffer
796	Octal tri-state buffer
797	Octal tri-state buffer
798	Octal tri-state buffer
804	Hex 2-input NAND line driver
805	Hex 2-input NOR line driver
808	Hex 2-input AND line driver
832	Hex 2-input OR line driver
848	8 to 3-line tri-state priority encoder
857	8-line multiplexer
873	Dual quad latch
874	Dual quad D-type bistable
876	Dual quad D-type bistable
878	Dual quad D-type bistable
879	Octal inv. D-type bistable
880	Dual quad inv. latch
881	4-bit ALU
882	32-bit look-ahead carry generator
901	Hex inv. buffer (TTL interface)
902	Hex buffer (TTL interface)
903	Hex inv. buffer (MOS interface)
904	Hex buffer (MOS interface)
905	12-bit successive approximation register
906	Buffer o.d.
907	Buffer o.d.
908	Dual h.v. CMOS driver
909	Quad comparator
910	256-bit RAM
911	4-digit 8-segment display controller

912	6-digit 8-segment display controller
914	Hex Sch. trigger
915	7-segment to BCD decoder
917	6-digit hex display controller
918	Dual h.v. CMOS driver
922	16-key keyboard encoder
923	20-key keyboard encoder
925	4-digit counter/7-segment display driver
926	4-digit counter/7-segment display driver
927	4-digit counter/7-segment display driver
928	4-digit counter/7-segment display driver
932	Phase detector
941	Octal tri-state buffer/line receiver/line driver
945	4-digit LCD up/down counter/latch/driver
946	4-digit LCD up/down counter/latch/driver
947	4-digit LCD up/down counter/latch/driver
956	4-digit 17-segment alpha-numeric display decoder/driver
1000	Buffered 00
1002	Buffered 02
1003	Buffered 03
1004	Buffered 04
1005	Buffered 05
1008	Buffered 08
1010	Buffered 10
1011	Buffered 11
1020	Buffered 20
1032	Buffered 32
1034	Hex buffer
1035	Hex buffer
1036	Quad 2-input NOR line driver
1240	Low power 240
1241	Low power 241
1242	Low power 242
1243	Low power 243
1244	Low power 244
1245	Low power 245
1616	16×16 multiplier
1620	Low power 620
1621	Low power 621
1622	Low power 622
1623	Low power 623
1638	Low power 638
1639	Low power 639
1640	Low power 640
1641	Low power 641
1642	Low power 642
1643	Low power 643
1644	Low power 644
1645	Low power 645
2620	Octal bus transceiver
2623	Octal bus transceiver
2640	Octal bus transceiver
2645	Octal bus transceiver

74 Series pin connections

00

01

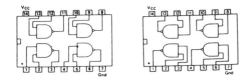

02

03

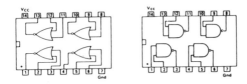

04

05

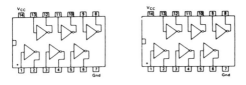

06

07

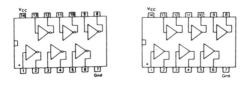

08

09

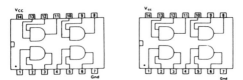

10

11

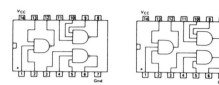

13

14

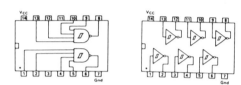

15

16

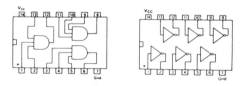

20

21

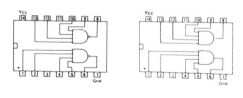

22

25

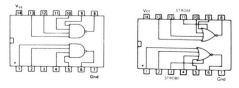

26

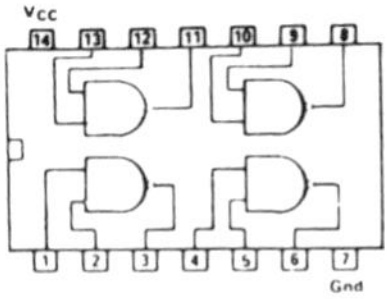

27

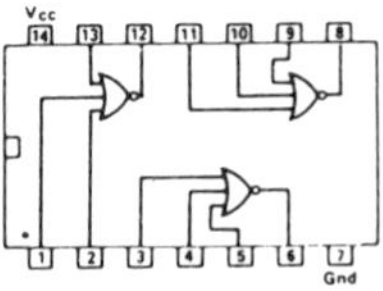

28

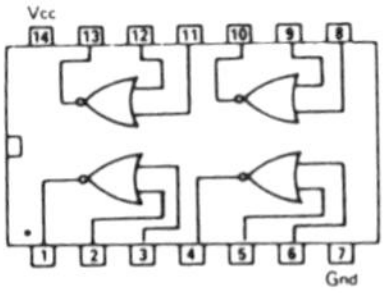

30

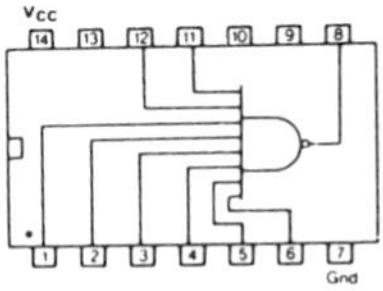

32

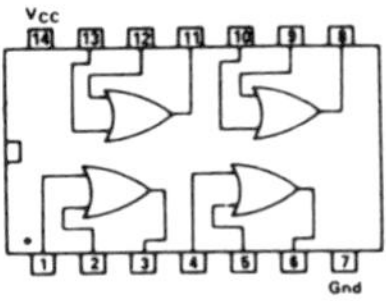

33

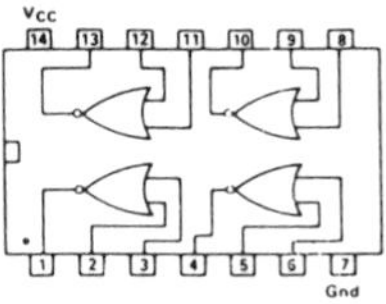

37

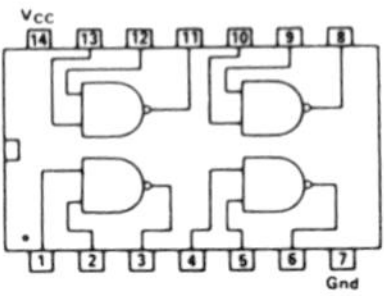

38

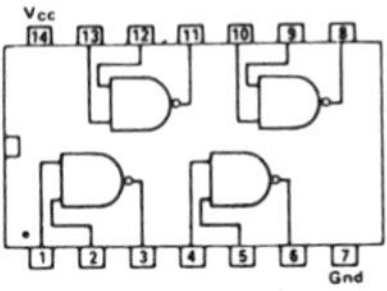

40

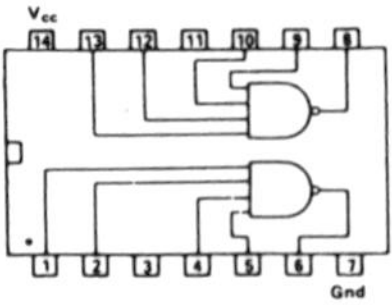

70

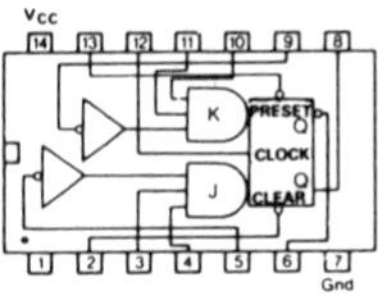

72

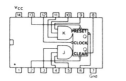

73

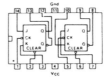

74

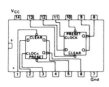

75

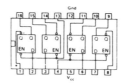

76

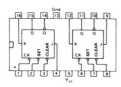

78

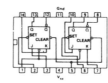

86

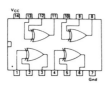

107

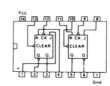

109

112

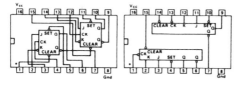

113

114

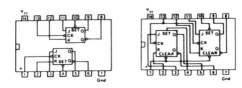

121

123

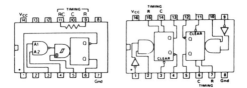

125

126

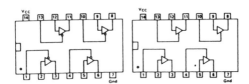

128

132

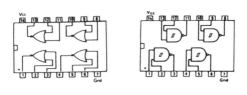

133

137

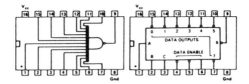

138

139

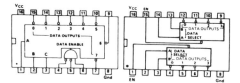

148

151

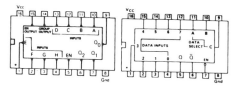

153

154

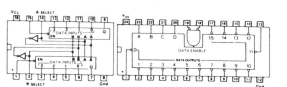

155

156

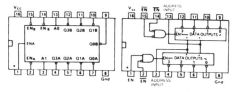

157

158

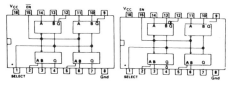

164

165

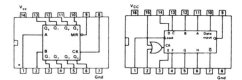

174

175

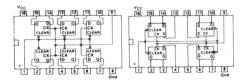

180

221

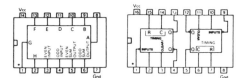

240

241

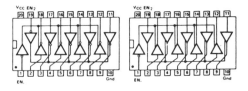

242

243

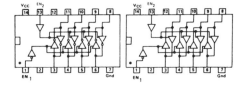

244

245

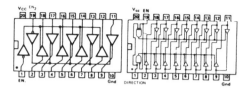

251

253

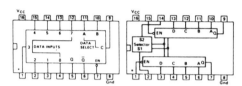

256

257

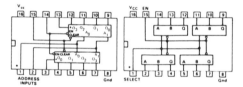

258

259

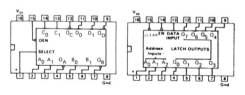

266

273

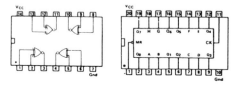

280

298

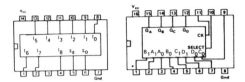

299

323

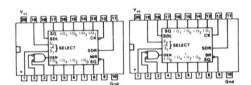

352

353

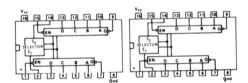

442

573

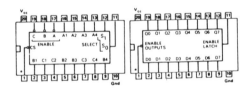

580

620

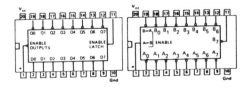

640 **643**

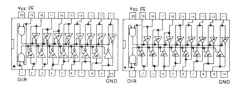

673

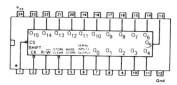

674

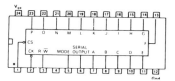

354 **356**

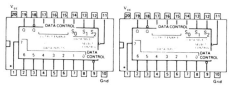

365 **366**

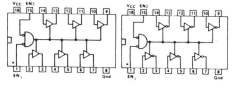

367   **368**

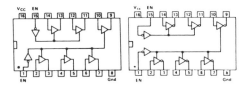

373   **374**

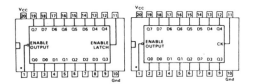

377   **378**

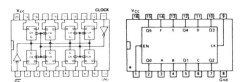

4000 Series

4001   Quad 2-input NOR
4002   Dual 4-input NOR
4006   18-bit shift register
4007   Dual CMOS transistor pair/inverter
4008   4-bit full adder
4009   Hex inverter/buffer
4010   Hex buffer
4011   Quad 2-input NAND
4012   Dual 4-input NAND
4013   Dual D-type bistable
4014   8-bit shift register
4015   Dual 4-bit shift register
4016   Quad analogue switch
4017   Decade counter
4018   Divide-by-N counter
4019   Quad 2-input AND/OR
4020   14-bit binary counter
4021   8-bit shift register
4022   Octal counter
4023   Triple 3-input NAND
4024   Seven-stage ripple counter

4025	Triple 3-input NOR
4026	7-segment display driver
4027	Dual J-K bistable
4028	BCD to decimal/binary to octal decoder
4029	Presettable binary/BCD up/down counter
4030	Quad 2-input exclusive-OR
4031	64-bit shift register
4032	Triple serial adder
4033	7-segment display driver
4034	8-bit bi-directional shift register
4035	4-bit PIPO shift register
4036	32-bit RAM
4037	Triple 3-input AND/OR
4038	Triple serial adder
4039	32-bit RAM
4040	12-bit binary counter
4041	Quad inverter/buffer
4042	Quad D-type latch
4043	Quad tri-state R-S latch
4044	Quad tri-state R-S latch
4045	21-bit binary counter
4046	Phase-locked loop
4047	Monostable/astable
4048	8-input multifunction gate
4049	Hex inverter/buffer
4050	Hex buffer
4051	Single 8-input analogue multiplexer
4052	Dual 4-input analogue multiplexer
4053	Triple 2-input analogue multiplexer
4054	BCD 7-segment display decoder/LCD driver
4055	BCD 7-segment display decoder/LCD driver
4056	BCD 7-segment display decoder/LCD driver
4057	Arithmetic logic unit
4059	Divide-by-N counter
4060	14-bit binary counter
4061	256-bit RAM
4062	200-bit shift register
4063	4-bit magnitude comparator
4066	Quad analogue switch
4067	1 to 16-line multiplexer/demultiplexer
4068	Single 8-input NAND
4069	Hex inverter
4070	Quad exclusive-OR
4071	Quad 2-input OR
4072	Dual 4-input OR
4073	Triple 3-input AND
4075	Triple 3-input OR
4076	Quad D-type register
4077	Quad 2-input exclusive-NOR
4078	Single 8-input NOR
4081	Quad 2-input AND
4082	Dual 4-input AND
4085	Dual 2-input AND/OR/invert
4086	Dual 2-input AND/OR/invert
4089	Binary rate multiplier
4093	Quad 2-input NAND
4094	8-stage tri-state register
4095	Single J-K bistable
4096	Single J-K bistable

4000 Series pin connections

4001

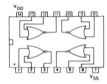

4002

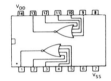

4011

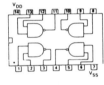

4012

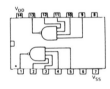

4013

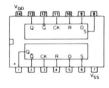

4023

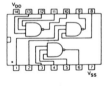

4042

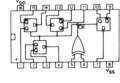

4049

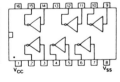

4050

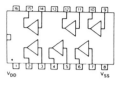

4068

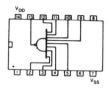

4069

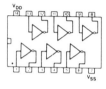

4070

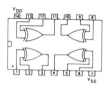

4071

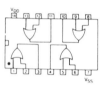

4072

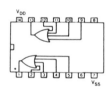

4073

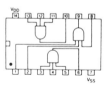

4075

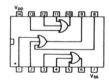

4076

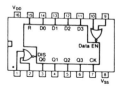

4077

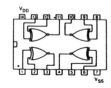

4078   **4081**

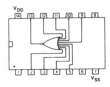   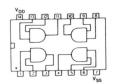

4093

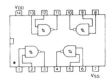

4500 Series

- 4501 Dual 4-input NAND/single 2-input OR/NOR
- 4502 Hex str. inverter/buffer
- 4503 Hex tri-state buffer
- 4504 Hex TTL-CMOS level shifter
- 4505 64-bit RAM
- 4506 Dual AND/OR/invert
- 4507 Quad exclusive-OR
- 4508 Dual 4-bit tri-state latch
- 4510 BCD up/down counter
- 4511 BCD to 7-segment latch/decoder/driver
- 4512 8-channel data selector
- 4513 BCD to 7-segment latch/decoder/driver
- 4514 4-bit latched input 1 to 16-line decoder
- 4515 4-bit latched input 1 to 16-line decoder
- 4516 Binary up/down counter
- 4517 Dual 64-bit shift register
- 4518 Dual BCD up-counter
- 4519 Quad 2-input multiplexer
- 4520 Dual 4-bit binary counter
- 4521 24-stage frequency divider
- 4522 BCD programmable divide-by-N
- 4524 256 × 4-bit ROM
- 4526 Binary programmable divide-by-N
- 4527 BCD rate multiplier
- 4528 Dual resettable monostable
- 4529 Dual 4-channel tri-state analogue data selector
- 4530 Dual 5-input majority gate
- 4531 12-bit parity tree
- 4532 8-bit priority encoder
- 4534 5-decade counter
- 4536 Programmable timer
- 4537 256 × 1-bit RAM

4500 Series pin connections

4502 **4508**

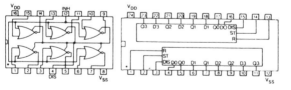

4512 **4514**

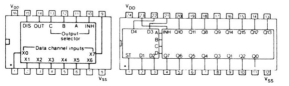

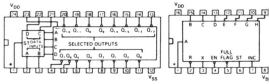

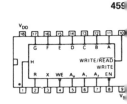

Electrical characteristics of typical logic gates

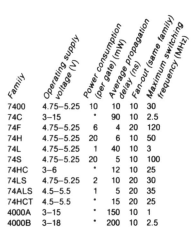

Family	Operating supply voltage (V)	Power consumption (per gate) (mW)	Average propagation delay (ns)	Fan-out (same family)	Maximum switching frequency (MHz)
7400	4.75–5.25	10	10	10	30
74C	3–15	*	90	10	2.5
74F	4.75–5.25	6	4	20	120
74H	4.75–5.25	20	6	10	50
74L	4.75–5.25	1	40	10	3
74S	4.75–5.25	20	5	10	100
74HC	3–6	*	12	10	25
74LS	4.75–5.25	2	10	20	30
74ALS	4.5–5.5	1	5	20	35
74HCT	4.5–5.5	*	15	20	25
4000A	3–15	*	150	10	1
4000B	3–18	*	200	10	2.5

*Depends on frequency: typically $20\,\mu W$ at 10 kHz, 2 mW at 2 MHz.

Fan-in and fan-out of logic gates

The fan-in of a logic gate provides a measure of the loading effect presented by its inputs and is usually expressed as the number of standard loads that it represents.

The fan-out of a logic gate provides a measure of the number of standard logic gate inputs that may be connected without the logic levels becoming illegal.

Typical values of fan-in and fan-out, expressed in terms of a standard TTL load, are shown below:

Family	Fan-in Low state	Fan-in High State	Fan-out Low state	Fan-out High state
7400	1	1	10	20
74F	0.375	0.5	12.5	25
74HC	0.05	0.05	2.5	2.5
74LS	0.25	0.5	5	10
74ALS	0.06	0.5	5	10
74HCT	0.05	0.05	2.5	2.5
4000	0.025	0.025	0.5	0.5

Standard TTL load

A standard TTL load (unit load) may be defined as:
   High state input current = 40 μA
   Low state input current = -1.6 mA
Typical conditions are illustrated below:

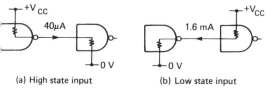

(a) High state input   (b) Low state input

TTL input and output current

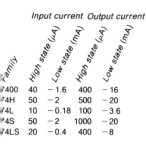

Family	Input current High state (μA)	Input current Low state (mA)	Output current High state (μA)	Output current Low state (mA)
7400	40	-1.6	400	-16
74H	50	-2	500	-20
74L	10	-0.18	100	-3.6
74S	50	-2	1000	-20
74LS	20	-0.4	400	-8

Interconnecting TTL families

Maximum number of inputs that may be connected

Family	7400	74H	74L	74S	74LS
74	10	8	40	8	20
74H	12	10	40	10	25
74L	2	1	10	1	5
74S	12	10	40	10	50
74LS	5	4	20	4	20

Logic levels and noise margins for CMOS and TTL

Logic levels are the range of voltages used to represent the logic states 0 and 1. With conventional positive logic these are as follows:

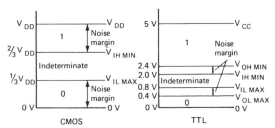

The noise margin is defined as the difference between:

(i) the minimum values of high state output and input voltage,
$V_O = _{MIN}$ and $V_I = _{MIN}$.
(ii) the maximum values of low state output and input voltage,
$V_{OL\ MAX}$ and $V_{IL\ MAX}$.

The noise margin for standard 7400-series TTL is usually 400 mV while that for CMOS is 0.33 V_{DD}.

Boolean algebra

Boolean operators
$\cdot$ = AND + = OR ⊕ = exclusive-OR $^{-}$ = NOT

Boolean identities
$0.0 = 0$	$0 + 0 = 0$
$0.1 = 0$	$0 + 1 = 1$
$1.0 = 0$	$1 + 0 = 1$
$1.1 = 1$	$1 + 1 = 1$
$A.0 = 0$	$A + 0 = A$

$A.1 = A \quad A + 1 = 1$
$A.A = A \quad A + A = A$
$A.\overline{A} = 0 \quad A + \overline{A} = 1$

$\overline{\overline{A}} = A \quad \overline{\overline{\overline{A}}} = \overline{A}$

$A + A.B = A \quad A + \overline{A}.B = A + B$
$(A + B).(A + C) = A + B.C$

$A \oplus B = A.\overline{B} + \overline{A}.B$

Associative law
$A + (B + C) = (A + B) + C \quad$ and $\quad A.(B.C) = (A.B).C$
$\qquad\qquad = A + B + C \qquad\qquad\qquad = A.B.C$

Commutative law
$A + B = B + A \quad$ and $\quad A.B = B.A$

Distributive law
$A.(B + C) = A.B + A.C \quad$ and $\quad A + (B.C) = (A + B).(A + C)$

De Morgan's theorem

$\overline{A.B} = \overline{A} + \overline{B} \qquad \overline{A + B} = \overline{A}.\overline{B}$
$\overline{A.B.C} = \overline{A} + \overline{B} + \overline{C} \qquad \overline{A + B + C} = \overline{A}.\overline{B}.\overline{C}$

Karnaugh maps

Karnaugh maps are a useful graphical technique for simplifying
complex logical functions involving between two and eight
variables; beyond that it is better to employ computer simulation.

The Karnaugh map consists of a square or rectangular array of
cells into which 0s and 1s may be placed to indicate false and true
respectively. Alternative representations of a Karnaugh map for
two variables are shown below:

The relationship between a truth table and a Karnaugh map is
illustrated in the following example, which plots the AND
function:

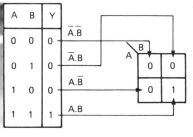

Karnaugh maps for the remaining basic logic functions (NAND, OR and NOR) for two variables are shown below:

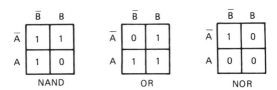

Adjacent cells within a Karnaugh map may be grouped together in rectangles of two, four, eight, etc. cells in order to effect a simplification.

Taking the NAND function, for example, the two groups of two adjacent cells in the map (below) correspond to $\overline{A}$ and $\overline{B}$. We thus conclude that:

$\overline{A.B} = \overline{A} + \overline{B}$ (De Morgan's theorem)

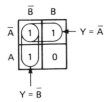

The technique of grouping cells together is an extremely powerful one. On a Karnaugh map showing four variables the relationship between the number of cells grouped together and the number of variables is as follows:

No. of cells	No. of variables
1	4
2	3
4	2
8	1

The following example shows how the function

$Y = A.\overline{B}.C.D + A.B.C.\overline{D} + A.B.\overline{C}.D + A.B.\overline{C}.\overline{D} + A.\overline{B}.C.D + A.\overline{B}.C.\overline{D}$

reduces to

$Y = A.B + A.C$

	$\bar{C}.\bar{D}$	$\bar{C}.D$	$C.D$	$C.\bar{D}$
$\bar{A}.\bar{B}$	0	0	0	0
$\bar{A}.B$	0	0	0	0
$A.B$	1	1	1	1
$A.\bar{B}$	0	0	1	1

It is also important to note that the map is a continuous surface
which links edge to edge. This allows cells at opposite extremes of
a row or column to be linked together. The four corner cells may
likewise be grouped together (provided they all contain 1!).

Some possible cell groupings are shown below:

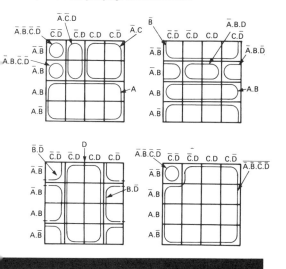

Power supplies

Most TTL and CMOS logic systems are designed to operate from
a single supply rail of nominally $+5\,\text{V}$. This voltage should be
regulated to within $\pm 5\%$ (i.e. it should not be allowed to fall
outside the range 4.75 V to 5.25 V) and the impedance of the
supply must be very low (typically 0.1 ohm or less) over a wide
range of frequencies (up to 35 MHz for standard TTL and CMOS
and up to 150 MHz for 'fast' and Schottky TTL).

The $+5\,\text{V}$ supply may be conveniently derived from a
monolithic three-terminal regulator as shown below. Regulators of
this type normally require an adequate heat sink (of around
4°C/W) and should be fitted with high-frequency decoupling
capacitors (of typically 220 nF). These should be mounted as close
to the regulator's terminals as possible.

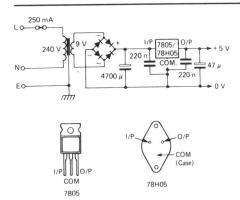

Under no circumstances should a TTL supply rail be allowed to exceed $+7\,V$ as this is likely to cause permanent damage to the integrated circuits. More elaborate power supplies may incorporate 'crowbar' protection in order to combat the effects of short-circuit failure within the regulator.

Care must also be exercised with supply distribution to the individual integrated circuits. Main $+5\,V$ and $0\,V$ rails should use PCB tracks of at least 5 mm width and generous $0\,V$ 'land' areas should be provided. (These can also be useful as a means of heat conduction from integrated circuits soldered directly to the PCB.)

Supply connectors and interconnecting leads should be adequately rated and all supply connections should be kept as short and direct as possible.

High-frequency decoupling capacitors (e.g. disk ceramic types) should be fitted as near to the individual i.c. supply pins as possible. At least one such capacitor (of between 4.7 nF and 100 nF) should be fitted for every three to four i.c. devices.

Low-frequency decoupling capacitors (electrolytic) should be fitted to main supply rails at regular points around the PCB. At least one capacitor (of between $4.7\,\mu F$ and $47\,\mu F$) should be fitted for every eight to ten i.c. devices.

Transient 'spikes' occurring on supply rails can manifest themselves in various ways, including spurious data errors and system crashes. Spikes can readily be detected using an oscilloscope (connected at various points to the $+5\,V$ rail) and dealt with by reinforcing the supply rail decoupling at strategic points. In severe cases ferrite bead inductors may be necessary in order to provide more effective decoupling.

Interfacing logic families

B-series CMOS to standard TTL

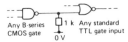

CMOS to LS-TTL

Any CMOS gate   Any LS-TTL gate input

TTL to CMOS

Any TTL gate   Any CMOS gate input

CMOS buffer to TTL

4049
4050
or 4502
CMOS buffers

Any two standard
TTL gate inputs or up to
six LS-TTL inputs

Microcomputer architecture

The essential constituents of any microcomputer system are:

(a) a central processing unit (CPU) which generally takes the form of a single VLSI device, the microprocessor;

(b) a memory which invariably comprises both read/write and read only devices (RAM and ROM respectively); and

(c) interface devices to facilitate input and output (I/O) for peripheral devices such as keyboards, disk drives, monitors and printers.

The individual elements of a microcomputer system are interconnected by means of a multiple connecting system known as a bus. In most systems there are three distinct buses: the address bus, the data bus, and the control bus.

The address bus is used to specify the memory locations (addresses) involved in data transfer while the data itself is transferred between devices using the data bus. The data bus, therefore, must be bidirectional — allowing data to be 'read' into and to be 'written' from the CPU.

The control bus comprises various lines used to distribute timing and control signals throughout the system. Important among these are: signals concerned with the direction of data transfer (to or from the CPU); signals which indicate that data is to be transferred to I/O rather than memory; and requests from external devices that require the attention of the CPU. The response to such 'interrupts' can be programmed in various ways, and a system of prioritization may often be desirable.

A system clock generator is responsible for providing an accurate and highly stable timing signal. This generator often forms part of the microprocessor itself.

The number of lines contained in the address and data buses depend upon the particular microprocessor employed. Most of today's microprocessors are capable of performing operations on binary numbers consisting of either 8 or 16 bits. They are thus known as 8-bit and 16-bit microprocessors respectively.

In a microcomputer based on an 8-bit microprocessor, the data bus has 8 separate lines. Similarly, in a 16-bit system the data bus will have 16 separate lines. Address buses for 8-bit systems invariably comprise 16 lines whereas those for 16-bit systems may consist of as many as 24 lines.

A further complication exists in the case of a number of microprocessors which, in order to minimize the CPU pin count (so that a 40-pin rather than a 64-pin package may be utilized), employ multiplexed data and address buses. Certain CPU pins are then used to convey both address and data information, the CPU outputting a signal which is used to latch the multiplexed information onto the respective bus.

Since a bus may be connected to many devices, the use of bus drivers/buffers is often desirable in order to reduce the loading on the CPU. Bus drivers/buffers are usually packaged in groups of eight (for obvious reasons) and may be unidirectional (e.g. for use with an address bus) or bidirectional (e.g. for use with a data bus). In the latter case devices are usually referred to as 'bus transceivers'.

The largest binary number that can appear on an 8-bit bus is 11111111 (or $2^8 - 1$) while that for a 16-bit bus is 1111111111111111 (or $2^{16} - 1$). Each address corresponds to a unique binary code, hence the linear addressable range (i.e. the total number of memory locations available without 'paging') will be dependent upon the number of address lines provided within the system. (The maximum number of individual memory locations that can exist in a system having n address lines is 2^n.)

The relationship between the number of address lines and the linear address range for three popular microprocessors is shown below:

CPU	Number of address lines	Linear address range (bytes)
Z80	16	64K
8086	20	1M
68000	24	16M

Signals on all lines, whether they be address, data, or control, can exist in only one of two states: logic 0 (low) or logic 1 (high). As far as individual devices sharing the data bus are concerned, a third 'high impedance' state exists whenever a device is in its de-selected or disabled state. This allows the CPU to communicate with other devices without the risk of a bus conflict. Bus transceivers can usually also be placed in a tri-state condition, thus permitting partial access to the bus for a second processor or other 'intelligent' device.

The address range corresponding to a particular device (e.g. ROM) is decoded from the address bus and used to generate an appropriate 'enable' signal. A TTL decoder (or demultiplexer) is often used in such an application.

Although the CPU is the heart of any microcomputer system, it may not be the only 'intelligent' device present. A second processor, for example, may be fitted, in order to perform numeric data processing (NDP), or a dedicated microprocessor may be incorporated in an 'intelligent keyboard'.

System VLSI devices other than CPU and memory (ROM and

RAM) may include memory controllers, counter/timers, and serial/parallel I/O chips. Such support devices not only serve to simplify the task of the CPU but also help to minimize the overall chip count.

Simplified model of a microcomputer system

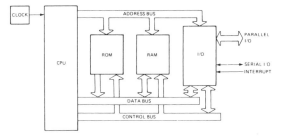

Typical 16-bit microcomputer system

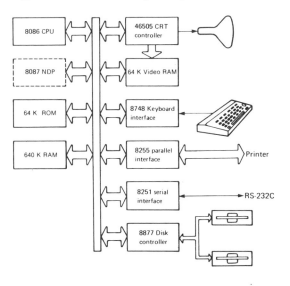

Memory maps

Portions of the address space comprising a microcomputer memory can be used in various ways. Some areas will be devoted to data and program storage, and must therefore have the capacity to be written to and read from (read/write memory), whereas other areas will be used for more permanent storage of the operating system, which will normally only permit reading (read only memory). In addition, on many home computers BASIC or other high level language interpreters are provided and these are invariably also contained in read only memory.

It is often convenient to think of a microcomputer memory as being divided into several contiguous blocks of appropriate size (e.g. 8K, 16K or 32K bytes). The resulting blocks can then be allocated various functions depending upon the particular system. A simple personal computer may, for example, have a total memory of 64K bytes, in which the operating system may exist in a block of 8K bytes, a BASIC interpreter may require a block of 16K bytes, and the remaining 40K bytes of memory may be filled by RAM. If 8K bytes of RAM are devoted to a bit-mapped screen, it should be apparent that a total of 32K bytes of RAM remains available for systems use, user programs and data.

In general, it is not necessary to draw memory maps to scale, nor is it necessary to show addresses in both decimal and hexadecimal format. Fortunately, most manufacturers provide memory maps for their systems and these can be a valuable aid to the computer engineer. It should, however, be noted that there are significant differences between memory maps for machines intended primarily for games/home use and those intended for more serious applications. Similarly, systems using different microprocessors often have quite different memory maps. A Z80-based microcomputer, for example, will normally have ROM at the bottom of memory while a 6502-based machine will have ROM at the top of memory.

Typical memory map for an 8-bit business microcomputer running CP/M

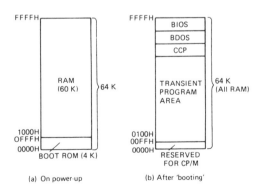

(a) On power-up

(b) After 'booting'

Typical memory map for a 16-bit personal computer running MS-DOS

ADDRESS (hex.)

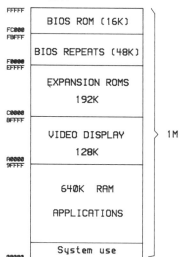

Typical memory map for an 8-bit home computer

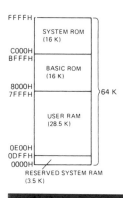

Internal architecture of a microprocessor

The microprocessor forms the heart of any microcomputer system and thus its operation is crucial to the entire system. The principal constituents of a microprocessor are:

(a) registers for temporary storage of addresses, instructions, and data;

(b) an arithmetic logic unit (ALU) able to perform a variety of arithmetic and logical operations; and
(c) a control unit to provide control and timing signals for the entire system.

Internal architecture tends to vary widely; however, there are a few common themes. The major microprocessor families, for example, tend to retain a high degree of upward compatibility, both in terms of the internal architecture of the CPU and its major support devices and the instruction set employed. This is clearly an important consideration in making new products attractive to the equipment manufacturer.

Some of the CPU registers are directly accessible to the programmer while others are not. Registers may also be classified as either 'dedicated' or 'general purpose'. In the former case the register is reserved for a particular function such as pointing to a memory location or holding the result of an ALU operation.

The following CPU registers are worthy of special note:

Program Counter (PC)/Instruction Pointer (IP)
The program counter contains the address of the next instruction byte to be executed. An arguably better name for this register, and that adopted by Intel, is the Instruction Pointer.

The contents of the program counter or instruction pointer is automatically incremented by the CPU each time an instruction byte (or word) is fetched.

Accumulator (A)
The Accumulator (A) functions both as a source and a destination register; not only is it usually the source of one of the data bytes (or words) required for an ALU operation but it is also the location in which the result of the operation is placed.

Index Registers (I, X, Y, IX, IY etc.)
Index registers are normally used to facilitate operations on tables of data stored in memory. This is achieved by means of a 'base address' for the table, which is stored in the index register. The 'effective address' is then determined by adding an 'offset' or 'displacement' contained within a relevant indexed instruction.

Stack Pointer (SP)
Most CPUs need to have access to an area of external read/write memory (RAM) which facilitates temporary storage of data. The stack operates on a last-in, first-out (LIFO) basis. Data is 'pushed' onto the stack and later 'pulled' off it. The stack pointer contains the address in memory of the last used stack location.

Some processors provide two independent stack pointers. One is used to maintain the System Stack (S or SSP) while the other is available to control the User Stack (U or USP).

Flag Register (F)/Status Register (S)/Condition Code Register (CCR)
The flag register contains information on the current state of the microprocessor and, in particular, signals the result of the last ALU operation. The flag register is not a register in the conventional sense; it is simply a collection of bistables which are set or reset. Each bistable generates a signal which can be considered to be a 'flag'. Commonly available flags are: zero (Z), overflow (V), negative (N), and carry (C).

Simplified model of the internal architecture of a microprocessor

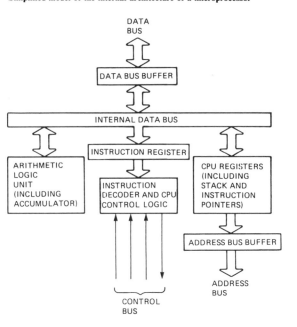

8-bit microprocessor architecture (8080 family)

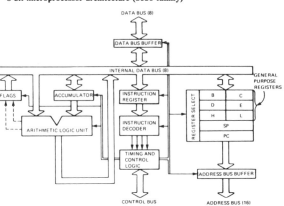

16-bit microprocessor architecture (8086 family)

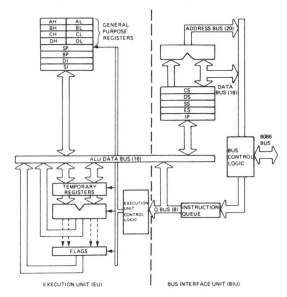

Some typical CPUs

6502

The 6502 was developed by MOS Technology as an improved 6800 device. The processor thus employs the same bus structure and is broadly compatible with the same range of peripheral support devices.

In the late 1970s and early 1980s the 6502 became widely accepted as an 'industry standard' 8-bit microprocessor, finding applications as varied as industrial process controllers and home computers.

The 6502 has only one general purpose data register (the accumulator), two 8-bit index registers (X and Y), an 8-bit stack pointer (S), and a 16-bit program counter (PC). An external single-phase clock is required, a typical frequency for which is 1 MHz. The device operates from a single +5 V supply.

The 6502 employs 13 addressing modes, 56 basic instructions, and has a total of 7 internal registers. Since the index registers are 8 rather than 16 bits wide, the 6502 requires a large number of addressing modes in order to achieve a full 64K indexed address range.

The following dedicated 6500 support devices are available:

6520   Parallel interface adaptor (PIA) with two 8-bit I/O ports
6522   Versatile interface adaptor (VIA) with two 8-bit I/O ports
       and two 16-bit timers
6532   RAM, I/O, Timer
6541   Keyboard/Display controller

6545 CRT controller
6551 Serial universal asynchronous receiver/transmitter
(UART)

The 6502 is 'second sourced' by Rockwell and Synertek. CMOS versions of the 6502 family are now readily available, including 65C02 (CPU), 65C21 (PIA), 65C22 (VIA), 65C51 (ACIA), and 65C102 (enhanced CPU). These pin and instruction set compatible devices will operate at up to 2 MHz with vastly reduced power consumption.

6502 basic configuration

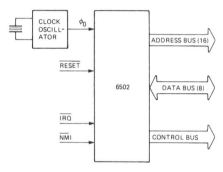

6502 register model

ACCUMULATOR (A)		
	INDEX REGISTER (X)	
	INDEX REGISTER (Y)	
PROGRAM COUNTER (PC)		
	STACK POINTER (S)	

6502 pin-out

0 V	1	40	$\overline{\text{RES}}$
RDY	2	39	ϕ_2
ϕ_1	3	38	SO
$\overline{\text{IRQ}}$	4	37	ϕ_0
NC	5	36	NC
$\overline{\text{NMI}}$	6	35	NC
SYNC	7	34	R/$\overline{\text{W}}$
+ 5 V	8	33	D0
A0	9	32	D1
A1	10	31	D2
A2	11	30	D3
A3	12	29	D4
A4	13	28	D5
A5	14	27	D6
A6	15	26	D7
A7	16	25	A15
A8	17	24	A14
A9	18	23	A13
A10	19	22	A12
A11	20	21	0 V

6502 instruction set

MNEMONIC	OPERATION	IMMEDIATE OP	n	#	ABSOLUTE OP	n	#	ZERO PAGE OP	n	#	ACCUM OP	n	#	IMPLIED OP	n	#	(IND, X) OP	n	#	(IND), Y OP	n	#	Z PAGE, X OP	n	#	ABS, X OP	n	#	ABS, Y OP	n	#	RELATIVE OP	n	#	INDIRECT OP	n	#	Z PAGE, Y OP	n	#	N	V	·	B	D	I	Z	C
A D C	A + M + C → A (4)(1)	69	2	2	6D	4	3	65	3	2							61	6	2	71	5	2	75	4	2	7D	4	3	79	4	3										N	V	·	·	·	·	Z	C
A N D	A ∧ M → A (1)	29	2	2	2D	4	3	25	3	2							21	6	2	31	5	2	35	4	2	3D	4	3	39	4	3										N	·	·	·	·	·	Z	·
A S L	C ← □□□□□ ← 0				0E	6	3	06	5	2	0A	2	1										16	6	2	1E	7	3													N	·	·	·	·	·	Z	C
B C C	BRANCH ON C = 0 (2)																															90	2	2							·	·	·	·	·	·	·	·
B C S	BRANCH ON C = 1 (2)																															B0	2	2							·	·	·	·	·	·	·	·
B E Q	BRANCH ON Z = 1 (2)																															F0	2	2							·	·	·	·	·	·	·	·
B I T	A ∧ M				2C	4	3	24	3	2																															M7	M6	·	·	·	·	Z	·
B M I	BRANCH ON N = 1 (2)																															30	2	2							·	·	·	·	·	·	·	·
B N E	BRANCH ON Z = 0 (2)																															D0	2	2							·	·	·	·	·	·	·	·
B P L	BRANCH ON N = 0 (2)																															10	2	2							·	·	·	·	·	·	·	·
B R K	BREAK (See Fig 1)													00	7	1																									·	·	·	1	·	·	·	·
B V C	BRANCH ON V = 0 (2)																															50	2	2							·	·	·	·	·	·	·	·
B V S	BRANCH ON V = 1 (2)																															70	2	2							·	·	·	·	·	·	·	·
C L C	0 → C													18	2	1																									·	·	·	·	·	·	·	0
C L D	0 → D													D8	2	1																									·	·	·	·	0	·	·	·
C L I	0 → I													58	2	1																									·	·	·	·	·	0	·	·
C L V	0 → V													B8	2	1																									·	0	·	·	·	·	·	·
C M P	A - M	C9	2	2	CD	4	3	C5	3	2							C1	6	2	D1	5	2	D5	4	2	DD	4	3	D9	4	3										N	·	·	·	·	·	Z	C
C P X	X - M	E0	2	2	EC	4	3	E4	3	2																															N	·	·	·	·	·	Z	C
C P Y	Y - M	C0	2	2	CC	4	3	C4	3	2																															N	·	·	·	·	·	Z	C
D E C	M - 1 → M				CE	6	3	C6	5	2													D6	6	2	DE	7	3													N	·	·	·	·	·	Z	·
D E X	X - 1 → X													CA	2	1																									N	·	·	·	·	·	Z	·
D E Y	Y - 1 → Y													88	2	1																									N	·	·	·	·	·	Z	·
E O R	A ∀ M → A (1)	49	2	2	4D	4	3	45	3	2							41	6	2	51	5	2	55	4	2	5D	4	3	59	4	3										N	·	·	·	·	·	Z	·
I N C	M + 1 → M				EE	6	3	E6	5	2													F6	6	2	FE	7	3													N	·	·	·	·	·	Z	·
I N X	X + 1 → X													E8	2	1																									N	·	·	·	·	·	Z	·
I N Y	Y + 1 → Y													C8	2	1																									N	·	·	·	·	·	Z	·
J M P	JUMP TO NEW LOC				4C	3	3																												6C	5	3				·	·	·	·	·	·	·	·
J S R	JUMP SUB (See Fig 2)				20	6	3																																		·	·	·	·	·	·	·	·
L D A	M → A (1)	A9	2	2	AD	4	3	A5	3	2							A1	6	2	B1	5	2	B5	4	2	BD	4	3	B9	4	3										N	·	·	·	·	·	Z	·

Mnemonic	Operation	IMMED	ABSOLUTE	ZERO PAGE	ACCUM	IMPLIED	(IND,X)	(IND),Y	Z.PAGE,X	ABS,X	ABS,Y	Z.PAGE,Y	N	V	B	D	I	Z	C
L D X	M → X (1)	A2 2 2	AE 4 3	A6 3 2						BE 4 3		B6 4 2	N	.	.	.	.	Z	.
L D Y	M → Y (1)	A0 2 2	AC 4 3	A4 3 2					B4 4 2	BC 4 3			N	.	.	.	.	Z	.
L S R	0 → [ ] → C		4E 6 3	46 5 2	4A 2 1				56 6 2	5E 7 3			0	.	.	.	.	Z	C
N O P	NO OPERATION					EA 2 1							.	.	.	.	.	.	.
O R A	A ∨ M → A	09 2 2	0D 4 3	05 3 2			01 6 2	11 5 2	15 4 2	1D 4 3	19 4 3		N	.	.	.	.	Z	.
P H A	A → Ms S − 1 → S					48 3 1							.	.	.	.	.	.	.
P H P	P → Ms S − 1 → S					08 3 1							.	.	.	.	.	.	.
P L A	S + 1 → S Ms → A					68 4 1							N	.	.	.	.	Z	.
P L P	S + 1 → S Ms → P					28 4 1							(RESTORED)						
R O L	[C ← [ ] ← C]		2E 6 3	26 5 2	2A 2 1				36 6 2	3E 7 3			N	.	.	.	.	Z	C
R O R	[C → [ ] → C]		6E 6 3	66 5 2	6A 2 1				76 6 2	7E 7 3			N	.	.	.	.	Z	C
R T I	RTRN INT					40 6 1							(RESTORED)						
R T S	RTRN SUB					60 6 1							.	.	.	.	.	.	.
S B C	A − M − C → A (1)(3)	E9 2 2	ED 4 3	E5 3 2			E1 6 2	F1 5 2	F5 4 2	FD 4 3	F9 4 3		N	V	.	.	.	Z	C
S E C	1 → C					38 2 1							.	.	.	.	.	.	1
S E D	1 → D					F8 2 1							.	.	.	1	.	.	.
S E I	1 → I					78 2 1							.	.	.	.	1	.	.
S T A	A → M		8D 4 3	85 3 2			81 6 2	91 6 2	95 4 2	9D 5 3	99 5 3		.	.	.	.	.	.	.
S T X	X → M		8E 4 3	86 3 2								96 4 2	.	.	.	.	.	.	.
S T Y	Y → M		8C 4 3	84 3 2					94 4 2				.	.	.	.	.	.	.
T A X	A → X					AA 2 1							N	.	.	.	.	Z	.
T A Y	A → Y					A8 2 1							N	.	.	.	.	Z	.
T S X	S → X					BA 2 1							N	.	.	.	.	Z	.
T X A	X → A					8A 2 1							N	.	.	.	.	Z	.
T X S	X → S					9A 2 1							.	.	.	.	.	.	.
T Y A	Y → A					98 2 1							N	.	.	.	.	Z	.

(1) ADD 1 TO N IF PAGE BOUNDARY IS CROSSED
(2) ADD 1 TO N IF BRANCH OCCURS TO SAME PAGE
     ADD 2 TO N IF BRANCH OCCURS TO DIFFERENT PAGE
(3) CARRY NOT = BORROW
(4) IF IN DECIMAL MODE Z FLAG IS INVALID
     ACCUMULATOR MUST BE CHECKED FOR ZERO RESULT

X   INDEX X
Y   INDEX Y
A   ACCUMULATOR
M   MEMORY PER EFFECTIVE ADDRESS
Ms MEMORY PER STACK POINTER

M7 MEMORY BIT 7 /
M6 MEMORY BIT 6
NO CYCLES
NO BYTES

+   ADD
−   SUBTRACT
∧   AND
∨   OR
⊻   EXCLUSIVE OR

6809

The 6809 was developed by Motorola as a successor to the 6800 device and as a rival to the 6502. The device uses an expanded 6800-type instruction set but incorporates a number of 16-bit instructions. To some extent, therefore, the 6809 forms a bridge between the second generation of 8-bit processors and the first generation of 16-bit processors.

The 6809 arrived rather too late to effectively rival the 6502 and Z80 devices in the mass production of 8-bit microcomputers, with only two manufacturers (Dragon Data and Tandy) adopting the device for the home computer boom of the early 1980s. The 6809 has, however, gained a large following in the industrial control sector where its power and elegance make it an attractive alternative to the 6502, 6800 and Z80. For this reason alone, the 6809 is likely to maintain its position as a versatile work-horse for many years to come.

The 6809 has two separate 8-bit accumulators (A and B). These may be used together to form a single 16-bit accumulator for use in 16-bit operations. Two 16-bit index registers (X and Y) are available, as are a 16-bit user stack pointer (U), 16-bit system stack pointer (S), and 16-bit program counter (PC).

The 6809 instruction set has 59 basic instructions including nine 16-bit accumulator/memory operations.

Typical 6800 family support devices include:

6821   Peripheral interface adaptor (PIA)
6828   Priority interrupt controller
6840   Programmable timer module
6845   CRT controller
6850   Asynchronous communications interface adaptor (ACIA)
6852   Synchronous serial data adaptor (SSDA)

The 6809 is 'second sourced' by AMI, Fairchild, and Hitachi. Since the device has retained bus compatibility with the 6800 and 6502 devices, a very wide range of support devices is available.

A CMOS version of the 6809 (HD6309) is available from Hitachi. The device operates with clock frequencies over the range 500 kHz to 8 MHz with a supply of 5 V ± 10% and features vastly reduced power consumption.

6809 basic configuration

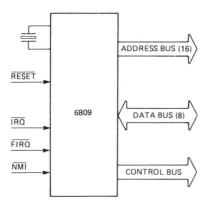

6809 register model

ACCUMULATOR (A)	ACCUMULATOR (B)
DIRECT PAGE (DP)	FLAGS (CC)
INDEX REGISTER (X)	
INDEX REGISTER (Y)	
USER STACK POINTER (U)	
SYSTEM STACK POINTER (S)	
PROGRAM COUNTER (PC)	

6809 pinout

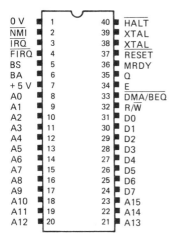

6809 instruction set

8-BIT ACCUMULATOR AND MEMORY	
Mnemonic(s)	**Operation**
ADCA, ADCB	Add memory to accumulator with carry
ADDA, ADDB	Add memory to accumulator
ANDA, ANDB	Add memory with accumulator
ASL, ALSA, ASLB	Arithmetic shift of accumulator or memory left
ASR, ASRA, ASRB	Arithmetic shift of accumulator or memory right
BITA, BITB	Bit test memory with accumulator
CLR, CLRA, CLRB	Clear accumulator or memory location
CMPA, CMPB	Compare memory from accumulator
COM, COMA, COMB	Complement accumulator or memory location
DAA	Decimal adjust A-accumulator

DEC, DECA, DECB	Decrement accumulator or memory location
EORA, EORB	Exclusive or memory with accumulator
EXG R1, R2	Exchange R1 with R2 (R1, R2 = A, B, CC, DP)
INC, INCA, INCB	Increment accumulator or memory location
LDA, LDB	Load accumulator from memory
LSL, LSLA, LSLB	Logical shift left accumulator or memory location
LSR, LSRA, ŁSRB	Logical shift right accumulator or memory location
MUL	Unsigned multiply (A x B→D)
NEG, NEGA, NEGB	Negate accumulator or memory
ORA, ORB	Or memory with accumulator
ROL, ROLA, ROLB	Rotate accumulator or memory left
ROR, RORA, RORB	Rotate accumulator or memory right
SBCA, SBCB	Subtract memory from accumulator with borrow
STA, STB	Store accumulator to memory
SUBA, SUBB	Subtract memory from accumulator
TST, TSTA, TSTB	Test accumulator or memory location
TFR, R1, R2	Transfer R1 to R2 (R1, R2 = A, B, CC, DP)

NOTE: A, B, CC, or DP may be pushed to (pulled from) either stack with PSHS, PSHU, (PULS, PULU) instructions

16-BIT ACCUMULATOR AND MEMORY

Mnemonic(s)	Operation
ADDD	Add memory to D accumulator
CMPD	Compare memory from D accumulator
EXG D, R	Exchange D with X, Y, S, U or PC
LDD	Load D accumulator from memory
SEX	Sign Extend B accumulator into A accumulator
STD	Store D accumulator to memory
SUBD	Subtract memory from D accumulator
TFR D, R	Transfer D to X, Y, S, U or PC
TFR R, D	Transfer X, Y, S, U or PC to D

INDEX REGISTER STACK POINTER

Mnemonic(s)	Operation
CMPS, CMPU	Compare memory from stack pointer
CMPX, CMPY	Compare memory from index register
EXG R1, R2	Exchange D, X, Y, S, U or PC with D, X, S, Y, U or PC

LEAS, LEAU	Load effective address into stack pointer
LEAX, LEAY	Load effective address into index register
LDS, LDU	Load stack pointer from memory
LDX, LDY	Load index register from memory
PSHS	Push any register(s) onto hardware stack (except S)
PSHU	Push any register(s) onto user stack (except U)
PULS	Pull any register(s) from hardware stack (except S)
PULU	Pull any register(s) from hardware stack (except U)
STS, STU	Store stack pointer to memory
STX, STY	Store index register to memory
TFR R1, R2	Transfer D, X, Y, S, U or PC to D, X, Y, S, U or PC
ABX	Add B accumulator to X (unsigned)

BRANCH

BCC, LBCC	Branch if carry clear
BCS, LBCS	Branch if carry set
BEQ, LBEQ	Branch if equal
BGE, LBGE	Branch if greater than or equal (signed)
BGT, LBGT	Branch if greater (signed)
BHI, LBHI	Branch if higher (unsigned)
BHS, LBHS	Branch if higher or same (unsigned)
BLE, LBLE	Branch if less than or equal (signed)
BLO, LBLO	Branch if lower (unsigned)
BLS, LBLS	Branch if lower or same (unsigned)
BLT, LBLT	Branch if less than (signed)
BMI, LBMI	Branch if minus
BNE, LBNE	Branch if not equal
BPL, LBPL	Branch if plus
BRA, LBRA	Branch always
BRN, LBRN	Branch never
BSR, LBSR	Branch to subroutine
BVC, LBVC	Branch if overflow clear
BVS, LBVS	Branch if overflow set

MISCELLANEOUS

ANDCC	AND condition code register
CWAI	AND condition code register, then wait for interrupt
NOP	No operation
ORCC	OR condition code register
JMP	Jump
JSR	Jump to subroutine
RTI	Return from interrupt
RTS	Return from subroutine
SW1, SW12, SW13	Software interrupt (absolute indirect)
SYNC	Synchronise with interrupt line

Z80

The Z80 is a powerful 8-bit microprocessor which has a total of
158 basic instructions (including bit set and test, and block move).
The Z80 was designed by Zilog as a very much enhanced 8080
device and yet retains full instruction set compatibility with that
device.

The Z80 has 17 internal registers including a duplicate set of
general purpose registers. Two 16-bit index registers (IX and IY)
are provided as well as a 16-bit stack pointer (SP) and 16-bit
program counter (PC). The device also provides for three interrupt
modes.

An interesting feature of the Z80 (and one which earned it
considerable popularity with manufacturers) is the internal
provision for refreshing dynamic RAM.

For control applications, the Z80 provides IN and OUT
instructions which permit reading and writing data to any one of
256 I/O ports. Memory and port addresses are distinguished using
the memory request ($\overline{\text{MREQ}}$) and input/output request ($\overline{\text{IORQ}}$)
lines.

The Z80 operates from a single $+5$ V supply and requires a
single-phase clock at typical frequencies of 4 MHz (Z80A) or
6 MHz (Z80B). It should also be noted that the clock input to the
Z80 normally requires a 390 Ω pull-up resistor.

Alternative sources for the Z80 include Fairchild (F3880),
Mostek (MK3880), NEC (μPD780C), and SGS-ATES (Z80A).

Z80 support devices include:

Z80-CTC (Z8430)	Counter/timer circuit
Z80-DART (Z8470)	Dual asynchronous receiver/transmitter
Z80-DMA (Z8410)	Direct memory access controller
Z80-PIO (Z8420)	Parallel input/output controller
Z80-SIO/0 (Z8440)	Serial input/output controller (with two synchronizing inputs)
Z80-SIO/2 (Z8442)	Serial input/output controller (with one synchronizing input and independent receiver and transmitter)

Support devices are coded with a suffix: A to indicate 4 MHz
operation, and B to indicate 6 MHz operation.

Z80 basic configuration

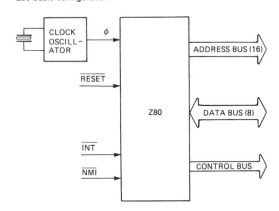

A CMOS version of the Z80 is available from NEC. This μPD7000PC device operates at up to 4 MHz with supplies of between 3 V and 6 V. Typical operating and standby currents are 16 mA and 100 μA respectively.

National Semiconductor produce a CMOS Z80-compatible device (the NSC800) which uses the full Z80 instruction set. The device is available in 1 MHz (NSC800N-1), 2.5 MHz (NSC800N), and 4 MHz (NSC800N-4) versions and it operates over a supply voltage range of 3 V to 12 V.

CMOS support devices (Z84C20 and Z84C30) are available from Toshiba, as is a Z80 CMOS clock generator (6497).

Z80 register model

MAIN REGISTER SET

ACCUMULATOR (A)	FLAGS (F)
(B)	(C)
(D)	(E)
(H)	(L)

ALTERNATE REGISTER SET

ACCUMULATOR (A')	FLAGS (F')
(B')	(C')
(D')	(E')
(H')	(L')

SPECIAL PURPOSE REGISTERS

INTERRUPT VECTOR (I)	MEMORY REFRESH (R)
INDEX REGISTER	(IX)
INDEX REGISTER	(IY)
STACK POINTER	(SP)
PROGRAM COUNTER	(PC)

Z80 pinout

A11	1	40	A10
A12	2	39	A9
A13	3	38	A8
A14	4	37	A7
A15	5	36	A6
Ø	6	35	A5
D4	7	34	A4
D3	8	33	A3
D5	9	32	A2
D6	10	31	A1
+5 V	11	30	A0
D2	12	29	OV
D7	13	28	RFSH
D0	14	27	M1
D1	15	26	RESET
INT	16	25	BUSRQ
NMI	17	24	WAIT
HALT	18	23	BUSAK
MREQ	19	22	WR
IORQ	20	21	RD

Z80 instruction set

	Mnemonic	Symbolic Operation	Comments
8-BIT LOADS	LD r, s	r ← s	s ≡ r, n, (HL), (IX+e), (IY+e)
	LD d, r	d ← r	d ≡ (HL), r (IX+e), (IY+e)
	LD d, n	d ← n	d ≡ (HL), (IX+e), (IY+e)
	LD A, s	A ← s	s ≡ (BC), (DE), (nn), I, R
	LD d, A	d ← A	d ≡ (BC), (DE), (nn), I, R
16-BIT LOADS	LD dd, nn	dd ← nn	dd ≡ BC, DE, HL, SP, IX, IY
	LD dd, (nn)	dd ← (nn)	dd ≡ BC, DE, HL, SP, IX, IY
	LD (nn), ss	(nn) ← ss	ss ≡ BC, DE, HL, SP, IX, IY
	LD SP, ss	SP ← ss	ss ≡ HL, IX, IY
	PUSH ss	(SP−1) ← ss$_H$; (SP−2) ← ss$_L$	ss ≡ BC, DE, HL, AF, IX, IY
	POP dd	dd$_L$ ← (SP); dd$_H$ ← (SP+1)	dd ≡ BC, DE, HL, AF, IX, IY
EXCHANGES	EX DE, HL	DE ← → HL	
	EX-AF, AF'	AF ← → AF'	
	EXX	$\begin{pmatrix} BC \\ DE \\ HL \end{pmatrix} ← → \begin{pmatrix} BC' \\ DE' \\ HL' \end{pmatrix}$	
	EX (SP), ss	(SP) ← → ss$_L$, (SP+1) ← → ss$_H$	ss ≡ HL, IX, IY
MEMORY BLOCK MOVES	LDI	(DE) ← (HL), DE ← DE+1 HL ← HL+1, BC ← BC−1	
	LDIR	(DE) ← (HL), DE ← DE+1 HL ← HL+1, BC ← BC−1 Repeat until BC = 0	
	LDD	(DE) ← (HL), DE ← DE−1 HL ← HL−1, BC ← BC−1	
	LDDR	(DE) ← (HL), DE ← DE−1 HL ← HL−1, BC ← BC−1 Repeat until BC = 0	
MEMORY BLOCK SEARCHES	CPI	A−(HL), HL ← HL+1 BC ← BC−1	
	CPIR	A−(HL), HL ← HL+1 BC ← BC−1, Repeat until BC = 0 or A = (HL)	A−(HL) sets the flags only. A is not affected
	CPD	A−(HL), HL ← HL−1 BC ← BC−1	
	CPDR	A−(HL), HL ← HL−1 BC ← BC−1, Repeat until BC=0 or A=(HL)	
8-BIT ALU	ADD s	A ← A + s	
	ADC s	A ← A + s + CY	CY is the carry flag
	SUB s	A ← A − s	
	SBC s	A ← A − s − CY	s ≡ r, n, (HL) (IX+e), (IY+e)
	AND s	A ← A ∧ s	
	OR s	A ← A ∨ s	
	XOR s	A ← A ⊕ s	
	CP s	A − s	s = r, n (HL) (IX+e), (IY+e)
	INC d	d ← d + 1	d = r, (HL)
	DEC d	d ← d − 1	(IX+e), (IY+e)
	ADD HL, ss	HL ← HL + ss	⎫ ss ≡ BC, DE
	ADC HL, ss	HL ← HL + ss + CY	⎬ HL, SP
	SBC HL, ss	HL ← HL − ss − CY	⎭
	ADD IX, ss	IX ← IX + ss	ss ≡ BC, DE, IX, SP

	Mnemonic	Symbolic Operation	Comments
16-BIT ARITHMETIC	ADD IY, ss	IY ← IY + ss	ss ≡ BC, DE, IY, SP
	INC dd	dd ← dd + 1	dd ≡ BC, DE, HL, SP, IX, IY
	DEC dd	dd ← dd − 1	dd ≡ BC, DE, HL, SP, IX, IY
MISCELLANEOUS GP ACC. & FLAG	DAA	Converts A contents into packed BCD following add or subtract.	Operands must be in packed BCD format
	CPL	A ← $\overline{A}$	
	NEG	A ← 00 − A	
	CCF	CY ← $\overline{CY}$	
	SCF	CY ← 1	
	NOP	No operation	
	HALT	Halt CPU	
	DI	Disable Interrupts	
	EI	Enable Interrupts	
	IM 0	Set interrupt mode 0	8080A mode
	IM 1	Set interrupt mode 1	Call to 0038$_H$
	IM 2	Set interrupt mode 2	Indirect Call
ROTATES AND SHIFTS	RLC s		
	RL s		
	RRC s		
	RR s		s ≡ r, (HL) (IX+e), (IY+e)
	SLA s		
	SRA s		
	SRL s		
	RLD		
	RRD		
BIT S, R. & T	BIT b, s	Z ← $\overline{s_b}$	Z is zero flag
	SET b, s	s_b ← 1	s ≡ r, (HL)
	RES b, s	s_b ← 0	(IX+e), (IY+e)
INPUT AND OUTPUT	IN A, (n)	A ← (n)	
	IN r, (C)	r ← (C)	Set flags
	INI	(HL) ← (C), HL ← HL + 1 B ← B − 1	
	INIR	(HL) ← (C), HL ← HL + 1 B ← B − 1 Repeat until B = 0	
	IND	(HL) ← (C), HL ← HL − 1 B ← B − 1	
	INDR	(HL) ← (C), HL ← HL − 1 B ← B − 1 Repeat until B = 0	
	OUT(n), A	(n) ← A	
	OUT(C), r	(C) ← r	
	OUTI	(C) ← (HL), HL ← HL + 1 B ← B − 1	
	OTIR	(C) ← (HL), HL ← HL + 1 B ← B − 1 Repeat until B = 0	
	OUTD	(C) ← (HL), HL ← HL − 1 B ← B − 1	
	OTDR	(C) ← (HL), HL ← HL − 1 B ← B − 1 Repeat until B = 0	

JUMPS	JP nn	PC ← nn		NZ	PO
	JP cc, nn	If condition cc is true	cc	Z	PE
		PC ← nn, else continue		NC	P
				C	M
	JR e	PC ← PC + e			
	JR kk, e	If condition kk is true	kk	NZ	NC
		PC ← PC + e, else continue		Z	C
	JP (ss)	PC ← ss	ss = HL, IX, IY		
	DJNZ e	B ← B - 1, if B ≠ 0			
		continue, else PC ← PC + e			

CALLS	CALL nn	(SP - 1) ← PC$_H$		NZ	PO
		(SP - 2) ← PC$_L$, PC ← nn	cc	Z	PE
	CALL cc, nn	If condition cc is false		NC	P
		continue, else same as		C	M
		CALL nn			

RESTARTS	RST L	(SP - 1) ← PC$_H$
		(SP - 2) ← PC$_L$, PC$_H$ ← 0
		PC$_L$ ← L

RETURNS	RET	PC$_L$ ← (SP),			
		PC$_H$ ← (SP + 1)			
	RET cc	If condition cc is false		NZ	PO
		continue, else same as RET	cc	Z	PE
	RETI	Return from interrupt,		NC	P
		same as RET		C	M
	RETN	Return from non-			
		maskable interrupt			

In the table the following abbreviations are used.

b	≡	a bit number in any 8-bit register or memory location
cc	≡	flag condition code

NZ	≡ non zero		PO	≡	Parity odd or no over flow
Z	≡ zero		PE	≡	Parity even or over flow
NC	≡ non carry		P	≡	Positive
C	≡ carry		M	≡	Negative (minus)

d	≡	any 8-bit destination register or memory location
dd	≡	any 16-bit destination register or memory location
e	≡	8-bit signed 2's complement displacement used in relative jumps and indexed addressing
L	≡	8 special call locations in page zero. In decimal notation these are 0, 8, 16, 24, 32, 40, 48 and 56
n	≡	any 8-bit binary number
nn	≡	any 16-bit binary number
r	≡	any 8-bit general purpose register (A, B, C, D, E, H, or L)
s	≡	any 8-bit source register or memory location
s$_b$	≡	a bit in a specific 8-bit register or memory location
ss	≡	any 16-bit source register or memory location
subscript "L"	≡	the low order 8 bits of a 16-bit register
subscript "H"	≡	the high order 8 bits of a 16-bit register
( )	≡	the contents within the ( ) are to be used as a pointer to a memory location or I/O port number

8-bit registers are A, B, C, D, E, H, L, I and R
16-bit register pairs are AF, BC, DE and HL
16-bit registers are SP, PC, IX and IY

8086

The Intel 8086 was the first true second-generation 16-bit microprocessor. Its arrival was extremely timely and coincided with the availability of low-cost high-capacity semiconductor memories. The 8086 thus rapidly became the first industry-standard 16-bit microprocessor. The 8086 instruction set has retained some compatibility with the 8-bit 8080 instructions and is well suited to efficient compilation from such high level languages as BASIC and Pascal.

The 8086 has 14 16-bit registers (including those that are the direct equivalents of 8080/8085 registers). The CPU has 20 address lines and thus provides for a 1M byte address range. The I/O address range, on the other hand, is 64K bytes.

Like many of its rival 16-bit processors, the 8086 uses a segmented address system. Four segment registers are provided: code segment (CS), stack segment (SS), data segment (DS) and extra segment (ES). A physical segment must start on a 16-byte address boundary (the four least significant address bits are all set to zero) and have a size of 64K bytes.

The actual 20-bit address is formed by extending the 16-bit segment address by shifting and adding four least significant zero bits (i.e. effectively multiplying the segment register contents by 16). The contents of the instruction pointer (IP), stack pointer (SP) or other 16-bit address register are then added to the result.

The 8086 operates from a single +5 V supply with typical clock frequencies of 5 MHz, 8 MHz and 10 MHz.

In order to avoid the use of a large package, the 8086 uses a multiplexed address/data bus; the lower 16 address lines share the 16 data bus lines.

The device can operate in one of two modes, 'max' or 'min'. Maximum mode is employed in multi-processor systems where an 8288 bus controller device decodes the 8086 S0, S1, and S2 lines to produce the necessary I/O and memory control signals.

Dedicated 8086 support devices include:

8087	Numeric data co-processor
8089	I/O processor with DMA
8207	Dynamic RAM controller
8208	Dynamic RAM controller
8237	DMA controller
8253	Timer/counter
8254	Timer/counter
8259A	Interrupt controller
8284A	Clock generator (essential for 8086-based systems)
8286	Data bus transceiver
8287	Data bus transceiver
8288	Bus controller (essential for 'max' mode)

The 8086 can also make use of the 8080 family of support devices.

The 8086 is 'second sourced' by AMD, Fujitsu, NEC, OKI, and Siemens. CMOS versions (80C86) are available from Harris and OKI.

8086 basic configuration

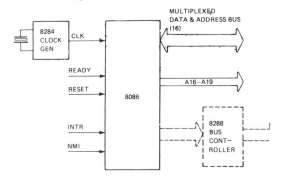

8086 register model

POINTER AND INDEX REGISTERS	
STACK POINTER	(SP)
BASE POINTER	(BP)
SOURCE INDEX	(SI)
DESTINATION INDEX	(DI)

GENERAL PURPOSE REGISTERS			
(AH)	ACC.	(AX)	(AL)
(BH)	BASE	(BX)	(BL)
(CH)	COUNT	(CX)	(CL)
(DH)	DATA	(DX)	(DL)

SEGMENT REGISTERS	
CODE SEGMENT	(CS)
DATA SEGMENT	(DS)
STACK SEGMENT	(SS)
EXTRA SEGMENT	(ES)

INSTRUCTION POINTER	(IP)
STATUS	(ST)

8086 pinout

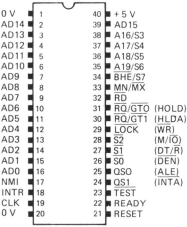

0 V	1	40	+ 5 V
AD14	2	39	AD15
AD13	3	38	A16/S3
AD12	4	37	A17/S4
AD11	5	36	A18/S5
AD10	6	35	A19/S6
AD9	7	34	$\overline{BHE}$/S7
AD8	8	33	MN/$\overline{MX}$
AD7	9	32	$\overline{RD}$
AD6	10	31	$\overline{RQ/GT0}$ (HOLD)
AD5	11	30	$\overline{RQ/GT1}$ (HLDA)
AD4	12	29	$\overline{LOCK}$ (WR)
AD3	13	28	$\overline{S2}$ (M/$\overline{IO}$)
AD2	14	27	$\overline{S1}$ (DT/$\overline{R}$)
AD1	15	26	$\overline{S0}$ (DEN)
AD0	16	25	QS0 (ALE)
NMI	17	24	QS1 (INTA)
INTR	18	23	TEST
CLK	19	22	READY
0 V	20	21	RESET

Note: Signals shown in brackets correspond to 'minimum'   de
when MN/$\overline{MX}$ is high.

8086 instruction set

GENERAL PURPOSE

MOV	Move byte or word
PUSH	Push word onto stack
POP	Pop word off stack
PUSHA	Push all registers on stack
POPA	Pop all registers from stack
XCHG	Exchange byte or word
XLAT	Translate byte

INPUT/OUTPUT

IN	Input byte or word
OUT	Output byte or word

ADDRESS OBJECT

LEA	Load effective address
LDS	Load pointer using DS
LES	Load pointer using ES

FLAG TRANSFER

LAHF	Load AH register from flags
SAHF	Store AH register in flags
PUSHF	Push flags onto stack
POPF	Pop flags off stack

ADDITION

ADD	Add byte or word
ADC	Add byte or word with carry
INC	Increment byte or word by 1
AAA	ASCII adjust for addition
DAA	Decimal adjust for addition

SUBTRACTION

SUB	Subtract byte or word
SBB	Subtract byte or word with borrow
DEC	Decrement byte or word by 1
NEG	Negate byte or word
CMP	Compare byte or word
AAS	ASCII adjust for subtraction
DAS	Decimal adjust for subtraction

MULTIPLICATION

MUL	Multiply byte or word unsigned
IMUL	Integer multiply byte or word
AAM	ASCII adjust for multiply

DIVISION

DIV	Divide byte or word unsigned
IDIV	Integer divide byte or word
AAD	ASCII adjust for division
CBW	Convert byte to word
CWD	Convert word to doubleword

MOVS	Move byte or word string
INS	Input bytes or word string
OUTS	Output bytes or word string
CMPS	Compare byte or word string
SCAS	Scan byte or word string
LODS	Load byte or word string
STOS	Store byte or word string
REP	Repeat
REPE/REPZ	Repeat while equal zero
REPNE/REPNZ	Repeat while not equal to zero

LOGICALS

NOT	'Not' byte or word
AND	'And' byte or word
OR	Inclusive 'or' byte or word
XOR	Exclusive 'or' byte or word
TEST	Test byte or word

SHIFTS

SHL/SAL	Shift logical/arithmetic left byte or word
SHR	Shift logical right byte or word
SAR	Shift arithmetic right byte or word

ROTATES

ROL	Rotate left byte or word
ROR	Rotate right byte or word
RCL	Rotate through carry left byte or word
RCR	Rotate through carry right byte or word

FLAG OPERATIONS

STC	Set carry flag
CLC	Clear carry flag
CMC	Complement carry flag
STD	Set direction flag
CLD	Clear direction flag
STI	Set interrupt enable flag
CLI	Clear interrupt enable flag

EXTERNAL SYNCHRONIZATION

HLT	Halt until interrupt or reset
WAIT	Wait for TEST pin active
ESC	Escape to extension processor
LOCK	Lock bus during next instruction

NO OPERATION

NOP	No operation

HIGH LEVEL INSTRUCTIONS

ENTER	Format stack for procedure entry
LEAVE	Restore stack for procedure exit
BOUND	Detects values outside prescribed range

CONDITIONAL TRANSFERS

JA/JNBE	Jump if above/not below nor equal
JAE/JNB	Jump if above or equal/not below
JB/JNAE	Jump if below/not above nor equal
JBE/JNA	Jump if below or equal/not above
JC	Jump if carry
JE/JZ	Jump if equal/zero
JG/JNLE	Jump if greater/not less nor equal
JGE/JNL	Jump if greater or equal/not less
JL/JNGE	Jump if less/not greater nor equal
JLE/JNG	Jump if less or equal/not greater
JNC	Jump if not carry
JNE/JNZ	Jump if not equal/not zero
JNO	Jump if not overflow
JNP/JPO	Jump if not parity/parity odd
JNS	Jump if not sign
JO	Jump if overflow
JP/JPE	Jump if parity/parity even
JS	Jump if sign

UNCONDITIONAL TRANSFERS

CALL	Call procedure
RET	Return from procedure
JMP	Jump

ITERATION CONTROLS

LOOP	Loop
LOOPE/LOOPZ	Loop if equal/zero
LOOPNE/LOOPNZ	Loop if not equal/not zero
JCXZ	Jump if register CX 0

INTERRUPTS

INT	Interrupt
INTO	Interrupt if overflow
IRET	Interrupt return

8088

The 8088 is an 8-bit data bus version of the 8086. The device has the same internal architecture as the 8086 and shares the same instruction set. This permits full software migration between the two systems and the same range of support devices.

The 8088 attracted much support from equipment manufacturers wishing to produce 16-bit microcomputers while retaining lower cost 8-bit data bus systems. The 8088 was thus adopted for the IBM PC, ACT Sirius, and Sanyo MBC-555 to name just three.

For other details see the 8086.

8088 basic configuration

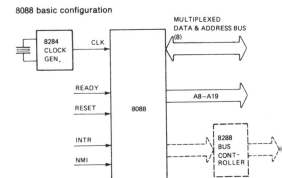

8088 register model

POINTER AND INDEX REGISTERS

| STACK POINTER (SP) |
| BASE POINTER (BP) |
| SOURCE INDEX (SI) |
| DESTINATION INDEX (DI) |

SEGMENT REGISTERS

CODE SEGMENT	(CS)
DATA SEGMENT	(DS)
STACK SEGMENT	(SS)
EXTRA SEGMENT	(ES)

GENERAL PURPOSE REGISTERS

(AH)	ACC	(AX)	(AL)
(BH)	BASE	(BX)	(BL)
(CH)	COUNT	(CX)	(CL)
(DH)	DATA	(DX)	(DL)

| INSTRUCTION POINTER | (IP) |
| STATUS (ST) |

8088 pinout

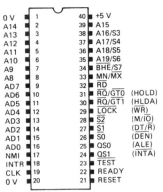

Note: Signals shown in brackets correspond to 'minimum' mode when MN/$\overline{\text{MX}}$ is high.

80286

Intel's 80286 is an advanced, high-performance microprocessor which has been optimized for multi-user and multi-tasking microcomputer systems. The 80286 offers a 16 M byte physical addressing range but incorporates memory management capabilities that can map up to a Gigabyte of virtual memory. Depending upon the application, the 80286 is up to six times faster than the standard 5 MHz 8086 while providing upward software compatibility with the 8086, 8088 and 80186 family of processors.

The 80286 has fifteen 16-bit registers of which fourteen are identical to those found in the 8086. The additional machine status word (MSW) register controls the operating mode of the processor and also records when a task switch takes place.

The bit functions within the MSW are summarized in the table:

Bit functions within the MSW

Bit	Name	Function
0	Protected enable (PE)	enables protected mode and can only be cleared by asserting the RESET signal
1	Monitor processor (MP)	allows WAIT instructions to cause a 'processor extension not present' exception (exception 7)
2	Emulate processor (EP)	causes a 'processor extension not present' exception (exception 7) on ESC instructions to allow emulation of a processor extension
3	Task switched (TS)	indicates that the next instruction using a processor extension will cause exception 7 (allowing software to test whether the current processor extension context belongs to the current task)

The machine status word is initialized with a value of FFF0H upon reset, the remainder of the 80286 registers being initialized as shown earlier for the 8086. The 80286 is packaged in either a 68-pin JEDEC type-A leadless chip carrier (LCC) or pin grid array (PGA).

In a typical 16-bit microprocessor system, the 80286 CPU enjoys the support of the following devices:

80287 Numeric data co-processor
82288 Bus controller
82284 Clock generator
82230 AT-bus chip
82231 AT-bus chip

In addition, 8-bit support devices (such as the 8259A) are often found in 80286-based systems.

Alternative sources for the 80286 include AMD, Fujitsu, Siemens and Harris Semiconductor Corp. The NEAT (New enhanced AT) chip set produced by C&T Corp. has integrated many of the functions of the AT support devices and provides manufacturers with a means of operating the 80286 CPU at either 16 or 20 MHz whilst the 8-bit expansion bus runs at a more sedate

8 MHz and memory is accessed at its upper limit of about 12 MHz. The NEAT chip set is thus instrumental in optimizing each part of the system to provide the fastest possible transfer of data.

80286 pin connections

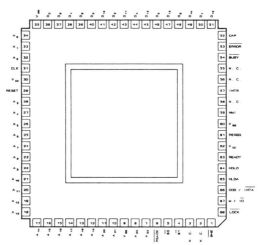

68000

The Motorola 68000 is an advanced 16-bit microprocessor which features 32-bit internal architecture. The 68000 contains a total of 32 registers, uses a 24-bit address and data buses respectively, and offers a 16M byte direct addressing range. The device is housed in a 64-pin DIL package.

The internal architecture of the 68000 is delightfully 'clean'; it has eight 32-bit data registers (somewhat confusingly known as D0 to D7) and seven 32-bit address registers (A0 to A6). In addition, there are two 32-bit stack pointers (USP and SSP) and one 32-bit program counter (PC).

The 68000 requires a single-phase clock input at either 8 MHz (68000-8) or 12 MHz (68000-12) and operates from a single +5 V supply.

The 68000 features 56 basic instructions. Operations may be based on bits, bytes (8 bits), words (16 bits), and long-words (32 bits). The CPU can operate in 'user' or 'supervisor' modes and a further 'trace' mode is provided which will generate an exception (trap) every time an instruction is executed.

The 68000 features asynchronous bus transfers; an acknowledge signal is required for data transfers on the bus. The 68000 is compatible with the range of 8-bit 68000 support devices. Dedicated 68000 peripheral devices include:

68430   Direct memory access controller (providing single-channel DMA control)

8450 Direct memory access controller (providing four DMA
      control channels with priorities)
8681 Dual channel universal asynchronous receiver/
      transmitter (UART)

Alternative sources for the 68000 include Hitachi and Signetics.
An 8-bit data bus version (68008) is also available. This device is
housed in a 48-pin DIL package.

68000 basic configuration

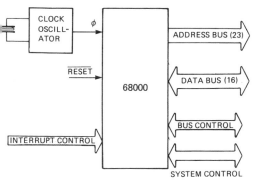

68000 register model

DATA REGISTERS

				(DØ)
				(D1)
				(D2)
				(D3)
				(D4)
				(D5)
				(D6)
				(D7)

ADDRESS REGISTERS

			(AØ)
			(A1)
			(A2)
			(A3)
			(A4)
			(A5)
			(A6)

SPECIAL PURPOSE REGISTERS

USER STACK POINTER	(USP)	(A7)
SUPERVISOR STACK POINTER	(SSP)	(A7)
PROGRAM COUNTER	(PC)	
	STATUS REGISTER	

68000 instruction set

Mnemonic	Description	Operation
ABCD	Add Decimal with Extend	(Destination)$_{10}$ + (Source)$_{10}$ → Destination
ADD	Add Binary	(Destination) + (Source) → Destination
ADDA	Add Address	(Destination) + (Source) → Destination
ADDI	Add Immediate	(Destination) + Immediate Data → Destination
ADDQ	Add Quick	(Destination) + Immediate Data → Destination
ADDX	Add Extended	(Destination) + (Source) + X → Destination
AND	AND Logical	(Destination) Λ (Source) → Destination
ANDI	AND Immediate	(Destination) Λ Immediate Data → Destination
ASL, ASR	Arithmetic Shift	(Destination) Shifted by < count > → Destination
B$_{CC}$	Branch Conditionally	If CC then PC + d → PC
BCHG	Test a Bit and Change	~ (< bit number >) OF Destination → Z ~ (< bit number >) OF Destination → < bit number > OF Destination
BCLR	Test a Bit and Clear	~ (< bit number >) OF Destination → Z 0 → < bit number > OF Destination
BRA	Branch Always	PC + d → PC
BSET	Test a Bit and Set	~ (< bit number >) OF Destination → Z 1 → < bit number > OF Destination
BSR	Branch to Subroutine	PC → SP@ − , PC + d → PC
BTST	Test a Bit	~ (< bit number >) OF Destination → Z
CHK	Check Register against Bounds	If Dn < 0 or Dn > (< ea >) then TRAP
CLR	Clear an Operand	0 → Destination
CMP	Compare	(Destination) − (Source)
CMPA	Compare Address	(Destination) − (Source)
CMPI	Compare Immediate	(Destination) − Immediate Data
CMPM	Compare Memory	(Destination) − (Source)
DB$_{CC}$	Test Condition, Decrement and Branch	If ~ CC then Dn − 1 → Dn, if Dn ≠ − 1 then PC + d → PC
DIVS	Signed Divide	(Destination) / (Source) → Destination
DIVU	Unsigned Divide	(Destination) / (Source) → Destination
EOR	Exclusive OR Logical	(Destination) ⊕ (Source) → Destination
EORI	Exclusive OR Immediate	(Destination) ⊕ Immediate Data → Destination
EXG	Exchange Register	Rx ↔ Ry
EXT	Sign Extend	(Destination) Sign-extended → Destination
JMP	Jump	Destination → PC
JSR	Jump to Subroutine	PC → SP@ − ; Destination → PC
LEA	Load Effective Address	Destination → An
LINK	Link and Allocate	An → SP@ − ; SP → An, SP + d → SP
LSL, LSR	Logical Shift	(Destination) Shifted by < count > → Destination
MOVE	Move Data from Source to Destination	(Source) → Destination
MOVE to CCR	Move to Condition Code	(Source) → CCR
MOVE to SR	Move to the Status Register	(Source) → SR
MOVE from SR	Move from the Status Register	SR → Destination
MOVE USP	Move User Stack Pointer	USP → An, An → USP
MOVEA	Move Address	(Source) → Destination
MOVEM	Move Multiple Registers	Registers → Destination (Source) → Registers
MOVEP	Move Peripheral Data	(Source) → Destination
MOVEQ	Move Quick	Immediate Data → Destination
MULS	Signed Multiply	(Destination) * (Source) → Destination
MULU	Unsigned Multiply	(Destination) * (Source) → Destination
NBCD	Negate Decimal with Extend	0 − (Destination)$_{10}$ − X → Destination
NEG	Negate	0 − (Destination) → Destination
NEGX	Negate with Extend	0 − (Destination) − X → Destination
NOP	No Operation	–
NOT	Logical Complement	~ (Destination) → Destination
OR	Inclusive OR Logical	(Destination) v (Source) → Destination
ORI	Inclusive OR Immediate	(Destination) v Immediate Data → Destination
PEA	Push Effective Address	Destination → SP@ −
RESET	Reset External Devices	
ROL, ROR	Rotate (Without Extend)	(Destination) Rotated by < count > → Destination
ROXL, ROXR	Rotate with Extend	(Destination) Rotated by < count > → Destination
RTE	Return from Exception	SP@ + → SR, SP@ + → PC
RTR	Return and Restore Condition Codes	SP@ + → CC, SP@ + → PC
RTS	Return from Subroutine	SP@ + → PC
SBCD	Subtract Decimal with Extend	(Destination)$_{10}$ − (Source)$_{10}$ − X → Destination
S$_{CC}$	Set According to Condition	If CC then 1's → Destination else 0's → Destination
STOP	Load Status Register and Stop	Immediate Data → SR, STOP
SUB	Subtract Binary	(Destination) − (Source) → Destination
SUBA	Subtract Address	(Destination) − (Source) → Destination
SUBI	Subtract Immediate	(Destination) − Immediate Data → Destination
SUBQ	Subtract Quick	(Destination) − Immediate Data → Destination
SUBX	Subtract with Extend	(Destination) − (Source) − X → Destination
SWAP	Swap Register Halves	Register [31 16] ↔ Register [15 0]
TAS	Test and Set an Operand	(Destination) Tested → CC, 1 → [7] OF Destination
TRAP	Trap	PC → SSP@ − ; SR → SSP@ − , (Vector) → PC
TRAPV	Trap on Overflow	If V then TRAP
TST	Test an Operand	(Destination) Tested → CC
UNLK	Unlink	An → SP, SP@ + → An

[ ] = bit number

68000 pinout

Pin	Signal		Pin	Signal
1	D4		64	D5
2	D3		63	D6
3	D2		62	D7
4	D1		61	D8
5	D0		60	D9
6	AS		59	D10
7	UDS		58	D11
8	LDS		57	D12
9	R/W		56	D13
10	DTACK		55	D14
11	BG		54	D15
12	BGACK		53	0 V
13	BR		52	A23
14	+5 V		51	A22
15	Ø		50	A21
16	0 V		49	+5 V
17	HALT		48	A20
18	RESET		47	A19
19	VMA		46	A18
20	EN		45	A17
21	VPA		44	A16
22	BERR		43	A15
23	IPL2		42	A14
24	IPL1		41	A13
25	IPL0		40	A12
26	FC2		39	A11
27	FC1		38	A10
28	FC0		37	A9
29	A1		36	A8
30	A2		35	A7
31	A3		34	A6
32	A4		33	A5

CPU data

Device coding	Internal architecture	Address bus	Data bus	Function code	Originator/ manufacturer	Family type
6500	8			C	Rockwell	6502
6502	8	16	8	G	Mostek	
65F11	8			C	Rockwell	6502
6800	8	16	8	G	Motorola	
6801	8			C	Motorola	6800
6802	8			C	Motorola	6800
6803	8			C	Motorola	6800
6805	8			C	Motorola	6800
6809	8/16	16	8	G	Motorola	6800
8035	8			C	Intel	8080
8039	8			C	Intel	8080
8048	8			C	Intel	8080
8049	8			C	Intel	8080
8080	8	16	8	G	Intel	
8085	8	16	8	G	Intel	8080
8086	16	20	16	G	Intel	(8080)
8088	16	20	8	G	Intel	8086
8096	16			C	Intel	8086

Device coding	Internal architecture	Address bus	Data bus	Function code	Originator/manufacturer	Family type
9440	16	16	16	G	Fairchild	
9900	16	16	16	G	Texas	
9980	16	14	8	G	Texas	9900
16008	8	16	8	G	National	(8080)
16016	16	16	16	G	National	(8080)
16032	16	24	16	E	National	
32032	32	24	32	E	National	
32100	32	32	32	E	AT&T	(32000)
32332	32	32	32	E	National	(32032)
68000	16/32	24	16	E	Motorola	
68008	16/32	20	16	E	Motorola	68000
68010	16/32	24	16	E	Motorola	68000
68020	32	32	32	E	Motorola	(68000)
68080	32	32	32	E	Motorola	(68000)
68200	16/32			C	Motorola	68000
80186	16	20	16	E	Intel	(8086)
80188	16	20	8	E	Intel	(8086)
80286	16	24	16	E	Intel	(8086)
80386	32	32	32	E	Intel	(8086)
80386DX	32	32	32	E	Intel	(8086)
80386SX	32	24	16	E	Intel	(8086)
80486	32	32	32	E	Intel	(8086)
88100	32	32	32	E	Motorola	(88000)
99105	16	16	16	E	Texas	(9900)
ARM	32	26	32	E	Acorn	
CP1600	16	16	16	G	GI	Nova
MN601	16	16	16	G	Data Gen.	Nova
NSC800	8	16	8	E	National	(Z80)
T414	32	32	32	E	Inmos	
T800	32	32	32	E	Inmos	(T414)
V20	16	20	8	E	NEC	(8088)
V30	16	20	16	E	NEC	(8086)
Z8	8			C	Zilog	
Z80	16	16	8	G	Zilog	(8080)
Z8000	32	32	32	G	Zilog	(Z8000)
Z8001	16	16	16	G	Zilog	Z8000
Z8002	16	16	16	G	Zilog	Z8000
Z8108	8/16	19	8	E	Zilog	(Z80)
Z8208	8/16	24	8	E	Zilog	(Z80)
Z8116	8/16	19	16	E	Zilog	(Z80)
Z8216	8/16	24	16	E	Zilog	(Z80)

Function codes: C = Microcontroller/microcomputer
E = Enhanced microprocessor
G = General purpose microprocessor

Brackets denote full or partial upward instruction set compatibility.

The Intel family of 16/32 bit microprocessors and associated support devices:

Feature	Microprocessor type					
	8086	8088	80186	80188	80286	80386
Data bus (bits)	16	8	16	8	16	32
Internal data bus (bits)	16	16	16	16	16	32
Clock rate (MHz)	5,8,10	5,8	6,8	6,8	6,8,10	16
Linear memory addressing range (M byte)	1	1	1	1	16	4000
I/O addressing range (K byte)	64	64	64	64	64	64
Coprocessor capability	Yes	Yes	Yes	Yes	Yes	Yes
Protected mode	No	No	No	No	Yes	Yes
Clock generator	8284A	8284A	On-chip	On-chip	82284	82384
Bus controller	8288	8288	On-chip	On-chip	82288	82288
Interrupt controller	8259A	8259A	On-chip	On-chip	8259A	8259A
DMA controller	8089/ 82258	8089/ 8237/ 82258	On-chip/ 82258	On-chip/ 82258	8089/ 82258	8237/ 82258
Timer/ counter	8253/ 8254	8253/ 8254	On-chip	On-chip	8253/ 8254	8253/ 8254
Maths coprocessor	8087	8087	8087	8087	80287	80287/ 80387
Chip select/ wait state logic	TTL	TTL	On-chip	On-chip	TTL	TTL
Supply (V)	5	5	5	5	5	5
Package	DIP	DIP	Leadless JEDEC-A	Leadless JEDEC-A	Leadless JEDEC-A	PGA
Pins	40	40	68	68	132	

Support devices

In order to assist in off-loading tasks from the CPU, most modern microcomputer systems employ a number of programmable support devices. These devices fall into the following general classes:

Arithmetic/numeric data co-processors

Arithmetic or numeric data co-processors are capable of performing arithmetic and logical operations on large integer numbers. Floating point operation is also made very much faster due to hardware rather than software implementation.

Clock generators

Specialized clock generators are required by a number of CPUs in order to provide a clock signal with particular characteristics; e.g. some processors require four-phase clocks while others require two-phase clocks in which the individual phases are non-overlapping. This can be much more easily achieved by using a dedicated clock generator chip than by using conventional TTL or CMOS logic.

CRT controllers

A considerable time penalty is paid when the CPU has to stop processing to periodically manipulate the video display. This task can readily be handled by an appropriate support chip which often operates in conjunction with its own reserved area of video RAM.

DMA controllers

Where a sophisticated bus system is employed, and particularly where 'fast' external devices are to be used (e.g. a hard disk), a DMA controller can be used to speed up data transfer by allowing external devices direct access to the system bus.

Graphic/video display processors (GDP/VDP)

These LSI devices are used to produce raster scan displays for video monitors and, in conjunction with a video modulator, television receivers.

The graphic display processor can normally be expected to generate all the necessary video and synchronizing signals as well as managing the storage and retrieval of display data from the dynamic screen-refresh memory.

Enhanced graphic display processors are capable of high speed vector plotting, interfacing with light pens, and organizing a multi plane (colour, backdrop, pattern, sprite etc.) dynamic memory.

GPIB controllers

Where a microcomputer is to be used with an IEEE-488 General Purpose Instrument Bus, a dedicated LSI controller can be used to handle the necessary protocol and control the GPIB bus/system interface.

Interrupt controllers

On systems employing a range of I/O devices, interrupts can be produced by any one of a number of peripherals. The use of a dedicated interrupt controller can permit faster real-time response and release the CPU from the task of periodically polling all peripheral devices that may require service.

Keyboard controllers

Keyboard controllers perform the mundane but nevertheless essential task of detecting and managing keyboard input. While some systems consign this task to what may be more properly described as a 'slave' processor, others make use of a specialized keyboard controller.

LAN controllers

LAN controllers perform data link control, data encoding/decoding, and logic-based collision detection associated with the operation of a local area network.

Memory controllers

Memory controllers assist with the management of external memory (of various types). Dynamic RAM controllers may be used to undertake the task of multiplexing the address bus signals (generating the requisite column address strobe, CAS, and row address strobe, RAS, signals) and periodically refreshing the memory.

Programmable parallel interface devices

Programmable parallel interface devices (see separate section) allow parallel (normally byte-wide) transfer of data to/from the system data bus. Devices normally incorporate tri-state bus buffers/drivers and output latches.

Programmable serial interface devices

Programmable serial interface devices (see separate section) facilitate serial data communication between the microcomputer system and remote peripherals or other microcomputers.

Programmable sound generators (PSG)

Given a suitable transducer and interface, a microprocessor is eminently capable of generating sounds. This, however, is a very inefficient solution to the problem of producing audible output from a microcomputer as it needlessly diverts the processor from other more important tasks. Sound generation is therefore a prime example of the need for programmable support devices.

Most programmable sound generators provide a number of internal registers which control the various attributes of the sounds generated (frequency, amplitude, envelope, etc.). In addition, these devices normally cater for several analogue output channels which may be subsequently mixed together before amplification to a level that will drive a loudspeaker.

Real-time clocks

A real-time clock can be implemented using a counter/timer chip in conjunction with a system clock, but a simpler and much more flexible solution is that of making use of a microprocessor-compatible real-time clock device. These are almost invariably CMOS devices and are designed to be operated in conjunction with battery back-up. Internal registers can be loaded with data corresponding to seconds, minutes, hours, days, weeks, months and even years. Interrupts can be programmed to occur at specified time intervals: e.g. from once every second to once every day.

Timers/counters

These devices perform such tasks as time base generation, event counting, and baud rate generation.

I/O control methods

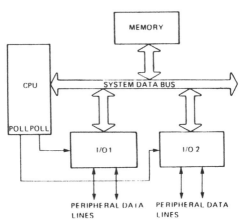

(a) CPU polling

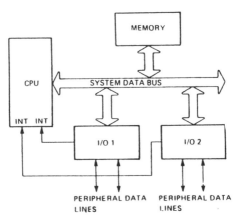

(b) Interrupt driven

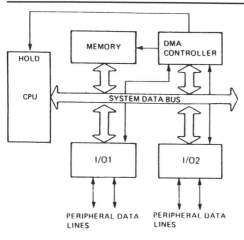

(c) DMA control

Simple parallel I/O interface (Z80-based systems)

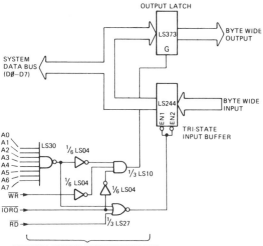

ADDRESS & CONTROL BUS DE-CODING LOGIC

Note: The interface is mapped to a port address of 255. Data is output from the port by first loading the accumulator with the output data and then using an OUT (255),A instruction. Data is input through the port by using an IN A,(255) instruction. The input data then appears in the accumulator.

Programmable parallel interface devices

Most microcomputers incorporate some form of programmable parallel input/output facility. This invariably takes the form of an LSI device variously known as a:

Peripheral interface adaptor	(PIA)	e.g. Motorola 6821
Programmable parallel interface	(PPI)	e.g. Intel 8255
Versatile interface adaptor	(VIA)	e.g. Rockwell 6522
Parallel input/output port	(PIO)	e.g. Zilog Z80-PIO

Such devices generally provide two separate 8-bit ports in which each of the eight bit lines can be configured, under software control, as an input or an output. Additional facilities found in certain more sophisticated devices include automatic handshaking (6522 and Z80-PIO) and internal timers/event counters (6522).

To permit direct connection to the system data bus, the parallel interface device invariably contains a bidirectional tri-state bus interface. Selection of the individual port registers is normally achieved using a subset of the system address bus. The programmable parallel interface thus appears as a number of specific memory addresses which may be selected by appropriate software instructions. The parallel interface device also utilizes the CPU control bus where, for example, a R/$\overline{W}$ signal is needed in order to determine the direction of data flow from/to the PIA.

The programmable parallel interface device is usually divided internally into two independent sections, A and B. Each section is equipped with three registers, the function of which will be discussed separately. In addition, bidirectional buffers are used to interface the peripheral lines. These buffers are generally TTL compatible and provide a limited current sink of typically 1.6 mA (i.e. one standard TTL load).

During a CPU write operation, the addressed data registers are loaded with the data currently present on the system data bus. The data is then latched onto those lines which have been programmed as outputs. During a CPU read operation the data present on those peripheral lines programmed as inputs is transferred to the system data bus.

The control registers allow the CPU to establish and control the operating modes of the peripheral control lines. In addition, bits are reserved for use as interrupt flags and as a means of selecting either output data or data direction registers. The various bits in the control registers may be accessed many times during a program to allow the CPU to change operating and interrupt modes as required by the particular peripheral device being controlled.

The data direction registers are used to determine which of the peripheral lines are configured as inputs and which are configured as outputs. Each bit position of the data registers corresponds to a particular peripheral line. A logic 1 written to the particular bit position designates the corresponding line as an output, and vice versa. Data direction and data registers often share the same address and selection between the two is made using one of the bits contained in the control register.

Internal registers of a typical programmable parallel I/O device

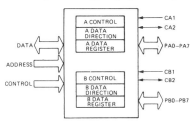

CPU interface to a programmable parallel I/O device

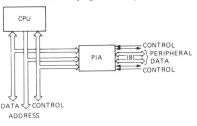

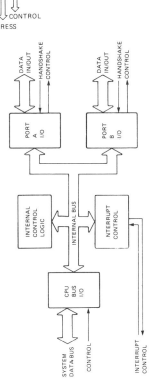

Internal architecture of the Z80-PIO

Pin connection data for popular programmable parallel I/O devices

6520

Pin	Signal	Pin	Signal
1	V_{SS}	40	CA1
2	PA0	39	$\overline{CA2}$
3	PA1	38	$\overline{IRQA}$
4	PA2	37	$\overline{IRQB}$
5	PA3	36	RS0
6	PA4	35	$\underline{RS1}$
7	PA5	34	$\overline{RES}$
8	PA6	33	D0
9	PA7	32	D1
10	PB0	31	D2
11	PB1	30	D3
12	PB2	29	D4
13	PB3	28	D5
14	PB4	27	D6
15	PB5	26	D7
16	PB6	25	EN
17	PB7	24	$\overline{CS2}$
18	CB1	23	CS3
19	CB2	22	CS1
20	V_{CC}	21	$R/\overline{W}$

6522

Pin	Signal	Pin	Signal
1	V_{SS}	40	CA1
2	PA0	39	CA2
3	PA1	38	RS0
4	PA2	37	RS1
5	PA3	36	RS2
6	PA4	35	$\underline{RS3}$
7	PA5	34	$\overline{RES}$
8	PA6	33	D0
9	PA7	32	D1
10	PB0	31	D2
11	PB1	30	D3
12	PB2	29	D4
13	PB3	28	D5
14	PB4	27	D6
15	PB5	26	D7
16	PB6	25	$\emptyset 2$
17	PB7	24	CS1
18	CB1	23	$\overline{CS2}$
19	CB2	22	$R/\overline{W}$
20	V_{CC}	21	$\overline{IRQ}$

6820

Pin	Signal	Pin	Signal
1	V_{SS}	40	CA1
2	PA0	39	$\overline{CA2}$
3	PA1	38	$\overline{IRQA}$
4	PA2	37	$\overline{IRQB}$
5	PA3	36	RS0
6	PA4	35	$\underline{RS1}$
7	PA5	34	RESET
8	PA6	33	D0
9	PA7	32	D1
10	PB0	31	D2
11	PB1	30	D3
12	PB2	29	D4
13	PB3	28	D5
14	PB4	27	D6
15	PB5	26	D7
16	PB6	25	EN
17	PB7	24	CS1
18	CB1	23	$\overline{CS2}$
19	CB2	22	CS0
20	V_{CC}	21	$R/\overline{W}$

8255

Pin	Signal	Pin	Signal
1	PA3	40	PA4
2	PA2	39	PA5
3	PA1	38	PA6
4	$\underline{PA0}$	37	$\underline{PA7}$
5	$\overline{RD}$	36	$\overline{WR}$
6	$\overline{CS}$	35	RESET
7	GND	34	D0
8	A1	33	D1
9	A0	32	D2
10	PC7	31	D3
11	PC6	30	D4
12	PC5	29	D5
13	PC4	28	D6
14	PC0	27	D7
15	PC1	26	V_{CC}
16	PC2	25	PB7
17	PC3	24	PB6
18	PB0	23	PB5
19	PB1	22	PB4
20	PB2	21	PB3

Z80 PIO

Pin	Signal	Pin	Signal
1	D2	40	D3
2	D7	39	D4
3	$\underline{D6}$	38	D5
4	$\overline{CE}$	37	$\overline{M1}$
5	$C/\overline{D}$	36	$\overline{IORQ}$
6	$B/\overline{A}$	35	$\overline{RD}$
7	PA7	34	PB7
8	PA6	33	PB6
9	PA5	32	PB5
10	PA4	31	PB4
11	GND	30	PB3
12	PA3	29	PB2
13	PA2	28	PB1
14	PA1	27	PB0
15	$\underline{PA0}$	26	+5 V
16	$\overline{ASTB}$	25	CLK
17	$\overline{BSTB}$	24	IEI
18	ARDY	23	$\overline{INT}$
19	D0	22	IEO
20	D1	21	BRDY

Programmable serial interface devices

Parallel data transfer is primarily suited to high speed operation over relatively short distances, a typical example being that of linking a microcomputer to an adjacent dot matrix printer. There are, however, a number of applications in which parallel data transfer is inappropriate, the most common example being data communication by means of telephone lines. In such cases data must be sent serially rather than in parallel form. Parallel data from the microprocessor must therefore be reorganized into a train of bits, one after another. An essential requirement of such an arrangement is a means of parallel-to-serial and serial-to-parallel data conversion.

When considering serial transmission of data, a distinction must be made between the two modes of transmission: synchronous and asynchronous. The former method requires a common clock signal to be present at both the sending and receiving ends of the synchronous serial data link. This signal is essential to the decoding process and may either be transmitted along a separate path or regenerated from synchronizing information accompanying the data.

In the asynchronous mode data is sent in a series of small 'packets'. Each packet contains additional 'start' and 'stop' bits which are used to signal the beginning and end of the packet. The position of each bit within the packet may thus be ascertained and the data decoded.

Like their parallel counterparts, programmable serial interface devices generally take the form of a single LSI device known variously as:

Asynchronous communications interface adaptor (ACIA) e.g. Motorola 6850
Synchronous serial data adaptor (SSDA) e.g. Motorola 6852
Universal asynchronous receiver/transmitter (UART) e.g. Intel 8256
Universal synchronous/asynchronous receiver/transmitter (USART) e.g. Intel 8251

Programmable serial interface devices contain a number of registers, including at least one SIPO (serial input, parallel output) and one PISO (parallel input, serial output) shift register. Alternatively, 'universal' shift registers may be employed. These devices can be programmed to operate in either SIPO or PISO modes.

When transmitting data, the appropriate shift register is loaded from the system data bus with data in conventional parallel form. The data is then written out as a serial bit stream by successive shifting.

The reverse process is used for receiving serial data. In this case the incoming data is loaded serially, each successive bit shifting further into the register until it becomes full. Data is then read out simultaneously onto the system bus.

Parallel to serial data conversion

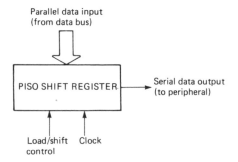

Serial to parallel data conversion

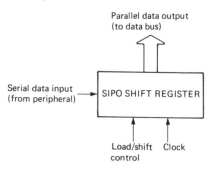

CPU interface to a programmable serial I/O device

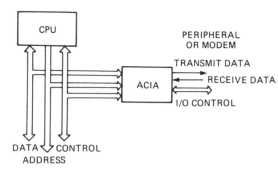

Pin connection data for popular programmable serial I/O devices

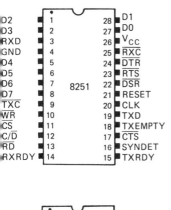

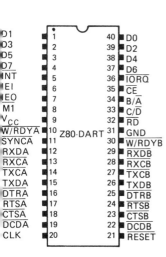

Basic cell configuration of semiconductor memories

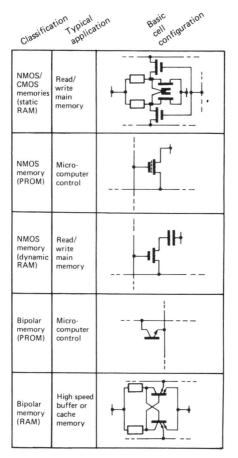

Classification	Typical application	Basic cell configuration
NMOS/ CMOS memories (static RAM)	Read/ write main memory	
NMOS memory (PROM)	Micro-computer control	
NMOS memory (dynamic RAM)	Read/ write main memory	
Bipolar memory (PROM)	Micro-computer control	
Bipolar memory (RAM)	High speed buffer or cache memory	

Semiconductor random access memory

A large proportion (typically 50 per cent or more) of the total addressable memory space of all microcomputers is devoted to read/write memory. This area of memory is used for a variety of purposes, most obvious of which is program and data storage. The term 'random access' simply refers to a memory device in which data may be retrieved from all locations with equal ease (i.e. access time is independent of actual memory address).

The basic element of a semiconductor random access memory is known as a 'cell'. Cells can be fabricated in one of two semiconductor technologies: MOS (metal oxide semiconductor) and bipolar. Bipolar memories are now rarely used in larger memories even though they offer much faster access times. Their disadvantage is associated with power supply requirements, since they need several voltage rails (both positive and negative) and use significantly more power then their MOS counterparts. The high speed of bipolar memories makes them useful for use in high speed buffer or 'cache' memories. These small capacity memories of typically 4K bytes, or less, permit high speed data transfer without the need for 'wait' states which would be necessary with conventional slower MOS memories.

Random access memories can be further divided into static and dynamic types. The important difference between the two types is that dynamic memories require periodic refreshing if they are not to lose their contents. In the normal course of events, this would be carried out whenever data was read and rewritten, but this technique cannot be relied upon to refresh all of the dynamic memory space and steps must be taken to ensure that all dynamic memory cells are refreshed periodically. This function has to be integrated with the normal operation of the microprocessor. Static memories do not need refreshing and can be relied upon to retain their memory until such time as new data is written or the power supply is interrupted (in which case all data is lost).

Semiconductor RAM data

Type	Size (bits)	Organization	Package	Technology
1256	262144	256K words × 1 bit	16-pin DIL	D/NMOS
2102A	1024	1K words × 1 bit	16-pin DIL	S/NMOS
2110	1024	1K words × 1 bit	16-pin DIL	S/ECL
2112	1024	256 words × 4 bits	16-pin DIL	S/ECL
2112A	1024	256 words × 4 bits	16-pin DIL	S/NMOS
2114	4096	1K words × 4 bits	18-pin DIL	S/NMOS
2118	16384	16K words × 1 bit	16-pin DIL	D/NMOS
2128	16384	2K words × 8 bits	24-pin DIL	S/NMOS
2142	4096	4K words × 1 bit	20-pin DIL	S/ECL
2147	4096	4K words × 1 bit	18-pin DIL	S/NMOS
2148	4096	1K words × 4 bits	18-pin DIL	S/NMOS
2149	4096	1K words × 4 bits	18-pin DIL	S/NMOS
2164	65536	64K words × 1 bit	16-pin DIL	D/NMOS
2167	16384	16K words × 1 bit	20-pin DIL	S/NMOS
2168	16384	4K words × 4 bits	20-pin DIL	S/NMOS
2169	4096	4K words × 4 bits	20-pin DIL	S/NMOS
2504	256	256 words × 1 bit	16-pin DIL	S/TTL
2510	1024	1K words × 1 bit	16-pin DIL	S/TTL
2511	1024	1K words × 1 bit	16-pin DIL	S/TTL
2600	65536	64K words × 1 bit	16-pin DIL	D/NMOS
2620	65536	16K words × 4 bits	18-pin DIL	D/NMOS
3764	65536	64K words × 1 bit	16-pin DIL	D/NMOS
4016	16384	2K words × 8 bits	24-pin DIL	S/NMOS

Type	Size (bits)	Organization	Package	Technology
4064	262144	64K words × 4 bits	18-pin DIL	D/NMOS
4116	16384	16K words × 1 bit	16-pin DIL	D/NMOS
4118	8192	1K words × 8 bits	24-pin DIL	S/NMOS
4161	65536	64K words × 1 bit	20-pin DIL	D/NMOS
4164	65536	64K words × 1 bit	16-pin DIL	D/NMOS
4256	262144	256K words × 1 bit	16-pin DIL	D/NMOS
4264	65536	64K words × 1 bit	16-pin DIL	D/NMOS
4334	4096	1K words × 4 bits	18-pin DIL	S/CMOS
4364	65536	8K words × 8 bits	28-pin DIL	S/CMOS
4416	65536	16K words × 4 bits	18-pin DIL	D/CMOS
4464	65536	8K words × 8 bits	28-pin DIL	S/CMOS
4564	65536	64K words × 1 bit	16-pin DIL	D/NMOS
4716	16384	16K words × 1 bit	16-pin DIL	D/NMOS
4801	8192	1K words × 8 bits	24-pin DIL	S/NMOS
4802	16384	2K words × 8 bits	24-pin DIL	S/NMOS
4816	16384	16K words × 1 bit	16-pin DIL	D/NMOS
4864	65536	64K words × 1 bit	16-pin DIL	D/NMOS
4865	65536	64K words × 1 bit	16-pin DIL	D/NMOS
5101	1024	256 words × 4 bits	22-pin DIL	S/CMOS
5114	4096	1K words × 4 bits	18-pin DIL	S/CMOS
5128	16384	2K words × 8 bits	24-pin DIL	S/CMOS
5257	4096	4K words × 1 bit	18-pin DIL	S/CMOS
5290	16384	16K words × 1 bit	16-pin DIL	D/NMOS
5516	16384	2K words × 8 bits	24-pin DIL	S/CMOS
5564	65536	8K words × 8 bits	28-pin DIL	S/CMOS
6116	16384	2K words × 8 bits	24-pin DIL	S/CMOS
6117	16384	2K words × 8 bits	24-pin DIL	S/CMOS
6147	4096	4K words × 1 bit	18-pin DIL	S/CMOS
6148	4096	1K words × 4 bits	18-pin DIL	S/CMOS
6164	65536	6K words × 8 bits	28-pin DIL	S/CMOS
6167	16384	16K words × 1 bit	20-pin DIL	S/CMOS
6168	16384	4K words × 4 bits	20-pin DIL	S/CMOS
6256	262144	256K words × 1 bit	16-pin DIL	D/NMOS
6264	65536	8K words × 8 bits	28-pin DIL	S/CMOS
6267	16384	16K words × 1 bit	20-pin DIL	S/CMOS
6287	65536	64K words × 1 bit	22-pin DIL	S/CMOS
6288	65536	16K words × 4 bits	22-pin DIL	S/CMOS
6665	65536	64K words × 1 bit	16-pin DIL	D/NMOS
6787	65536	64K words × 1 bit	22-pin DIL	S/CMOS
6788	65536	16K words × 4 bits	22-pin DIL	S/CMOS
9016	16384	16K words × 1 bit	16-pin DIL	D/NMOS
9044	4096	4K words × 1 bit	18-pin DIL	S/NMOS
9064	65536	64K words × 1 bit	16-pin DIL	D/NMOS
9101	1024	256 words × 4 bits	22-pin DIL	S/MOS
9111	1024	256 words × 4 bits	18-pin DIL	S/MOS
9112	1024	256 words × 4 bits	16-pin DIL	S/MOS
9114	4096	1K words × 4 bits	18-pin DIL	S/NMOS
9122	1024	256 words × 4 bits	22-pin DIL	S/MOS
9128	2048	2K words × 8 bits	24-pin DIL	S/MOS
9150	1024	1K words × 4 bits	24-pin DIL	S/NMOS
9151	1024	1K words × 4 bits	24-pin DIL	S/NMOS
99C68	16384	4K words × 4 bits	20-pin DIL	S/CMOS
99C88	65536	8K words × 8 bits	28-pin DIL	S/CMOS
10415	1024	1K words × 1 bit	16-pin DIL	S/ECL

Type	Size (bits)	Organization	Package	Technology
10422	1024	256 words × 4 bits	24-pin DIL	S/ECL
10470	4096	4K words × 1 bit	18-pin DIL	S/ECL
10474	4096	1K words × 4 bits	24-pin DIL	S/ECL
10480	16384	16K words × 1 bit	20-pin DIL	S/ECL
41128	131072	2 × 64K words × 1 bit	16-pin DIL	D/NMOS
41256	262144	256K words × 1 bit	16-pin DIL	D/NMOS
41257	262144	256K words × 1 bit	16-pin DIL	D/NMOS
41416	65536	16K words × 4 bits	18-pin DIL	D/NMOS
43256	262144	32K words × 8 bits	28-pin DIL	S/CMOS
48Z02	16384	2K words × 8 bits	24-pin DIL	S/CMOS
48416	65536	16K words × 4 bits	18-pin DIL	D/NMOS
50256	262144	256K words × 1 bit	16-pin DIL	D/NMOS
50257	262144	256K words × 1 bit	16-pin DIL	D/NMOS
50464	262144	64K words × 4 bits	18-pin DIL	D/NMOS
50465	262144	64K words × 4 bits	18pin DIL	D/NMOS
51256	282144	256K words × 1 bit	16-pin DIL	D/NMOS
51528	262144	256K words × 1 bit	18-pin DIL	D/NMOS
62256	262144	32K words × 8 bits	28-pin DIL	S/CMOS
65256	262144	32K words × 8 bits	28-pin DIL	S/CMOS
66202	262144	32K words × 8 bits	30-pin DIL	S/CMOS
66203	1048575	128K words × 8 bits	32-pin DIL	S/CMOS
81257	262144	256K words × 1 bit	16-pin DIL	D/NMOS
81416	65536	16K words × 4 bits	18-pin DIL	D/NMOS
93412	1024	256K words × 4 bits	22-pin DIL	S/TTL
93415	1024	1K words × 1 bit	16-pin DIL	S/TTL
511000	1048576	1M words × 1 bit	18-pin DIL	D/NMOS
511001	1048576	1M words × 1 bit	18-pin DIL	D/NMOS
511002	1048576	1M words × 1 bit	18-pin DIL	D/NMOS

Pin connection data for popular RAM devices

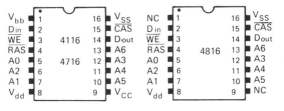

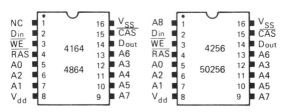

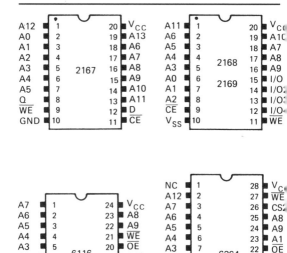

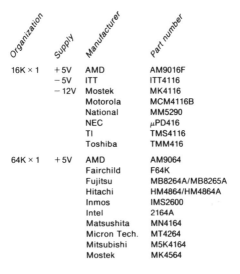

Dynamic RAM equivalents

Organization	Supply	Manufacturer	Part number
16K × 1	+ 5V	AMD	AM9016F
	− 5V	ITT	ITT4116
	− 12V	Mostek	MK4116
		Motorola	MCM4116B
		National	MM5290
		NEC	μPD416
		TI	TMS4116
		Toshiba	TMM416
64K × 1	+ 5V	AMD	AM9064
		Fairchild	F64K
		Fujitsu	MB8264A/MB8265A
		Hitachi	HM4864/HM4864A
		Inmos	IMS2600
		Intel	2164A
		Matsushita	MN4164
		Micron Tech.	MT4264
		Mitsubishi	M5K4164
		Mostek	MK4564

Organization	Supply	Manufacturer	Part number
		Motorola	MCM6665A
		National	NMC4164
		NEC	μPD4164
		Oki	MSM3764
		Siemens	HYB4164
		TI	TMS4164
		Toshiba	TMM4164
		Tristar	KM4164A
16K × 4	+5V	Fujitsu	MB81416
		Hitachi	HM48416A
		Inmos	IMS2620
		Mitsubishi	M5M4416
		TI	TMS4416
256K × 1	+5V	Fujitsu	MB81256/MB81257
		Hitachi	HM50256/HM50257
		Micron Tech.	MT1256
		Mitsubishi	M5M4256
		Motorola	MCM6256
		NEC	μPD41256/μPD41257
		Oki	MSM37256
		TI	TMS4256/TMS4257
		Toshiba	TMM41256
		Western Elec.	WCM41256
64K × 4	+5V	Hitachi	HM50464/HM50465
		Micron Tech.	MT4064
		NEC	μPD41256
		TI	TMS4464

Note: There may be minor variations in refresh requirements and that although the devices listed in each group are equivalent, they may not be identical in *every* respect.

Typical CMOS battery-backed supply arrangement

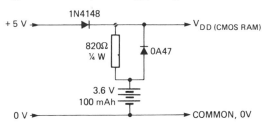

Semiconductor read only memory

As its name implies, read only memory is memory which, once programmed, can only be read from and not written to. It may thus be described as 'non-volatile' since its contents are not lost when the supply is disconnected. This facility is of course necessary for the long-term semi-permanent storage of operating systems and high level language interpreters. To change the operating system or language it is necessary to replace the ROM. This is a simple matter because ROMs are usually plug-in devices.

The following types are in common use:

Mask ROM
This relatively expensive process is suitable for high-volume production (several thousand units, or more) and involves the use of a mask with which programs links within the ROM chip. These links establish a permanent pattern of bits in the row/column matrix of the memory. The customer (computer manufacturer) must supply the ROM manufacturer with the programming information from which the mask is generated.

Programmable ROM (PROM)
This is a somewhat less expensive process than mask programming and is suitable for small/medium scale production. The memory cells consist of nichrome or polysilicon fuse links between rows and columns. These links can, by application of a suitable current pulse, be open-circuited or 'blown'. PROMs are ideal for prototype use and programming can be carried out by the computer manufacturer using relatively inexpensive equipment. When a PROM has been thoroughly tested, and provided that volume production can be envisaged, it is normal for the device to be replaced by a conventional mask programmed ROM.

Erasable PROM (EPROM)
Unlike the two previous types of ROM, the EPROM can be re-programmed. EPROMs are manufactured with a window which allows light to fall upon the semiconductor memory cell matrix. The EPROM may be erased by exposure to a strong ultraviolet light source over a period of several minutes, or tens of minutes. Once erasure has taken place, any previously applied bit pattern is completely removed; the EPROM is 'blank' and ready for programming. The programming process is carried out by the manufacturer from master software using a dedicated programming device which supplies pulses to establish the state of individual memory cells. This process usually takes several minutes (though some EPROM programmers can program several devices at once) and, since EPROMs tend to be relatively expensive, this process is clearly unsuitable for anything other than very small scale production. Furthermore, it should be noted that EPROMs tend to have rather different characteristics from PROMs and ROMs and thus subsequent volume production replacement may cause problems.

Electrically alterable ROM (EAROM) or electrically erasable programmable ROM (EEPROM)
The EAROM can be both read to and written from. Unlike the random access memory (RAM) the EAROM is unsuitable for use in the read/write memory section of a computer since the writing process takes a considerable time (typically a thousand times longer than the reading time). EAROMs are relatively recent and fairly expensive devices. As such, they have not found many applications in the microcomputer field. It should be noted that a reasonable compromise for semi-permanent data and program storage could take the form of low power consumption CMOS RAM fitted with back-up batteries. In certain circumstances such a

system can be relied upon to retain stored information, at relatively low cost, for a year or more. Such an arrangement is an attractive low-cost alternative to the use of EAROM or EEPROM devices.

Semiconductor ROM data

Type	Size (bits)	Organization	Package	Technology
2332	32768	4K words × 8 bits	24-pin DIL	MASK ROM
2364	65536	8K words × 8 bits	28-pin DIL	MASK ROM
2516	16384	2K words × 8 bits	24-pin DIL	EPROM/ NMOS
2532	32768	4K words × 8 bits	24-pin DIL	EPROM/ NMOS
2564	65536	8K words × 8 bits	28-pin DIL	EPROM/ NMOS
2708	8192	1K words × 8 bits	24-pin DIL	EPROM/ NMOS
2716	16384	2K words × 8 bits	24-pin DIL	EPROM/ NMOS
27C16	16384	2K words × 8 bits	24-pin DIL	EPROM/ CMOS
2732	32768	4K words × 8 bits	24-pin DIL	EPROM/ NMOS
27C32	32768	4K words × 8 bits	24-pin DIL	EPROM/ NMOS
2764	65536	8K words × 8 bits	28-pin DIL	EPROM/ NMOS
27C64	65536	8K words × 8 bits	28-pin DIL	EPROM/ CMOS
2816	16384	2K words × 8 bits	24-pin DIL	EEPROM/ NMOS
2817	16384	2K words × 8 bits	28-pin DIL	EEPROM/ NMOS
2864	65536	8K words × 8 bits	28-pin DIL	EEPROM/ NMOS
4732	32768	4K words × 8 bits	24-pin DIL	MASK ROM
4764	65536	8K words × 8 bits	24-pin DIL	MASK ROM
9306	256	16 words × 16 bits	8-pin DIL	EEPROM/ NMOS
27128	131072	16K words × 8 bits	28-pin DIL	EPROM/ NMOS
27C128	131072	16K words × 8 bits	28-pin DIL	EPROM/ CMOS
27256	262144	32K words × 8 bits	28-pin DIL	EPROM/ NMOS
27C101	1048576	128K words × 8 bits	32-pin DIL	EPROM/ CMOS
27C256	262144	32K words × 8 bits	28-pin DIL	EPROM/ CMOS
27512	524288	64K words × 8 bits	28-pin DIL	EPROM/ NMOS

Type	Size (bits)	Organization	Package	Technology
27C301	1048576	128K words × 8 bits	32-pin DIL	EPROM/CMOS
27C512	524288	64K words × 8 bits	28-pin DIL	EPROM/CMOS
43128	131072	16K words × 8 bits	28-pin DIL	MASK ROM
47128	131072	16K words × 8 bits	28-pin DIL	MASK ROM
47256	262144	32K words × 8 bits	28-pin DIL	MASK ROM
47C256	262144	32K words × 8 bits	28-pin DIL	MASK ROM
47C512	524288	64K words × 8 bits	28-pin DIL	MASK ROM
48016	16384	2K words × 8 bits	24-pin DIL	EAROM/MOS
61366	65536	8K words × 8 bits	24-pin DIL	MASK ROM
613128	131072	16K words × 8 bits	28-pin DIL	MASK ROM
613256	262144	32K words × 8 bits	28-pin DIL	MASK ROM
ER3400	4096	1K words × 4 bits	22-pin DIL	EAROM/MOS
27C1024	1048576	64K words × 16 bits	40-pin DIL	EPROM/CMOS
47C1024	1048576	128K words × 8 bits	28-pin DIL	MASK ROM

Pin connection data for popular EPROM devices

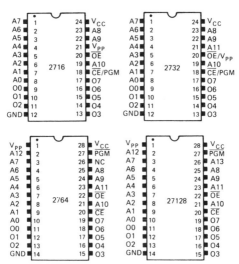

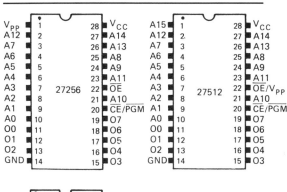

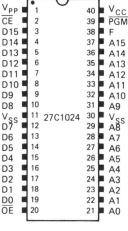

Pin connection data for popular EEPROM/EAROM devices

Storage capacities of mass memories

Medium	Typical capacity (bits)	(bytes)	Equivalent text (A4 pages)	Typical data transfer rate (bits/sec)
Semiconductor ROM	128K	16K	4	4M
Semiconductor RAM	512K	64K	16	4M
Magnetic tape (microdrive)	1M	128K	64	16K
Magnetic tape (0.125 inch cassette)	1M	128K	64	1.2K
Magnetic bubble memory	1M	128K	64	64K
Floppy disk (5.25 ins.)	8M	1M	512	250K
Magnetic tape (0.25 inch cartridge)	16M	20M	1K	100K
Winchester hard disk	160M	20M	10M	4M
Magnetic tape (0.5 inch reel)	256M	32M	16K	800K
WORM laser disk/CD ROM	800M	100M	50K	2.5M

Magnetic disk storage

Magnetic disks are undoubtedly the most popular form of on-line storage for use with computers both large and small. Magnetic disk drives are available in various forms, from the high capacity multi-platter hard disk drives commonly found in mainframe and minicomputer installations to the tiny 3 inch drives used in the smaller personal computers. Despite the obvious outward differences between such devices, essentially they share the same principle of operation; that of writing a magnetic pattern of binary data in the surface oxide coating of a disk. The magnetic pattern is written and read using a small coil contained in a read/write head. The coil itself forms part of a magnetic circuit in which the highest flux density is concentrated in a gap which, depending upon the type of drive, rides either immediately above, or in contact with, the surface of the disk. The main features of each of the popular types of drive are summarized below.

Winchester disks

Today's Winchester disks are the direct descendants of the large multi-platter disk drives used on many mainframe computers of a decade or more ago. Unlike these bulky and extremely expensive units, the modern mini-Winchester drive provides a relatively inexpensive mass storage device in a neat and compact package.

IBM's first Winchester disk drives in the early 1970s were 14 inches in diameter but, in common with the reduction in size of most computer equipment, they rapidly shrank, first to 8 inches and then to 5.25 inches. Storage capacities of up to 650M byte in a package no larger than that occupied by a conventional full-height 5.25 inch floppy disk drive and up to 85M byte in a 3.5 inch micro-Winchester are now commonplace.

The read/write head of a Winchester disk drive rides on a thin cushion of air immediately above the disk surface. This prevents wear on the disk and head surfaces yet maintains efficient magnetic coupling between the head and the disk. To exclude particles of dust, dirt and smoke (which may otherwise lodge between the head and disk surface), the entire disk assembly is housed in a tightly sealed enclosure. Winchester disks rotate at around 3000rpm and offer fast access times (typically 625K bit/sec).

Unfortunately, Winchester disk drives need rather careful handling since permanent damage can be caused by bumping or jolting the drive (both when in use and when in transit). This is likely to cause the head to 'crash' against the oxide surface of the disk.

Winchester technology has evolved using largely non-exchangeable media, but some effort has been put into producing a removable Winchester cartidge and several manufacturers are working in this area. The problems of maintaining reliability with removable media are, however, not easily overcome!

8 inch floppy disks

The standard 8 inch floppy disk was originally developed by IBM as part of the IBM 3740 key-to-disk data-entry system. These were the forerunners of the ubiquitous 5.25 inch mini-floppy disk. The system uses interchangeable media contained within a low-friction protective mylar sleeve. Storage capacities of between 250K byte and 2M byte are common. In recent years, however, the 8 inch disk has rapidly faded from popularity having largely been replaced by lower cost 5.25 inch mini-floppy technology.

5.25inch floppy disk

Mini-floppy disks have a diameter of 5.125 inches (130.2 mm) and the disk sleeve is 5.25 inches (133.4 mm) square. Disks are available in both hard- and soft-sectored formats, the latter enjoying by far the greater popularity.

Hard-sectored disks have a series of index holes which indicate the start of each sector. The sectors on soft-sectored disks have to be written during the formatting process, which effectively writes a framework of tracks and sectors in which the data is subsequently placed.

Mini-floppy disk drives are often categorized by their height in relation to those which first became available (i.e. full-height drives). In recent years there has been a trend towards more compact drives in order to permit a consequent saving of space in the equipment to which they are fitted. This is, of course, particularly important where drives are to be fitted in portable equipment.

The first mini-floppy disk drive to gain popularity was the SA400 from Shugart Associates. This 35 (or 40) track drive provides an unformatted capacity of 125K bytes in single density (FM) or 250K bytes in double density (MFM). The data transfer rates are respectively 125K bit/sec and 250k bit/sec. The drive provides an average latency of 100 ms, a stepping time (track to track) of 20 ms and an average access time of 280 ms. The drive requires d.c. supplies of $+12\,V \pm 5\%$ at 0.9 A (typical) and $+5\,V \pm 5\%$ at 0.5 A (typical).

In recent years, the FD-50 series of full-height drives from Teac have achieved immense popularity (the FD-50A being compatible with Shugart's SA400). Half-height drives have also become increasingly popular, with modern devices by Hitachi, Mitsubishi, and Tandon (among others) offering storage capacities well in excess of the SA400 and almost comparable with the smaller hard disks.

3.5 inch floppy disks

The Sony 3.5 inch floppy disk drive was the first 3.5 inch drive to appear in quantity and was largely an extension and improvement of the existing 5.25 inch standard. Many manufacturers have adopted this new standard, which is based upon 40 or 80 tracks at 67.5 or 135 tracks per inch with track–track stepping times of 6 ms and 3 ms respectively. Storage capacities of up to 400K byte per side are thus possible using double density (MFM) recording.

The 3.5 inch disk system is based upon a disk (having less than half the surface area of its 5.25 inch counterpart) housed in a rigid plastic cassette. The disk is provided with an automatic shutter which protects the magnetic surface from accidental contact (a perennial problem with the 5.25 inch mini-floppy disk). Write protection is provided by means of a sliding write-protect tab. The disk is soft-sectored and typically provides approximately 500K byte and 1M byte of unformatted storage on single- and double sided-drives respectively.

3 inch floppy disks

Although the 3.5 inch drive seems to have very largely set the standard for a compact mini-floppy, a number of other drives have appeared at around 3 inches diameter. Most notable among these are Teac's FD30A and Hitachi's HFD30S. These units have both sensibly retained full software formatting compatibility with their 5.25 inch predecessors. Hardware compatibility extends with the use of the standard 34-way disk bus (including PCB edge connector), disk rotation speed and number of tracks per inch.

Other 3 inch drives do exist (including one which uses a single spiral track) but seem unlikely to gain a large following in the industry as a whole.

Microdrives, stringy floppies, and wafadrives

From time to time, attempts have been made to provide a low-cost alternative to disk storage yet one which is faster and more reliable than using compact cassette tapes. Although none of the above methods can be strictly described as disk-based storage media, they all attempt, in some way, to emulate disk storage using a continuous loop of magnetic tape running at high speed.

The first 'stringy floppy' tape drive to be produced in large quantities was that from Exatron, which was designed to be used with the popular Tandy TRS-80 home computer.

None of the few systems currently available can be described as particularly satisfactory (at least when compared with conventional disk storage) and indeed their cost-effectiveness is now somewhat questionable in the light of the falling price of 5.25 inch and 3.5 inch disk drives. Despite this, one major manufacturer (Sinclair) has doggedly promoted its own Microdrive system which is both loved and hated by its devotees!

8 inch disk media format

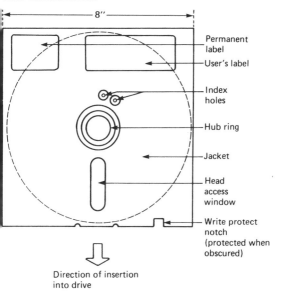

Direction of insertion
into drive

5.25 inch disk media format

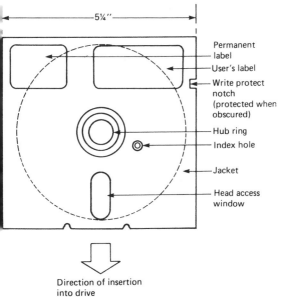

Direction of insertion
into drive

3.5 inch disk media format

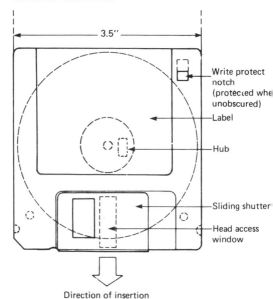

3 inch disk media format

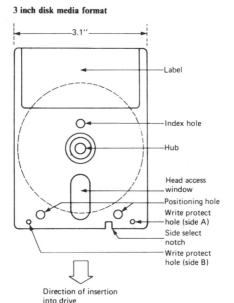

Magnetic recording techniques

The two most commonly employed recording techniques use either frequency modulation (FM) or modulated frequency modulation (MFM). Both methods involve writing a serial pulse train comprising both data and clock pulses) to the disk.

Single density (IBM 3740 standard)

In the case of single-density recording (FM) a clock pulse is present at the start of each bit cell. In this method, a 1 is written by including a pulse in the centre of the cell (i.e. between consecutive clock pulses).

Double density (IBM System 34 standard)

In the double-density recording method things are a little more complex and, whereas a 1 is again written by placing a pulse in the centre of the bit cell, a clock pulse is only written at the start of a cell when a 0 appears in both the preceding cell and the cell in question.

Single-density (FM) recording signal

The example shows a byte comprising the hex character D2
Rules: 1. Write a clock bit at the start of each bit cell.
2. If the data is a 1, write a data bit at the centre of the bit cell.

Double-density (MFM) recording signal

The example shows a byte comprising the hex character D2
Rules: 1. If the data is a 1, write a data bit at the centre of the bit cell.
2. Write a clock bit at the start of a bit cell if no data was written in the last bit cell and no data bit will be written in the next bit cell.

IBM 3740 disk format

The IBM format applies to the vast majority of 8 inch disk systems and, with minor changes (such as the number of tracks and/or sectors), to many of the mini-floppy systems in current use. The main points are listed below.

Track format

The disk has 77 concentric tracks, numbered physically from 00 to 76, with track 00 being the outermost track. During initialization, any two tracks (other than track 00) may be designated as 'bad' and the remaining 75 data tracks are numbered in logical sequence from 00 to 74.

Sector format

Each track is divided into 26, 15 or 8 sectors of 128, 256, or 512 bytes length respectively. The first sector is numbered 01, and is physically the first sector after the index mark. The remaining sectors are not necessarily numbered in physical sequence, the numbering scheme being determined at initialization.

Each sector consists of a number of fields separated by gaps. An ID field is used to identify the sector, while a data field contains the information stored. The beginning of each field is indicated by six synchronizing bytes of 00H followed by one byte mark.

Address marks

Address marks are unique patterns, one byte in length, which are used to identify the beginning of ID and data fields and to synchronize the de-serialising circuitry with the first byte of each field. Address mark bytes are different from all other data bytes in that certain bit cells do not contain a clock bit (all other data byte have clock bits in every bit cell). Four different types of address mark are employed to identify different types of field, as follows.

(a) Index address mark The index address mark is located at the beginning of each track and is a fixed number of bytes in advance of the first record. (N.B. Not used in the mini-floppy format.)

(b) ID address mark The ID address mark byte is located at the beginning of each ID field on the disk.

(c) Data address mark The data address mark byte is located at the beginning of each non-deleted data field on the disk.

(d) Deleted data address mark The deleted data address mark byte is located at the beginning of each deleted data field on the disk.

The clock and data patterns used for the various address marks are:

Address mark type	Clock pattern	Data pattern
Index	D7	FC
ID	C7	FE
Data	C7	FB
Deleted data	C7	F8
Bad track ID	C7	FE

ID field

The ID field precedes the data field and contains a total of seven bytes (including the ID address mark). The ID field contains the track number, side number, sector number, and sector length byte as well as a two-byte cyclic redundancy code (CRC) checksum. The relationship between the sector length byte and the length of the subsequent data field is:

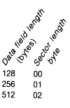

Data field length (bytes)	Sector length byte
128	00
256	01
512	02

Data field
The data field comprises a single-byte data address mark (DAM) followed by the stored data and a trailing two-byte cyclic redundancy code checksum. The data is either 128, 256, or 512 bytes in length.

CRC characters
The 16-bit CRC character is generated using the polynomial $X^{16} + X^{12} + X^5 + 1$, normally initialized to FFH. Its generation includes all characters except the CRC in the ID or data field.

Bad track format
The format is the same as that used for good tracks with the exception that the track number, side number, sector number, and sector length are all set to FFH.

IBM 3740 floppy disk format

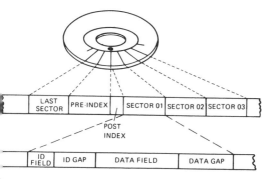

ID field organization (IBM 3740)

One byte

ID ADDRESS MARK	TRACK NUMBER (00–74)	SIDE NUMBER (00–01)	SECTOR NUMBER (01–26)	SECTOR LENGTH (00–02)	CRC (MSB)	CRC (LSB)

Data field organization (IBM 3740)

One byte

DATA ADDRESS MARK	DATA		CRC (MSB)	CRC (LSB)

IBM 3740 format: Gap type and designation

Gap type	Gap designation	Length (bytes)	Content
1	Post-index	22	16 of FFH followed by 6 of 00H
2	ID	17	11 of FFH followed by 6 of 00H
3	Data	33	27 of FFH followed by 6 of 00H
4	Pre-index	274 (nom)	FFH

Note: 00H is sync. and FFH is filler.

10-sector 80-track single-density format (BBC Microcomputer disk systems)

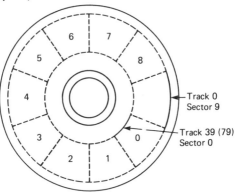

Disk drive mechanics

Floppy disk drives invariably consist of a chassis incorporating the following components:

1. A drive mechanism to rotate the disk at a constant speed.
2. A read/write head mounted on a precision positioning assembly, invariably driven by a stepper m .or.
3. Control circuitry which interprets inputs from the disk controller and generates signals to:
(a) start the drive motor
(b) implement write protection so that protected disks cannot be overwritten
(c) drive the head position actuator which moves the head from track to track
(d) activate the head load solenoid which moves the head against the disk
(e) locate the physical index which indicates the start of each track.
4. Read/write circuitry (invariably mounted on the same PCB as the control circuitry) which interfaces the read/write head to produce/accept TTL-compatible signal levels.

CUSTOMER RECEIPT

Birmingham Corporation Street
Unit 9 Old Santander Building 23 CorpSt Birmingham West
Midlands , B2 4LP
09/04/2022 13:03:52
RECEIPT NO.: 8601
MID: XXX85993   TID: XXXX6742
AID: A0000000031010
Visa Debit
XXXXXXXXXXXX0024
PAN SEQ NO. : 00

SALE :   GBP2.00
TOTAL :   GBP2.00

PLEASE DEBIT MY ACCOUNT
NO CARDHOLDER VERIFICATION
CONTACTLESS
PLEASE KEEP THIS RECEIPT FOR YOUR RECORDS
AUTH CODE:097800

A precision servo-controlled d.c. motor is used to maintain the disk speed at 300 rpm ± 1.5% for a mini-floppy drive, or 360 rpm ± 1.5% for a standard 8 inch floppy drive. Coupling to the disk rotating spindle is normally achieved by means of a rubber drive belt; however, some modern units use direct drive from the motor to the spindle/flywheel assembly.

The drive spindle engages with the centre of the disk (which is usually reinforced by means of additional hub rings) such that the disk rotates within its outer sleeve. The material of the sleeve is chosen so that friction between disk and sleeve is minimal.

Unlike larger hard disks, where the read/write heads ride on a thin cushion of air above the disk surface, the read/write head of a floppy disk makes physical contact with the disk surface (i.e. it is permanently 'crashed') through an elongated hole provided in the sleeve.

The presence (or absence) of a write-protect notch is detected by means of an LED and phototransistor and, if present, write operation is inhibited. Another photo-detector arrangement is used to locate the start of recorded tracks by means of the physical index hole in the disk.

The read/write head assembly is accurately positioned through the use of a precision spiral cam. This cam has a V-groove with a ball-bearing follower which is attached to the head carriage assembly. Precise track selection is accomplished as the cam is rotated in small discrete increments by a stepping motor.

The read/write heads themselves have straddle erase elements which provide erased areas between adjacent data tracks, hence minimizing the effects of data overlap between adjacent tracks when disks written on one drive are read by another.

To ensure a very high degree of compliance with the read/write head, precise registration of the diskette is essential. This is accomplished, with the diskette held in a plane perpendicular to the read/write head, by a platen located in the base casting. The head is loaded against the disk by means of the head load solenoid and a spring-loaded pressure pad is used to maintain contact between the head and the oxide-coated disk surface.

Floppy disk controllers

Floppy disk controllers (FDC) facilitate the storage and retrieval of data in the sectors and tracks, which are written on the disk during the formatting process. The disk controller is thus an extremely complex device, being capable of both formatting the disk and then writing/reading the data on it.

Since neither the user nor the programmer is concerned with the actual organization of data in tracks and sectors, a disk operating system (DOS) is required to carry out management and housekeeping associated with the maintenance of disk files.

The FDC has the following principal functions:

1. Formatting the disk with the required number of tracks and sectors as determined by the DOS.
2. Accepting and executing commands issued by the CPU. These commands are loaded (via the data bus) into a command register within the FDC.
3. Maintaining various internal registers which:
(a) reflect the current status of the controller;

(b) indicate the current track over which the read/write head is positioned; and

(c) hold the address of the desired sector position.

4. Providing an interface to the CPU bus, so that:

(a) during the write process, incoming parallel data from the bus is converted to a serial self-clocking data stream for writing to the floppy disk; and

(b) during the read process, incoming serial data from the floppy disk is separated from the accompanying clock, and fed to a serial-to-parallel shift register before outputting to the data bus.

5. Generating the necessary cyclic redundancy check (CRC) characters and appending these to the write data stream at the appropriate time.

Each disk drive contains its own interface to the bus which links all the drives in a system to the FDC. The most commonly used bus arrangement is that originated by Shugart and first employed with the SA400 drive. This bus uses a 34-way connector, the 17 odd-numbered lines of which are common earth. It should be noted that, since the drive requires an appreciable current, the +12 V and +5 V power lines require a separate connector.

CPU interface to a floppy disk controller

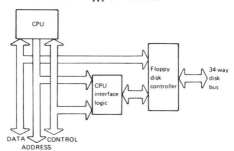

179x floppy disk controller pinout

n.c.	1	40	+12 V
$\overline{WE}$	2	39	IRQ
$\overline{CS}$	3	38	DRQ
$\overline{RE}$	4	37	$\overline{DDEN}$ (note 3)
A0	5	36	$\overline{WPRT}$
A1	6	35	$\overline{IP}$
$\overline{DAL0}$	7	34	$\overline{TR00}$
$\overline{DAL1}$	8	33	WF/VFOE
$\overline{DAL2}$	9	32	READY
(note 2) $\overline{DAL3}$	10	31	WD
$\overline{DAL4}$	11	30	WG
$\overline{DAL5}$	12	29	TG43
$\overline{DAL6}$	13	28	HLD
$\overline{DAL7}$	14	27	RAWREAD
STEP	15	26	RCLK
DIRC	16	25	(note 1)
EARLY	17	24	CLK
LATE	18	23	$\overline{HLT}$
$\overline{MR}$	19	22	TEST
0 V	20	21	+5 V

Notes: 1. RG when X = 1,3; SSO when X = 5,7

2. Bus non-inverted when X = 3,7

3. Not connected when X = 2,4

8271 floppy disk controller pinout

```
                   ┌──────⌄──────┐
FAULT RESET/OPO ■  │ 1        40 │  ■ + 5 V
      SELECT 0  ■  │ 2        39 │  ■ LOW CURRENT
         CLK    ■  │ 3        38 │  ■ LOAD HEAD
        RESET   ■  │ 4        37 │  ■ DIRECTION
        READY1  ■  │ 5        36 │  ■ SEEK/STEP
       SELECT1  ■  │ 6        35 │  ■ WR ENABLE
        DACK    ■  │ 7        34 │  ■ INDEX
         DRQ    ■  │ 8        33 │  ■ WR PROTECT
          RD    ■  │ 9        32 │  ■ READY 0
          WR    ■  │ 10       31 │  ■ TRK0
         INT    ■  │ 11       30 │  ■ COUNT/OPI
         DB0    ■  │ 12       29 │  ■ WR DATA
         DB1    ■  │ 13       28 │  ■ FAULT
         DB2    ■  │ 14       27 │  ■ UNSEP DATA
         DB3    ■  │ 15       26 │  ■ DATA WINDOW
         DB4    ■  │ 16       25 │  ■ PLO/SS
         DB5    ■  │ 17       24 │  ■ CS
         DB6    ■  │ 18       23 │  ■ PLOC
         DB7    ■  │ 19       22 │  ■ A1
         0 V    ■  │ 20       21 │  ■ A0
                   └─────────────┘
```

34-way Shugart floppy disk bus pin assignment

Pin number	Designation	Common abbrev.	Function
2	Not connected	n.c.	See note 4
4	HEAD LOAD	HLD	Output from FDC, active low, activates the head load solenoid (see note 3)
6	DRIVE SELECT 4	DS4	Output from FDC, active low, selects drive 4
8	INDEX	IP	Input to FDC, active low
10	DRIVE SELECT 1	DS1	Output from FDC, active low, selects drive 1
12	DRIVE SELECT 2	DS2	Output from FDC, active low, selects drive 2
14	DRIVE SELECT 3	DS3	Output from FDC, active low, selects drive 3
16	MOTOR ON	MOTOR	Output from FDC, active low, activates drive motor
18	DIRECTION	DIRC	Output from FDC, selects stepping direction; step out when high, step in when low
20	STEP	STEP	Output from FDC, activates head stepper motor; steps on positive-going edge
22	WRITE DATA	WDATA	Output from FDC, inactive high, pulsed low with data
24	WRITE GATE	WG	Output from FDC, write data when low, read data when high

Pin number	Designation	Common abbrev.	Function
26	TRACK 00	TR00	Input to FDC, low when head positioned over track 00
28	WRITE PROTECT	WPRT	Input to FDC, active low, indicates that disk has been protected
30	READ DATA	RDATA	Input to FDC, inactive high, pulsed low
32	SIDE SELECT	SIDE	Output from FDC, selects side (double-sided drives only)
34	READY	RDY	Input to FDC, active low (see note 3)

Notes: 1. Odd-numbered pins (1 to 33) are 0 V or GROUND.
2. There are some minor variations in the names used for the various lines. In particular, drive selects may be numbered DS0 to DS3 rather than DS1 to DS4.
3. HEAD LOAD and READY signals are not always provided.
4. Pin 2 may either be 'not connected' or 'reserved' for some special purpose.

Pin assignment for a standard 34-way floppy disk bus

1	2	not connected, reserved, or 0 V
3	4	IN USE or HEAD LOAD, HLD
5	6	DRIVE SELECT 4, DS4
7	8	INDEX, IP
9	10	DRIVE SELECT1, DS1
11	12	DRIVE SELECT 2, DS2
13	14	DRIVE SELECT 3, DS3
15	16	MOTOR ON, MOTOR
17	18	DIRECTION SELECT, DIRC
19	20	STEP, STEP
21	22	WRITE DATA, WD
23	24	WRITE GATE, WG
25	26	TRACK 00, TR00
27	28	WRITE PROTECTED, WPRT
29	30	READ DATA, RDATA
31	32	SIDE SELECT, SIDE
33	34	READY, RDY

GND or 0 V { 17

Normally lower side ◄——— ———► Normally upper side

Note: Edge view of double sided PCB (0.1" pad spacing)

Disk drive power connections

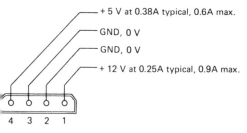

    —— + 5 V at 0.38A typical, 0.6A max.
    —— GND, 0 V
    —— GND, 0 V
    —— + 12 V at 0.25A typical, 0.9A max.

    4   3   2   1

Note: Pin view of PCB mounting connector (0.2'' pin spacing)

Characteristics of common 5.25 inch floppy disk drives

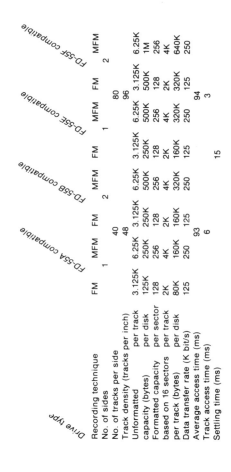

Drive type	FD-55A compatible		FD-55B compatible		FD-55E compatible		FD-55F compatible	
Recording technique	FM	MFM	FM	MFM	FM	MFM	FM	MFM
No. of sides	1		2		1		2	
No. of tracks per side	40		40		80		80	
Track density (tracks per inch)	48		48		96		96	
Unformatted capacity (bytes) per track	3.125K	6.25K	3.125K	6.25K	3.125K	6.25K	3.125K	6.25K
per disk	125K	250K	250K	500K	250K	500K	500K	1M
Formatted capacity (bytes) per sector	128	256	128	256	128	256	128	256
based on 16 sectors per track	2K	4K	2K	4K	2K	4K	2K	4K
per track	80K	160K	160K	320K	160K	320K	320K	640K
per disk	125	250	125	250	125	250	125	250
Data transfer rate (K bit/s)								
Average access time (ms)	93				94			
Track access time (ms)	6				3			
Settling time (ms)			15					

Typical floppy disk capacities

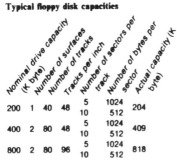

Nominal drive capacity (K byte)	Number of surfaces	Number of tracks	Tracks per inch	Number of sectors per track	Number of bytes per sector	Actual capacity (K byte)
200	1	40	48	5	1024	204
				10	512	
400	2	80	48	5	1024	409
				10	512	
800	2	80	96	5	1024	818
				10	512	

Typical Winchester disk capacities

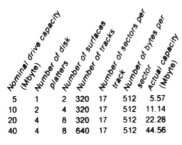

Nominal drive capacity (Mbyte)	Number of disk platters	Number of surfaces	Number of tracks	Number of sectors per track	Number of bytes per sector	Actual capacity (Mbyte)
5	1	2	320	17	512	5.57
10	2	4	320	17	512	11.14
20	4	8	320	17	512	22.28
40	4	8	640	17	512	44.56

Typical pin assignment for a Winchester disk controller

```
49 ┌──────────────────────────  //  ──────
   └──────────────────────────  //  ──────
50
```

Pin number	Signal/function
2	Data line 0
4	Data line 1
6	Data line 2
8	Data line 3
10	Data line 4
12	Data line 5
14	Data line 6
16	Data line 7
36	$\overline{\text{BUSY}}$
38	$\overline{\text{ACKNOWLEDGE}}$
40	$\overline{\text{RESET}}$
42	$\overline{\text{MESSAGE}}$
44	$\overline{\text{SELECT}}$
46	$\overline{\text{COMMAND}}$/DATA
48	$\overline{\text{REQUEST}}$
50	$\overline{\text{INPUT}}$/OUTPUT

Note: All odd-numbered pins (1 to 49) are ground (GND)·

The IBM PC

Of the seven million, or so, personal computers regularly in use in Western Europe, a very significant proportion is accounted for by the IBM PC, PC-XT, PC-AT and numerous 'compatibles'. These machines, more than any other, have set the standard for personal computers in the 1980s and have attracted a software base which outstrips all other machines.

IBM's first effort, the original PC, was announced in 1981 and first appeared in 1982. The PC had an 8088 processor, 64K to 256K of System Board RAM (expandable to 640K with 384K fitted in expansion slots). The PC supported two 360K floppy disk drives, an 80 column × 25 line display, and 16 colours with an appropriate Colour Graphics Adapter (CGA).

The original PC comprised of three units; system unit, keyboard, and display. The system unit itself comprises of three items; system board, power supply, and disk storage. In addition to an 8088 CPU (or 8086 CPU in some PC-compatibles) the original PC used approximately 100 integrated circuit devices including an 8237A DMA controller (DMAC), 8253 programmable interval timer (PIT), 8255A programmable parallel interface, 8259A programmable interrupt controller (PIC), 8284A clock generator, and 8288 bus controller. A socket was also provided, for an 8087 mathematics co-processor (or numeric data processor, NDP).

The original PC was quickly followed by the PC-XT. This machine, an improved PC with a single 360K floppy drive and a 10M hard disk, was introduced in 1983. The PC-XT was followed in 1984 by a more enhanced machine, the PC-AT. This machine uses an 80286 microprocessor (rather than the 8088 used in its predecessors) and offers 256K of system board RAM. The standard AT provides 1.2M and 20M of floppy and hard disk storage respectively.

Whilst IBM were blazing a trail, many other manufacturers were close behind. The standards set by IBM attracted much interest from other manufacturers, notable amongst which were Compaq and Olivetti, who were not merely content to produce machines with an identical specification but went on to make significant improvements. Other manufacturers were happy to 'clone' the PC; indeed, one could be excused for thinking that the highest accolade that could be offered by the computer press was that a machine was 'PC-compatible'!

PC port addresses

Device	PC-XT	PC-AT
8237A DMA controller	000-00F	000-01F
8259A interrupt controller	020-021	020-03F
8253/8254 timer	040-043	040-05F
8255 PPI	060-063	n/a
8042 keyboard controller	n/a	060-06F
DMA page register	080-083	080-09F
NMI mask register	0A0-0A7	070-07F
Second 8259A interrupt controller	n/a	0A0-0BF
Second 8237A DMA controller	n/a	0C0-0DF
Maths coprocessor	n/a	0F0-0FF

Device	PC-XT	PC-AT
Games controller	200-20F	200-207
Expansion unit	210-217	n/a
Second parallel printer	n/a	278-27F
Second serial port	2F8-2FF	2F8-2FF
Prototype card	300-31F	300-31F
Fixed (hard) disk	320-32F	1F0-1F8
First parallel printer	378-37F	378-37F
SDLC	380-38F	380-38F
BSC	n/a	3A0-3AF
Monochrome adapter	3B0-3BF	3B0-3BF
Colour graphics adapter	3D0-3DF	3D0-3DF
Disk controller	3F0-3F7	3F0-3F7
First serial port	3F8-3FF	3F8-3FF

Useful PC memory locations

Address (hex)	Number of bytes	Function
0410	2	Installed equipment list (see separate table)
0413	2	Usable memory
0417	2	Keyboard status
043E	1	Disk calibration. Bits 0 to 3 correspond to drives 0 to 3 respectively. A reset bit indicates that 'recalibration' is necessary for the disk concerned.
043F	1	Disk drive motor status. Bits 0 to 3 correspond to the motors fitted to drives 0 to 3. A set bit indicates that the motor concerned is running.
0440	1	Drive motor count. Set to 37 after a disk operation and is decremented at each clock 'tick' thereafter. The drive motor power is removed when the count reaches zero.
0441	2	Disk status (see separate table)
0442	7	Disk controller status
0449	1	Current video mode
044A	2	Current screen column width (value in hexadecimal)
046C	4	Master clock count (incremented by one on each clock 'tick')
0472	2	Set to 1234 hex during a keyboard reboot. This requires the use of CTRL-ALT-DEL keys.
0500	1	Screen print byte 00 indicates normal ready status, 01 indicates that a screen print is in operation. FF indicates that an error occurred during a screen print operation.

Note: All addresses are given in hexadecimal

Equipment list word (address 0410H)

Bit number	Meaning
0	Set if disk drives are present
1	Unused (reset)
2 and 3	System board RAM size:

Bit 2	Bit 3	RAM
0	0	16K
1	0	32K
1	1	64K/256K

4 and 5   Initial video mode:

Bit 4	Bit 5	Mode
1	0	40 column colour
0	1	80 column colour
1	1	80 column monochrome

6 and 7   Number of disk drives plus 1, i.e.:

Bit 6	Bit 7	Number of drives
0	0	1
1	0	2
0	1	3
1	1	4

8	Reset if DMA chip installed (standard)
9 to 11	Number of RS-232C serial ports installed
12	Set if a games adapter is installed
13	Set if a serial printer is installed
14 and 15	Number of printers installed

Disk status byte (address 0411H)

Bit number / Function

0	Set if an invalid disk command has been requested
1	Set if address mark on diskette is not found
2	Set if sector not found (this error occurs if the disk is damaged or has not been formatted)
3	Set if a disk DMA error has occurred
4	Set if a CRC error has occurred
5	Set if the disk controller device is not responding
6	Set if a track seek operation has failed
7	Set if the disk has 'timed out' (i.e. failed to respond in the preset time)

Video mode byte (address 0449H)

Byte value
Current video mode

0	40 column text, monochrome
1	40 column text, 16 colours
2	60 column text, monochrome
3	80 column text, 16 colours
4	Medium resolution graphics, 4 colours
5	Medium resolution graphics, 4 grey scale
6	High resolution graphics, 2 colours
7	Monochrome adapter mode
8	Low resolution graphics, 16 colours
9	Medium resolution graphics, 16 colours
10	High resolution graphics, 4 colours
13	Medium resolution graphics, 16 colours
14	High resolution graphics, 16 colours
15	Special high resolution graphics, 4 colours

PC video display

The video display provided by a PC will depend upon the type of graphics adapter card fitted. The PC will operate in a variety of different video modes supported by a number of different graphics standards including colour graphics adapter (CGA), enhanced graphics adapter (EGA), and video graphics array (VGA).

The extent of memory (present within the appropriate graphics adapter card) required to display a screen in text mode is determined by the number of character columns and lines and also on the number of colours displayed. In modes 0 to 6 and 8, a total of 16 K bytes is reserved for display memory whilst in mode 7 (monochrome 80 × 25 characters) the requirement is for only 4 K bytes (colours are not displayed).

In modes 0 to 3, less than 16 K bytes is used by the screen at any one time. For these modes, the available memory is divided into pages. Note that only one page can be displayed at any particular time. Displayed pages are numbered 0 to 7 in modes 0 and 1, and 0 to 3 in modes 2 and 3.

The extent of display memory required in a graphics mode depends upon the number of pixels displayed (horizontal × vertical) and also on the number of colours displayed. Provided that a display adapter has sufficient RAM fitted, the concept of screen pages also applies to graphics modes. Again, it is only possible to display one page at a time.

Graphics adapter standards

Mode Display type	Colours	Screen resolution (note 1)	MDA	CGA	EGA	MCGA	VGA	HGA (note 3)
00H Text	16	40 × 25		*	*	*	*	
01H Text	16	40 × 25		*	*	*	*	
02H Text	16	80 × 25		*	*	*	*	

Mode Display type	Colours	Screen resolution (note 1)	MDA	CGA	EGA	MCGA	VGA	HGA (note 3)
03H Text	16	80 × 25	★	★	★	★	★	
04H Graphics	4	320 × 200	★	★	★	★	★	
05H Graphics	4	320 × 200	★	★	★	★	★	
06H Graphics	2	640 × 200	★	★	★	★	★	
07H Text	Mono	80 × 25	★		★		★	★
08H Graphics	16	160 × 200	(note 2)					
09H Graphics	16	320 × 200	(note 2)					
0AH Graphics	4	640 × 200	(note 2)					
0BH (note 4)								
0CH (note 4)								
0DH Graphics	16	320 × 200			★		★	
0EH Graphics	16	640 × 200			★		★	
0FH Graphics	Mono	640 × 350			★		★	
10H Graphics	16	640 × 350			★		★	
11H Graphics	2	640 × 480				★	★	
12H Graphics	16	640 × 480					★	
13H Graphics	256	320 × 200				★	★	

Notes: 1 Resolutions are quoted in (columns × lines) for text displays and (horizontal × vertical) pixels for graphics displays.

2 Applies only to the PC Junior.

3 The Hercules Graphics Adapter card successfully combines the graphics (but not colour) capabilities of the CGA adapter with the high quality text display of the MDA adapter.

4 Reserved mode.

Power on self-test (POST)

The IBM power on self test (POST) checks the system hardware during initialization and performs the following checks:

(a) system board
(b) memory expansion adapter
(c) fixed disk and disk drive adapter
(d) keyboard
(e) disk drives
(f) fixed disk drive

As a result of the POST, error codes are displayed which indicate the area in which a fault has been detected. The following error codes relate to the PC-AT:

Code	Functional element
1xx	System board
2Øx	Memory board
3Øx	Keyboard
4xx	Display (monochrome)
5xx	Display (colour)

Code   Functional element

6xx   Disk drive
7xx   Maths coprocessor
9xx   Serial/parallel adapter—parallel port
10xx   Alternative serial/parallel adapter—parallel port
11xx   Serial/parallel adapter—serial port
12xx   Alternative serial/parallel adapter—serial port
13xx   Games control adapter
14xx   Graphics printer
15xx   SDLC adapter
17xx   Fixed disk drive
20xx   BSC adapter
21xx   Alternative BSC adapter
29xx   Colour printer
NB: x = any digit

IBM PS/2

IBM's second generation of personal computers, personal system 2, is based on four machines; models 30, 50, 60 and 80. The smallest of these, model 30, is based on 8086 CPU and has dual 720K/1.4M 3.5″ floppy disk drives and 640K of RAM. Models 50 and 60 use the 80286 CPU with 1M of RAM (expandable) and fixed disk drives of 20M (model 50), 44M (model 60).

IBM's top-of-the-range machine, the model 80, employs a 80386 CPU and a 1.4M 3.5″ floppy disk drive. Three different fixed disk/RAM configurations are available for the model 80 and these are based on 44M fixed disk/1M RAM, 70M fixed disk/2M RAM, and 115M fixed disk/2M RAM. Models 30 and 50 are designed for conventional desk-top operation whilst models 60 and 80 both feature 'vertical' floor-standing systems units with front access panels for the fixed disk tray. PS/2 family has an impressive expansion capability and the following devices are supported by models 50, 60 and 80:

(a) Monochrome display (8503)
(b) Colour display (8512)
(c) Colour display (8513) (medium resolution)
(d) Colour display (8514) (high resolution)
(e) Memory expansion kits/cards
(f) Second fixed disk (44M/70M/115M)
(g) External 5.25″ floppy disk drive
(h) Tape streamer (6157)
(i) Optical disk (internal or external 3363)
(j) Dual asynchronous communications adapter
(k) Internal modem (30/1200 baud)
(l) IBM PC network (LAN) adapter
(m) IBM token-ring (LAN) adapter
(n) Multi-protocol adapter (asynchronous/BSC/SDLC/HDLC)
(o) System 36/38 workstation emulator adapter

Powers of two

n	2^n	n	2^n	n	2^n
0	1	9	512	18	262 144 (256K)
1	2	10	1 024 (1K)	19	524 288 (512K)
2	4	11	2 048 (2K)	20	1 048 576 (1M)
3	8	12	4 096 (4K)	21	2 097 152 (2M)
4	16	13	8 192 (8K)	22	4 194 304 (4M)
5	32	14	16 384 (16K)	23	8 388 608 (8M)
6	64	15	32 768 (32K)	24	16 777 216 (16M)
7	128	16	65 536 (64K)		
8	256	17	131 072 (128K)		

Decimal/hexadecimal/octal/binary/ASCII conversion table

Decimal	Hexadecimal	Octal	Binary	ASCII character
0	00	000	00000000	NUL
1	01	001	00000001	SOH
2	02	002	00000010	STX
3	03	003	00000011	ETX
4	04	004	00000100	EOT
5	05	005	00000101	ENQ
6	06	006	00000110	ACK
7	07	007	00000111	BEL
8	08	010	00001000	BS
9	09	011	00001001	HT
10	0A	012	00001010	LF
11	0B	013	00001011	VT
12	0C	014	00001100	FF
13	0D	015	00001101	CR
14	0E	016	00001110	SO
15	0F	017	00001111	SI
16	10	020	00010000	DLE
17	11	021	00010001	DC1
18	12	022	00010010	DC2
19	13	023	00010011	DC3
20	14	024	00010100	DC4
21	15	025	00010101	NAK
22	16	026	00010110	SYN
23	17	027	00010111	ETB
24	18	030	00011000	CAN
25	19	031	00011001	EM
26	1A	032	00011010	SUB
27	1B	033	00011011	ESC
28	1C	034	00011100	FS
29	1D	035	00011101	GS
30	1E	036	00011110	RS
31	1F	037	00011111	US
32	20	040	00100000	space
33	21	041	00100001	!
34	22	042	00100010	''

Decimal	Hexadecimal	Octal	Binary	ASCII character
35	23	043	00100011	#
36	24	044	00100100	$
37	25	045	00100101	%
38	26	046	00100110	&
39	27	047	00100111	'
40	28	050	00101000	(
41	29	051	00101001	)
42	2A	052	00101010	*
43	2B	053	00101011	+
44	2C	054	00101100	,
45	2D	055	00101101	−
46	2E	056	00101110	.
47	2F	057	00101111	/
48	30	060	00110000	0
49	31	061	00110001	1
50	32	062	00110010	2
51	33	063	00110011	3
52	34	064	00110100	4
53	35	065	00110101	5
54	36	066	00110110	6
55	37	067	00110111	7
56	38	070	00111000	8
57	39	071	00111001	9
58	3A	072	00111010	:
59	3B	073	00111011	;
60	3C	074	00111100	<
61	3D	075	00111101	=
62	3E	076	00111110	>
63	3F	077	00111111	?
64	40	100	01000000	@
65	41	101	01000001	A
66	42	102	01000010	B
67	43	103	01000011	C
68	44	104	01000100	D
69	45	105	01000101	E
70	46	106	01000110	F
71	47	107	01000111	G
72	48	110	01001000	H
73	49	111	01001001	I
74	4A	112	01001010	J
75	4B	113	01001011	K
76	4C	114	01001100	L
77	4D	115	01001101	M
78	4E	116	01001110	N
79	4F	117	01001111	O
80	50	120	01010000	P
81	51	121	01010001	Q
82	52	122	01010010	R
83	53	123	01010011	S
84	54	124	01010100	T
85	55	125	01010101	U
86	56	126	01010110	V
87	57	127	01010111	W

Decimal	Hexadecimal	Octal	Binary	ASCII character
88	58	130	01011000	X
89	59	131	01011001	Y
90	5A	132	01011010	Z
91	5B	133	01011011	[
92	5C	134	01011100	\
93	5D	135	01011101	]
94	5E	136	01011110	-
95	5F	137	01011111	__
96	60	140	01100000	`
97	61	141	01100001	a
98	62	142	01100010	b
99	63	143	01100011	c
00	64	144	01100100	d
01	65	145	01100101	e
02	66	146	01100110	f
03	67	147	01100111	g
04	68	150	01101000	h
05	69	151	01101001	i
06	6A	152	01101010	j
07	6B	153	01101011	k
08	6C	154	01101100	l
09	6D	155	01101101	m
10	6E	156	01101110	n
11	6F	157	01101111	o
12	70	160	01110000	p
13	71	161	01110001	q
14	72	162	01110010	r
15	73	163	01110011	s
16	74	164	01110100	t
17	75	165	01110101	u
18	76	166	01110110	v
19	77	167	01110111	w
20	78	170	01111000	x
21	79	171	01111001	y
22	7A	172	01111010	z
23	7B	173	01111011	{
24	7C	174	01111100		
25	7D	175	01111101	}
26	7E	176	01111110	-
27	7F	177	01111111	DEL
28	80	200	10000000	
29	81	201	10000001	
30	82	202	10000010	
31	83	203	10000011	
32	84	204	10000100	
33	85	205	10000101	
34	86	206	10000110	
35	87	207	10000111	
36	88	210	10001000	
37	89	211	10001001	
38	8A	212	10001010	
39	8B	213	10001011	
40	8C	214	10001100	

Decimal	Hexadecimal	Octal	Binary	ASCII character
141	8D	215	10001101	
142	8E	216	10001110	
143	8F	217	10001111	
144	90	220	10010000	
145	91	221	10010001	
146	92	222	10010010	
147	93	223	10010011	
148	94	224	10010100	
149	95	225	10010101	
150	96	226	10010110	
151	97	227	10010111	
152	98	230	10011000	
153	99	231	10011001	
154	9A	232	10011010	
155	9B	233	10011011	
156	9C	234	10011100	
157	9D	235	10011101	
158	9E	236	10011110	
159	9F	237	10011111	
160	A0	240	10100000	
161	A1	241	10100001	
162	A2	242	10100010	
163	A3	243	10100011	
164	A4	244	10100100	
165	A5	245	10100101	
166	A6	246	10100110	
167	A7	247	10100111	
168	A8	250	10101000	
169	A9	251	10101001	
170	AA	252	10101010	
171	AB	253	10101011	
172	AC	254	10101100	
173	AD	255	10101101	
174	AE	256	10101110	
175	AF	257	10101111	
176	B0	260	10110000	
177	B1	261	10110001	
178	B2	262	10110010	
179	B3	263	10110011	
180	B4	264	10110100	
181	B5	265	10110101	
182	B6	266	10110110	
183	B7	267	10110111	
184	B8	270	10111000	
185	B9	271	10111001	
186	BA	272	10111010	
187	BB	273	10111011	
188	BC	274	10111100	
189	BD	275	10111101	
190	BE	276	10111110	
191	BF	277	10111111	
192	C0	300	11000000	
193	C1	301	11000001	

Decimal	Hexadecimal	Octal	Binary	ASCII character
194	C2	302	11000010	
195	C3	303	11000011	
196	C4	304	11000100	
197	C5	305	11000101	
198	C6	306	11000110	
199	C7	307	11000111	
200	C8	310	11001000	
201	C9	311	11001001	
202	CA	312	11001010	
203	CB	313	11001011	
204	CC	314	11001100	
205	CD	315	11001101	
206	CE	316	11001110	
207	CF	317	11001111	
208	D0	320	11010000	
209	D1	321	11010001	
210	D2	322	11010010	
211	D3	323	11010011	
212	D4	324	11010100	
213	D5	325	11010101	
214	D6	326	11010110	
215	D7	327	11010111	
216	D8	330	11011000	
217	D9	331	11011001	
218	DA	332	11011010	
219	DB	333	11011011	
220	DC	334	11011100	
221	DD	335	11011101	
222	DE	336	11011110	
223	DF	337	11011111	
224	E0	340	11100000	
225	E1	341	11100001	
226	E2	342	11100010	
227	E3	343	11100011	
228	E4	344	11100100	
229	E5	345	11100101	
230	E6	346	11100110	
231	E7	347	11100111	
232	E8	350	11101000	
233	E9	351	11101001	
234	EA	352	11101010	
235	EB	353	11101011	
236	EC	354	11101100	
237	ED	355	11101101	
238	EE	356	11101110	
239	EF	357	11101111	
240	F0	360	11110000	
241	F1	361	11110001	
242	F2	362	11110010	
243	F3	363	11110011	
244	F4	364	11110100	
245	F5	365	11110101	
246	F6	366	11110110	

Decimal	Hexadecimal	Octal	Binary	ASCII character
247	F7	367	11110111	
248	F8	370	11111000	
249	F9	371	11111001	
250	FA	372	11111010	
251	FB	373	11111011	
252	FC	374	11111100	
253	FD	375	11111101	
254	FE	376	11111110	
255	FF	377	11111111	

ASCII control characters

Hexadecimal	ASCII character	Meaning	Keyboard entry
00	NUL	Null	CTRL-@
01	SOH	Start of heading	CTRL-A
02	STX	Start of text	CTRL-B
03	ETX	End of text	CTRL-C
04	EOT	End of transmission	CTRL-D
05	ENQ	Enquiry	CTRL-E
06	ACK	Acknowledge	CTRL-F
07	BEL	Bell	CTRL-G
08	BS	Backspace	CTRL-H
09	HT	Horizontal tabulation	CTRL-I
0A	LF	Line feed	CTRL-J
0B	VT	Vertical tabulation	CTRL-K
0C	FF	Form feed	CTRL-L
0D	CR	Carriage return	CTRL-M
0E	SO	Shift out	CTRL-N
0F	SI	Shift in	CRTL-O
10	DLE	Data link escape	CTRL-P
11	DC1	Device control one	CTRL-Q
12	DC2	Device control two	CTRL-R
13	DC3	Device control three	CTRL-S
14	DC4	Device control four	CTRL-T
15	NAK	Negative acknowledge	CTRL-U
16	SYN	Synchronous idle	CTRL-V
17	ETB	End of transmission	CTRL-W
18	CAN	Cancel	CTRL-X
19	EM	End of medium	CTRL-Y
1A	SUB	Substitute	CTRL-Z
1B	ESC	Escape	CTRL-[
1C	FS	File separator	CTRL-\
1D	GS	Group separator	CTRL-]
1E	RS	Record separator	CTRL-
îF	US	Unit separator	CTRL- —

Divisors of 255 with remainders

Divisor (n)	255/n	Remainder	Divisor (n)	255/n	Remainder	Divisor (n)	255/n	Remainder
1	255	0	44	5	35	87	2	81
2	127	1	45	5	30	88	2	79
3	85	0	46	5	25	89	2	77
4	63	3	47	5	20	90	2	75
5	51	0	48	5	15	91	2	73
6	42	3	49	5	10	92	2	71
7	36	3	50	5	5	93	2	69
8	31	7	51	5	0	94	2	67
9	28	3	52	4	47	95	2	65
10	25	5	53	4	43	96	2	63
11	23	2	54	4	39	97	2	61
12	21	3	55	4	35	98	2	59
13	19	8	56	4	31	99	2	57
14	18	3	57	4	27	100	2	55
15	17	0	58	4	23	101	2	53
16	15	15	59	4	19	102	2	51
17	15	0	60	4	15	103	2	49
18	14	3	61	4	11	104	2	47
19	13	8	62	4	7	105	2	45
20	12	15	63	4	3	106	2	43
21	12	3	64	3	63	107	2	41
22	11	13	65	3	60	108	2	39
23	11	2	66	3	57	109	2	37
24	10	15	67	3	54	110	2	35
25	10	5	68	3	51	111	2	33
26	9	21	69	3	48	112	2	31
27	9	12	70	3	45	113	2	29
28	9	3	71	3	42	114	2	27
29	8	23	72	3	39	115	2	25
30	8	15	73	3	36	116	2	23
31	8	7	74	3	33	117	2	21
32	7	31	75	3	30	118	2	19
33	7	24	76	3	27	119	2	17
34	7	17	77	3	24	120	2	15
35	7	10	78	3	21	121	2	13
36	7	3	79	3	18	122	2	11
37	6	33	80	3	15	123	2	9
38	6	27	81	3	12	124	2	7
39	6	21	82	3	9	125	2	5
40	6	15	83	3	6	126	2	3
41	6	9	84	3	3	127	2	1
42	6	3	85	3	0	128	1	127
43	5	40	86	2	83			

Note: This table (and the one that follows) can be used to determine the optimum size for logical records associated with random access disk files. The divisor and remainder give respectively the number of fields (assumed equal size) and the number of wasted bytes.

Divisors of 256 with remainders

Divisor (n)	256/n	Remainder	Divisor (n)	256/n	Remainder	Divisor (n)	256/n	Remainder
1	256	0	44	5	36	87	2	82
2	128	0	45	5	31	88	2	80
3	85	1	46	5	26	89	2	78
4	64	0	47	5	21	90	2	76
5	51	1	48	5	16	91	2	74
6	42	4	49	5	11	92	2	72
7	36	4	50	5	6	93	2	70
8	32	0	51	5	1	94	2	68
9	28	4	52	4	48	95	2	66
10	25	6	53	4	44	96	2	64
11	23	3	54	4	40	97	2	62
12	21	4	55	4	36	98	2	60
13	19	9	56	4	32	99	2	58
14	18	4	57	4	28	100	2	56
15	17	1	58	4	24	101	2	54
16	16	0	59	4	20	102	2	52
17	15	1	60	4	16	103	2	50
18	14	4	61	4	12	104	2	48
19	13	9	62	4	8	105	2	46
20	12	16	63	4	4	106	2	44
21	12	4	64	4	0	107	2	42
22	11	14	65	3	61	108	2	40
23	11	3	66	3	58	109	2	38
24	10	16	67	3	55	110	2	36
25	10	6	68	3	52	111	2	34
26	9	22	69	3	49	112	2	32
27	9	13	70	3	46	113	2	30
28	9	4	71	3	43	114	2	28
29	8	24	72	3	40	115	2	26
30	8	16	73	3	37	116	2	24
31	8	8	74	3	34	117	2	22
32	8	0	75	3	31	118	2	20
33	7	25	76	3	28	119	2	18
34	7	18	77	3	25	120	2	16
35	7	11	78	3	22	121	2	14
36	7	4	79	3	19	122	2	12
37	6	34	80	3	16	123	2	10
38	6	28	81	3	13	124	2	8
39	6	22	82	3	10	125	2	6
40	6	16	83	3	7	126	2	4
41	6	10	84	3	4	127	2	2
42	6	4	85	3	1	128	2	0
43	5	41	86	2	84			

Flowchart symbols

 Direction of flow

 Start of flow chart

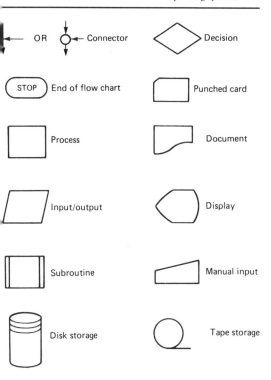

- ← OR   ⦶ ← Connector   ◇ Decision

- (STOP) End of flow chart   ▢ Punched card

- ▢ Process   ▱ Document

- ▱ Input/output   ⬠ Display

- ▣ Subroutine   ▱ Manual input

- ⬟ Disk storage   ◯ Tape storage

Operating systems

In general, an operating system is simply a collection of system
programs which allow the user to run applications software
without having to produce the hardware-specific routines required
for such mundane tasks as keyboard and disk I/O. The operating
system thus frees the programmer from the need to be aware of the
hardware configuration and presents him with what is, in effect, a
'virtual machine' whose characteristics are more tractable than the
underlying 'physical machine'.

One obvious advantage of the 'virtual machine' concept is that,
provided a form of the operating system is available for a range of
machines, a high degree of software portability is ensured.

As a minimum, an operating system can normally be expected to
perform the following tasks:

(a) accept keyboard entry of commands and data
(b) create, copy and delete disk files
(c) load programs and data files from disk into RAM
(d) maintain some form of directory of disk files
(e) save programs and data files from RAM to disk.

Operating systems may either be contained in ROM (as

'firmware') or be loaded from disk into RAM when the system is initialized ('booted') on power-up. There are obvious advantages and disadvantages with both of these techniques.

Operating systems normally include a number of commands for manipulating files. These include those for naming, renaming, sorting and copying files. Files are referred to by a 'file specification' (filespec) which, in complete form, comprises:

(a) the drive specification (drivespec) or drive name, comprising a single letter or number;
(b) the filename, which normally comprises a string of up to eight alphanumeric characters;
(c) an extension to the filename, which is normally up to three characters in length.

The extension is usually used to indicate either the type of file or the group of files to which the file belongs. The following are typical examples:

ACC	an accessory file
ASC	a pure ASCII text file
ASM	an assembler source file
BAS	a BASIC program file
BAT	a batch processing file (a file that contains a sequence of system commands which will be automatically executed when the file is loaded)
BIN	a binary file
C	a C program file
CMD	a directly executable utility program (command file)
COM	a compiled object code file/command file
DAT	a data file
DOC	a document file (normally ASCII)
DVR	a driver program
EXE	see CMD
FLT	a device filter
H	a header file (containing predefined symbols and C functions)
IMG	a binary image file for loading directly into memory
LIB	a library file (used in the linking process)
LNK	a link control file
LOG	a LOGO program file
LST	a list file
O	an object code file
OBJ	an object code file
OVn	an overlay (n denotes the overlay number, e.g. OV3 is the third overlay file)
PRG	a directly executable application program (program file)
REL	a relocatable object code file
RND	a random access data file
S	a source code file
SEQ	a sequential access data file
SUB	a submit file (see BAT and CP/M)
SYS	a system file
TXT	a word-processor text file (usually ASCII)

The drivespec is usually followed by a colon or other separator. Where no drivespec is given the drive is taken to be the current (default) drive. The filename is followed by the extension (usually optional). Where the extension is omitted, the system assumes (or supplies) a default extension (CMD when the command line interpreter is active, BAS when the BASIC interpreter is active, and so on). The filename and its extension are normally separated by a full-stop (period) or slash (/).

The following are examples of some complete filenames:

A: CONFIG/SYS	a system file called CONFIG stored in drive A
A: CMDFILE.ASM	an assembler source code file called CMDFILE and contained in drive A
B: INVOICE.BAS	a BASIC program called INVOICE stored in drive B
B: INVOICE.DAT	a data file called INVOICE stored in drive B
HELP.TXT	a text file called HELP stored in the default drive

CP/M

Most microcomputer operating systems can trace their origins in the original CP/M operating system developed by Gary Kildall and written as a software development aid for use with the Intel 8080 microprocessor. In its original form, CP/M was supplied on an 8 inch IBM format floppy disk.

CP/M was subsequently extensively developed and marketed by Digital Research. It now exists in a variety of forms, including those for use with Intel and Motorola 16-bit microprocessor families.

CP/M became the *de facto* operating system for most 8080, 8085 and Z80 8-bit microprocesser-based microcomputers. The wealth of business software written under CP/M guarantees its long term survival, even though it can hardly be described as 'user friendly'.

The following major variants of CP/M are in existence:

CP/M-80	the original 8080-based operating system
CP/M-2.2	improved and enhanced version of CP/M
CP/M-plus	enhanced CP/M with Z80 macro-assembler, faster disk throughput, and banked memory
CP/M-86	CP/M for 8086 family microprocessors
CP/M-68K	CP/M for 68000 family microprocessors
Concurrent CP/M	CP/M which permits time-sharing of the CPU between two or more tasks
MP/M-86	a very much enhanced multi-processing operating system for the 8086 family microprocessors

The following program modules are contained in the CPM.SYS file:

CCP	Console Command Processor (a user interface which parses command lines)
BDOS	Basic Disk Operating System
BIOS	Basic I/O System

CP/M establishes a reserved area of read/write memory which is known as the Transient Program Area (TPA). Application programs are then loaded into this area. The CCP is responsible for communicating with the user, and accepting and acting upon input commands from the console.

CP/M commands

The following represent a typical subset of CP/M commands:

A:	specifies drive A as the current disk drive
B:	specifies drive B as the current disk drive

DIR	displays a directory of files contained in the current disk drive (may be appended with a filename or filematch)
DDT	invokes the dynamic debugger (may be appended with a filename)
DUMP	displays the content of a diskfile (the filename must be appended and should include any extension)
ED	invokes the editor (any filename appended must be a text file and any extension must be included)
ERA	erases the specified files (a wild card filematch is provided using an asterisk for either filename or extension; e.g. ERA *.DAT erases all files with the extension DAT from the current disk drive)
FORMAT	formats a disk
LOAD	converts a HEX (the default extension) file into a command file (having a COM extension)
PIP	copies, combines and transfers specified files between peripheral devices
REN	renames an existing file with a specified new name (extensions must be included)
SAVE	saves contents of memory in a disk file (filename and extension must be provided)
STAT	displays status information and/or assigns devices
SUBMIT	a batch processor which executes a sequence of commands contained in the specified submit file (having a SUB extension)
SYSGEN	initializes a system disk
TYPE	displays the contents of a specified ASCII file on the console screen

Notes: 1. Not all of the above commands are appropriate to a particular version of CP/M.
2. Commands such as DIR, ERA, REN, and TYPE are intrinsic CP/M commands.
3. Commands such as FORMAT, PIP, STAT and SUBMIT refer to CP/M utilities.

MS-DOS

With the advent of 16-bit machines and the appearance of the IBM PC, a new and more powerful operating system was required. Digital Research produced an 8086-based version of CP/M (known as CP/M-86) however, Microsoft produced a rival product (PC-DOS) which was adopted by IBM for use with the PC. Microsoft quickly also developed an operating system (MS-DOS) for use with compatible machines. This operating system (now approaching version 5) is currently the world's most popular microcomputer operating system.

MS-DOS devices

The MS-DOS operating system can be configured for operation with a wide variety of peripheral devices including various types of monitor (CGA, HGA, EGA, VGA etc.), serial and parallel printers and modems. Each individual hardware configuration requires its own particular I/O provision and this is achieved by means of a piece of software known as a device driver. A number of device drivers (e.g. those which deal with the standard serial and parallel ports) are resident within the BIOS ROM. Others which may be required must be loaded into RAM during system initialization.

MS-DOS channels

In order to simplify the way in which MS-DOS handles input and output, the system recognizes the names of its various I/O devices. This may, at first, appear to be unnecessarily cumbersome but it is instrumental in allowing MS-DOS to redirect data. This feature can be extremely useful when, for example, output normally destined for the printer is to be redirected to an auxiliary serial port.

The following I/O channels are recognized by MS-DOS:

Channel	Meaning	Function	Notes
COM 1: and COM2:	Communications	Serial I/O	Via RS-232 ports
CON:	Console	Keyboard (input) and screen (output)	This channel is equivalent to that which would be associated with a computer terminal.
LPT1: LPT2: and LPT3:	Line printer	Parallel printer (output)	This interface conforms to the Centronics standard.
PRN:	Printer	Serial or parallel printer (output)	
NUL:	Null device	Simulated I/O	Provides a means of simulating a physical I/O channel without data transfer taking place.

The COPY command (see page 143) can be used to transfer data from one device to another. As an example, the command:

COPY CON: PRN:

copies data from the keyboard (console input device) to the printer.

Similarly, the command:

COPY CON: COM1:

copies data from the keyboard to the serial port (COM1). In either case, the end-of-file character, <CTRL-Z> or <F6>, must be entered to abort the command.

Redirection

The ability to redirect data is an extremely useful facility. The < and > characters are used within certain MS-DOS commands to indicate redirection of input and output data. Hence:

TYPE A: README. DOC > PRN:

can be used to redirect the normal screen output produced by the TYPE command to the printer. In this case, the content of a file named README.DOC (present in the root directory of the disk in drive A:) is sent to the printer.

Finally, the MODE command can be used to establish redirection of printer output from the (default) parallel port to a serial port. This facility is extremely useful where a serial printer has to be used in place of the (more usual) parallel printer. For further information see page 150.

MS-DOS command entry

MS-DOS responds to command lines typed at the console and terminated with a <RETURN> or <ENTER> keystroke. A command line is thus composed of a command keyword, an optional command tail, and <RETURN>. The command keyword identifies the command (or program) to be executed. The command tail can contain extra information relevant to the command, such as a filename or other parameters. Each command line must be terminated using <RETURN> or <ENTER> (not shown in the examples which follow).

As an example, the following command can be used to display a directory of all assembly language source code files (i.e. those with an ASM extension) within a directory named SYSDEV in drive A, indicating the size of each:

DIR A:\SYSDEV*.ASM

Note: In this example and the examples which follow, we have omitted the prompt generated by the system (indicating the current drive).

It should be noted that the command line can be entered in any combination of upper-case or lower-case characters. MS-DOS converts all letters in the command line to upper-case before interpreting them. Furthermore, whilst a command line generally immediately follows the system prompt, MS-DOS permits spaces between the prompt (>) and the command keyword.

As characters are typed at the keyboard, the cursor moves to the right in order to indicate the position of the next character to be typed. Depending upon the keyboard used, a <BACKSPACE>, or <DELETE> key can be used to delete the last entered character and move the cursor backwards one character position. Alternatively, a combination of the CONTROL and H keys (i.e. <CTRL-H>) may be used instead.

If it is necessary to repeat or edit the previous command, the <F1> (or right-arrow) key may be used to reproduce the command line, character by character, on the screen. The left-arrow key permits backwards movement through the command line for editing purposes. The <F3> key simply repeats the last command in its entirety.

MS-DOS control characters

The following 'control characters' have special meanings within MS-DOS:

Control character	Hex.	Function
<CTRL-C>	03	Terminates the current program (if possible) and returns control to the user.
<CTRL-G>	07	Sounds the audible warning device (bell). Can only be used as part of a program of batch file.
<CTRL-H>	08	Moves the cursor back by one space (i.e. the same as the <BACKSPACE> key) and deletes the character present at that position.

Control character	Hex.	Function
\<CTRL-I\>	09	Tabs the cursor right by a fixed number of columns (usually eight). Performs the same function as the \<TAB\> key.
\<CTRL-J\>	10	Issues a line feed and carriage return, effectively moving the cursor to the start of the next line.
\<CTRL-L\>	12	Issues a form feed instruction to the printer.
\<CTRL-M\>	13	Produces a carriage return (i.e. has the same effect as \<RETURN\>).
\<CTRL-P\>	16	Toggles screen output to the printer (i.e. after the first \<CTRL-P\> is issued, all screen output will be simultaneously echoed to the printer. A subsequent \<CTRL-P\> will disable the simultaneous printing of the screen output). Note that \<CTRL-PRT.SC.\> has the same effect as \<CTRL-P\>.
\<CTRL-S\>	19	Pauses screen output during execution of the TYPE command (\<CTRL-NUM.LOCK\> has the same effect).
\<CTRL-Z\>	26	Indicates the end of a file (can also be entered using \<F6\>).

Note: Whilst not a control character, the simultaneous depression of \<CTRL-ALT-DEL\> can be used to terminate the current program and perform a warm system reset. This particular combination of keys should only be used in the last resort as it will clear the system memory and any program or data present in RAM will be lost!

File specifications

Many of the MS-DOS commands make explicit reference to files. A file is simply a collection of related information stored on a disk. Program files comprise a series of instructions to be executed by the processor whereas data files simply contain a collection of records. A complete file specification has four distinct parts; a drive specifier, a filename, a filetype, and a password. The drive specifier is a single letter followed by a colon which separates it from the filename which follows. The filename comprises 1 to 8 characters whilst the filetype is usually specified in a 1 to 3 character extension. The filetype extension is separated from the filename by means of a full stop. A complete file specification (or 'filespec') thus takes the form:

[drive specifier]: [filename].[filetype]

As an example, the following file specification refers to a file named PROCESS and having a COM filetype stored on the disk in drive A:

A:PROCESS.COM

MS-DOS allows files to be grouped together within directories and sub-directories. Directory and sub-directory names are separated by means of the backslash (\) character. Directories and sub-directories are organized in a heirarchical (tree) structure and thus complete file specifications must include directory information. The following general format is used:

[drive specifier]:\[directory name(s)]\[filename].[filetype]

The base directory (i.e. that which exists at the lowest level in the heirarchical structure) is known as the 'root directory'. The root directory is accessed by default when we simply specify a drive name without further reference to a directory. Thus:

A:PROCESS.COM

refers to a file in the root directory whilst:

A:\APPS\PROCESS.COM

refers to an identically named file resident in the APPS sub-directory.

Sub-directories can be extended to any practicable level. As an example:

A:\APPS\DATA\PROCESS.DAT

refers to a file named PROCESS.DAT present in the DATA sub-directory within a directory which is itself named APPS.

When it is necessary to make explicit reference to the root directory, we can simply use a single backslash character as follows:

A:\

File extensions

The filetype extension provides a convenient mechanism for distinguishing different types of file and MS-DOS provides various methods for manipulating groups of files having the same filetype extension. We could, for example, delete all of the assembly language source code files present in the root directory of the disk in drive A using a single command of the form:

ERA A:*.ASM

Alternatively, we could copy all of the executable (EXE) files from one disk in drive A to another in drive B using the command:

COPY A:*.EXE B:\

The following are a selection of the most commonly used filetype extensions:

Extension	Type of file
ARC	A compressed format archive file.
ASC	An ASCII text file.
ASM	An assembly language source code file.
BAK	A back-up file (often created automatically by a text editor which renames the source file with this extension and the revised file assumes the original file specification).
BAS	A BASIC program source file.
BAT	A batch file which contains a sequence of operating system commands.
BIN	A binary file (comprising instructions and data in binary format).
BLD	A binary file to be loaded into BASIC using the BLOAD command.

Extension	*Type of file*
C	A source code file written in the C language.
CBL	A COBOL source code file.
COB	A COBOL source code file.
COM	An executable program file in small memory format (i.e. confined to a single 64 K byte memory segment).
CRF	A cross reference file (for processing by a utility which will produce a cross reference listing of symbols for debugging purposes).
DAT	A date file (usually presented in either binary or ASCII format).
DEV	A device driver file (loaded by CONFIG.SYS at bootup.
DOC	A document file (not necessarily presented in standard ASCII format).
EXE	An executable program file in large memory format (i.e. not confined to a 64 K byte memory model).
FMT	A format or display spec. file used by dBASE III.
FOR	A FORTRAN source code file.
HEX	A file presented in hexadecimal (an intermediate format sometimes used for object code).
INI	An initialization file which may contain a set of inference rules and/or environment variables.
LIB	A library file (containing multiple object code files).
LST	A listing file (usually showing the assembly code corresponding to each source code instruction together with a complete list of symbols).
MAK	A make file generated by a make utility (i.e. MAKE). A make file contains information which allows a compiler to identify together the various modules and include files required in the compilation process.
MAP	A map file generated by a linker utility (i.e. LINK). A map file consists of a list of symbols and their corresponding addresses.
OBJ	An object code file.
OVL	A program overlay file.
PAS	A Pascal source code file.
PGM	A binary program file or overlay.
PIF	A program information file used by Microsoft Windows.
PRN	A printer file (output from certain programs which can later be directed to the printer). The program may contain print formatting codes along with the text.
SYS	A device driver loaded by CONFIG.SYS at bootup.
TMP	A temporary file (created by some programs and then later erased).
TXT	A text file (usually in ASCII format).
WKS	A data worksheet (created by Lotus 1–2–3 or another spreadsheet program).
$$$	A temporary file (created by some programs and then later erased).

Wildcard characters
MS-DOS allows the user to employ wildcard characters when
specifying files. The characters, * and ?, can be used to replace
complete fields and individual characters respectively within a file
specification. MS-DOS will search, then carry out the required
operation on all files for which a match is obtained.

The following examples illustrate the use of wildcard characters:

A:*.ASM   refers to all files having an ASM extension
            present in the root directory of drive A
C:\MC*.*   refers to all files (regardless of name or
            extension) present in the directory named MC
            on drive C
B:\PROC?.C refers to all files having a C extension present in
            the TURBO directory on the disk in drive B
            which have PROC as their first three letters and
            any alphanumeric character in the fourth
            character place

A match will occur for each of the following files:
PROC1.C PROC2.C PROC3.C PROCA.C PROCB.C etc.

MS-DOS commands
A distinction must be made between MS-DOS commands which
relate to the resident part of the operating system (internal
commands) and those which involve other utility programs
(external commands). Intrinsic commands are executed
immediately whereas extrinsic commands require the loading of
transient utility programs from disk and hence there is a short
delay before the command is acted upon.

In the case of external commands, MS-DOS checks only the
command keyword. Any parameters which follow are passed to the
utility program without checking.

Internal MS-DOS commands
The following are some of the most commonly used internal MS-
DOS commands and their functions:

Command	Function
BREAK	The BREAK command disables the means by which it is possible to abort a running program. This facility is provided by means of the <CTRL-C> or <CTRL-BREAK> key combinations and it normally only occurs when output is being directed to the screen or the printer. BREAK accepts two parameters, ON and OFF. Examples: BREAK ON enables full <CTRL-C> or <CTRL-BREAK> key checking (it is important to note that this will normally produce a dramatic reduction in the speed of execution of a program); BREAK OFF restores normal <CTRL-C> or <CTRL-BREAK> operation (i.e. the default condition)
CD	See CHDIR
CHDIR	The CHDIR command allows users to display or change the current directory. CHDIR may be abbreviated to CD. Examples: CHDIR A: displays the current directory path for the disk in drive A;

| *Command* | *Function* |

CHDIR C:\APPS changes the directory path to APPS on drive C; CD D:\DEV\PROCESS changes the directory path to the sub-directory PROCESS within the directory named DEV on drive D; CD\ changes the directory path to the root directory of the current drive

LS The screen may be cleared using the CLS command

OPY The COPY command can be used to transfer a file from one disk to another using the same or a different filename. The COPY command is effective when the user has only a single drive. The COPY command must be followed by one or two file specifications. When only a single file specification is given, the command makes a single drive copy of a file. The copied file takes the same filename as the original and the user is prompted to insert the source and destination disks at the appropriate point. Where both source and destination file specifications are included, the file is copied to the specified drive and the copy takes the specified name. Where only a destination drive is specified (i.e. the destination filename is omitted) the COPY command copies the file to the specified drive without altering the filename. COPY may be used with the '*' and '?' wildcard characters in order to copy all files for which a match is found (see page 142). Examples: COPY A:ED.COM copies the file ED.COM present on the disk in drive A to another disk inserted in the same drive. The COPY utility generates prompts during the process; COPY A:ED.COM B: copies the file ED.COM present on the disk in drive A to the disk present in drive B. The copy will be given the name ED.COM

ATE The DATE command allows the date to be set or displayed. Examples: DATE displays the date on the screen and also prompts the user to make any desired changes. The user may press <RETURN> to leave the settings unchanged; DATE 12–27–91 sets the date to 27th December 1991

EL See ERASE

IR The DIR command displays the names of all non-system files in the directory. Variations of the command allow the user to specify the drive to be searched and the types of files to be displayed. Further options govern the format of the directory display. Examples: DIR displays all files in the current default directory; DIR B: displays all files on the disk in drive B (but without changing the default drive to B); A:DIR changes the default drive to A (root directory) and then displays the contents of the root directory of the disk in drive A; DIR*.BAS displays all files with a BAS extension present in the current default directory drive;

Command	Function

DIR C:\DEV.* displays all files named DEV (regardless of their type or extension) present in the root directory of drive C (the hard disk); DIR C:\MC*.BIN displays all files having a BIN extension present in the sub-directory named MC on drive C (the hard disk); DIR/W displays a directory listing in 'wide' format (excluding size and creation date/time information) of the current default directory.

ERASE The ERASE command is used to erase a filename from the directory and release the storage space occupied by a file. The ERASE command is identical to the DEL command and the two may be used interchangeably. ERASE may be used with the * and ? wildcard characters in order to erase all files for which a match occurs. Examples: ERASE PROG1.ASM erases the file named PROG1.ASM from the disk placed in the current default drive; ERASE B:TEMP.DAT erases the file named TEMP.DAT from the disk placed in drive B; ERASE C:*.COM erases all files having a COM extension present on the disk in drive C; ERASE A:PROG1.* erases all files named PROG1 (regardless of their type extension) present on the disk currently in drive A

MKDIR The MKDIR command is used to make a new directory or sub-directory. The command may be abbreviated to MD. Examples: MKDIR APPS creates a sub-directory named APPS within the current directory (note that the MKDIR command is often used after a CHDIR).

PATH The PATH command may be used to display the current directory path. Alternatively, a new directory path may be established using the SET PATH command. Examples: PATH displays the current directory path (a typical response would be PATH = C:\PCTOOLS); SET PATH = C:\DOS makes the directory path C:\DOS

PROMPT The PROMPT command allows the user to change the system prompt. The PROMPT command is followed by a text string which replaces the system prompt. Special characters may be inserted within the string, as follows:

$d	current date
$e	escape character
$g	>
$h	backspace and erase
$1	<
$n	current drive
$p	current directory path
$q	=
$t	current time
$v	DOS version number
$$	$
$	newline

Command	Function
	Examples: PROMPT tg changes the prompt to the current time followed by a >. PROMPT Howard Associates PLC $-? changes the prompt to Howard Associates PLC followed by a carriage return and newline on which a ? is displayed; PROMPT restores the normal system prompt (e.g. C>)
RD	See RMDIR
RENAME	The RENAME command allows the user to rename a disk file. RENAME may be used with the * and ? wildcard characters in order to rename all files for which a match occurs. RENAME may be abbreviated to REN. Examples: RENAME PROG2.ASM PROG1.ASM renames PROG1.ASM to PROG2.ASM on the disk placed in the current default drive; REN A:HELP.DOC HELP.TXT renames the file HELP.DOC to HELP.TXT on the disk placed in drive A; REN B:CONTROL.* PROG1.* renames all files with name PROG1 (regardless of type extension) to CONTROL (with identical extensions) found on the disk placed in drive B
RMDIR	The RMDIR command is used to remove a directory. RMDIR may be abbreviated to RD. The command cannot be used to remove the current directory and any directory to be removed must be empty and must not contain further sub-directories. Example: RMDIR ASSEM removes the directory ASSEM from the current directory
SET	The SET command is used to set the environment variables (see PATH)
TIME	The TIME command allows the time to be set or displayed. Examples: TIME displays the time on the screen and also prompts the user to make any desired changes. The user may press <RETURN> to leave the settings unchanged; TIME 14:30 sets the time to 2.30 p.m.
TYPE	The TYPE command allows the user to display the contents of an ASCII (text) file on the console screen. The TYPE command can be used with options which enable or disable paged mode displays. The <CTRL-S> key combination may be used to halt the display and <CTRL-Q> used to restart. <CTRL-C> may be used to abort the execution of the TYPE command and exit to the system. The file may be simultaneously echoed to the printer by means of <CTRL-P> which should be used before issuing the TYPE command. A second <CTRL-P> can be issued to disable the echo facility. Example: TYPE B:PROG1.ASM will display the contents of a file called PROG1.ASM stored on the disk placed in drive B. The file will be sent to the screen
VER	The VER command displays the current DOS version

Command	Function
VERIFY	The VERIFY command can be used to enable or disable disk file verification. VERIFY ON enables verification whilst VERIFY OFF disables verification. If VERIFY is used without ON or OFF, the system will display the state of verification (on or off)
VOL	The VOL command may be used to display the volume label of a disk

External MS-DOS commands

Unlike internal commands, these commands will not function unless the appropriate MS-DOS utility program is resident in the current (default) directory. External commands are simply the names of utility programs (normally resident in the DOS sub-directory). If you need to gain access to these utilities from any directory or sub-directory, then the following lines should be included in your AUTOEXEC.BAT file:

SET PATH = C:\DOS

The foregoing assumes that you have created a sub-directory called DOS on the hard disk and that this sub-directory contains the MS-DOS utility programs. The following are the most commonly used commands and their functions:

Command	Function
APPEND	The APPEND command allows the user to specify drives, directories and sub-directories which will be searched through when a reference is made to a particular data file. The APPEND command follows the same syntax as the PATH command (see page 144)
ASSIGN	The ASSIGN command allows users to re-direct files between drives. ASSIGN is particularly useful when a RAM disk is used to replace a conventional disk drive. Examples: ASSIGN A = D results in drive D being searched for a file whenever a reference is made to drive A. The command may be countermanded by issuing a command of the form: ASSIGN A = A; alternatively, all current drive assignments may be over-ridden by simply using: ASSIGN
ATTRIB	The ATTRIB command allows the user to examine and/or set the attributes of a single file or a group of files. The ATTRIB command alters the file attribute byte (which appears within a disk directory) and which determines the status of the file. (e.g. read-only). Examples: ATTRIB A:\PROCESS.DOC displays the attribute status of copies the file PROCESS.DOC contained in the root directory of the disk in drive A; ATTRIB + R A:\PROCESS.DOC changes the status of the file PROCESS.DOC contained in the root directory of the disk in drive A so that it is a read-only file. This command may be countermanded by issuing a command of the form: ATTRIB –R A:\PROCESS.DOC

Command	Function
BACKUP	

BACKUP

The BACKUP command may be used to copy one or more files present on a hard disk to a number of floppy disks for security purposes. It is important to note that the BACKUP command stores files in a compressed format (i.e. not in the same format as that used by the COPY command). The BACKUP command may be used selectively with various options including those which allow files to be archived by date. The BACKUP command usually requires that the target disks have been previously formatted however, from MS-DOS V3.3 onwards, an option to format disks has been included. Examples: BACKUP C:*.*A: backs up all of the files present on the hard disk. This command usually requires that a large number of (formatted) disks are available for use in drive A. Disks should be numbered so that the data can later be RESTORED in the correct order; BACKUP C:\DEV*.C A: backs up all of the files with a C extension present within the DEV sub-directory on drive C; BACKUP C:\PROCESS*.BAS A:/D:01–01–89 backs up all of the files with a BAS extension present within the PROCESS sub-directory of drive C that were created or altered on or after 1st January 1990; BACKUP C:\COMMS*.* A:/F backs up all of the files present in the COMMS sub-directory of drive C and formats each disk as it is used

CHKDSK

The CHKDSK command reports on disk utilization and provides information on total disk space, hidden files, directories, and user files. CHKDSK also gives the total memory and free memory available. CHKDSK incorporates options which can be used to enable reporting and to repair damaged files. Example: CHKDSK C:\DEV*.ASM/F/V checks the specified disk and directory, examining all files with an ASM extension, reporting errors and attempting to correct them

COMP

The COMP command may be used to compare two files on a line by line or character by character basis. The following options are available:
/A   use ... to indicate differences;
/B   perform comparison on a character basis;
/C   do not report character differences;
/L   perform line comparison for program files;
/N   add line numbers;
/T   leave tab characters;
/W   ignore white space at beginning and end of lines;
Example: COMP /B PROC1.ASM PROC2.ASM carries out a comparison of the files PROC1.ASM and PROC2.ASM on a character by character basis

Command	Function
DISKCOMP	The DISKCOMP command provides a means of comparing two (floppy) disks. DISKCOMP accepts drive names as parameters and the necessary prompts are generated when a single-drive disk comparison is made. Examples: DISKCOMP A: B: compares the disk in drive A with that placed in drive B
EXE2BIN	The EXE2BIN utility converts, where possible, an EXE program file to a COM program file (which loads faster and makes less demands on memory space). The command will not operate on EXE files that require more than 64 K bytes of memory space (including space for the stack and data storage) and/or those that make reference to other memory segments (i.e. CS, DS, ES, and SS must all remain the same within the program). Example: EXE2BIN PROCESS will search for the program PROCESS.EXE and generate a program PROCESS.COM
FASTOPEN	The FASTOPEN command provides a means of rapidly accessing files. The command is only effective when a hard disk is fitted and should ideally be used when the system is initialized (e.g. from within the AUTOEXEC.BAT file). The command retains details of files within memory and must not be used concurrently with the commands ASSIGN, JOIN, and/or SUBST. Example: FASTOPEN C:32 enables fast opening of files and provides for the details of up to 32 files to be retained in RAM
FDISK	The FDISK utility allows users to format a hard (fixed) disk. Since the command will render any existing data stored on the disk inaccessible, FDISK should be used with extreme caution. Furthermore improved hard disk partitioning and formatting utilities are normally supplied when a hard disk is purchased. These should be used in preference to FDISK whenever possible
FIND	The FIND command can be used to search for a character string within a file. Options include: /C display the line number(s) where the search string has been located; /N number the lines to show the position within the file; /V display all lines which do not contain the search string; Example: FIND/C 'outport' C:\DEV\PROCESS.C searches the file PROCESS.C present in the DEV sub-directory for occurrences of outport. When the search string is located, the command displays the appropriate line number
FORMAT	The FORMAT command is used to initialize a floppy or hard disk. The command should be used with caution since it will generally not be possible to recover any data which was

Command	Function

previously present. Various options are available including:

/1	single-sided format;
/8	format with 8 sectors per track;
/B	leave space for system tracks to be added (using the SYS command);
/N:8	format with 8 sectors per track;
/S	write system tracks during formatting (note that this must be the last option specified when more than one option is required;
/T:80	format with 80 tracks;
/V	format and then prompt for a volume label;

Examples: FORMAT A: formats the disk placed in drive A; FORMAT B:/S formats the disk placed in drive B as a system disk

JOIN The JOIN command provides a means of associating a drive with a particular directory path. The command must be used with care and must not be used with ASSIGN, BACKUP, DISKCOPY, FORMAT etc.

KEYB The KEYB command invokes the MS-DOS keyboard driver. KEYB replaces earlier utilities (such as KEYBUK) which were provided with MS-DOS versions prior to V3.3. The command is usually incorporated in an AUTOEXEC.BAT file and must specify the country letters required. Example: KEYB UK selects the UK keyboard layout

LABEL The LABEL command allows a volume label (maximum 11 characters) to be placed in the disk directory. Example: LABEL A: PROCESS will label the disk present in drive A as PROCESS. This label will subsequently appear when the directory is displayed

MODE The MODE command can be used to select from a range of screen and printer options. MODE is an extremely versatile command and offers a wide variety of options. Examples: MODE LPT1: 120,6 initializes the parallel printer LPT1 for printing 120 columns at 6 lines per inch; MODE LPT2: 60,8 initializes the parallel printer LPT2 for printing 60 columns at 8 lines per inch; MODE COM1: 1200,N,8,1 initializes the COM1 serial port for 1200 baud operation with no parity, eight data bits and one stop bit; MODE COM2: 9600,N,7,2 initializes the COM2 serial port for 9600 baud operation with no parity, seven data bits and two stop bits; MODE 40 sets the screen to 40 column text mode; MODE 80 sets the screen to 80 column mode; MODE BW80 sets the screen to monochrome 40 column text mode; MODE CO80 sets the screen to colour 80 column mode. The MODE command can also be used to permit

Command	Function

	redirection of printer output. Example: MODE LPT1: = COM1: redirects output from the (default) parallel port to the RS–232 serial port. Normal operation can be restored by the command: MODE LPT1:
PRINT	The PRINT command sends the contents of an ASCII text file to the printer. Printing is carried out as a background operation and data is buffered in memory. The default buffer size is 512 bytes however the size of the buffer can be specified using /B: (followed by required buffer size in bytes). When the utility is first entered, the user is presented with the opportunity to redirect printing to the serial port (COM1:). A list of files (held in a queue) can also be specified. Examples; PRINT README.DOC prints the file README.DOC from the current directory; PRINT /B: 4096 HELP1.TXT HELP2.TXT HELP3.TXT establishes a print queue with the files HELP1.TXT, HELP2.TXT, and HELP3.TXT and also sets the print buffer to 4 K bytes. The files are sent to the printer in the specified sequence
RESTORE	The RESTORE command was used to replace files on the hard disk which were previously saved on floppy disk(s) using the BACKUP command. Various options are provided (including restoration of files created before or after a specified date. Examples: RESTORE C:\DEV\PROCESS.COM restores the files PROCESS.COM in the sub-directory named DEV on the hard disk partition, C. The user is prompted to insert the appropriate floppy disk (in drive A); RESTORE C:\BASIC /M restores all modified (altered or deleted) files present in the sub-directory named BASIC on the hard disk partition, C
SYS	The SYS command creates a new boot disk by copying the hidden MS-DOS system files. SYS is normally used to transfer system files to a disk which has been formatted with the /S or /B option. SYS cannot be used on a disk which has had data written to it after initial formatting
TREE	The TREE command may be used to display a complete directory listing for a given drive. The listing starts with the root directory.
XCOPY	The XCOPY utility provides a means of selectively copying files. The utility creates a copy which has the same directory structure as the original. Various options are provided:
	/A only copy files which have their archive bit set (but do not reset the archive bits);
	/D only files which have been created (or that have been changed) after the specified date;

Command	Function	
	/M	copy files which have their archive bit set but reset the archive bits (to avoid copying files unnecessarily at a later date);
	/P	prompt for confirmation of each copy;
	/S	copy files from sub-directories;
	/V	verify each copy;
	/W	prompt for disk swaps when using a single drive machine;

Example: XCOPY C:\SYSDEV*.* A:/M copy all files present in the SYSDEV sub-directory of drive C:. Files will be copied to the disk in drive A:. Only those files which have been modified (i.e. had their archive bits set) will be copied

Batch files

Batch files provide a means of avoiding the tedium of repeating a sequence of operating system commands many times over. Batch files are nothing more than straightforward ASCII text files which contain the commands which are to be executed when the name of the batch is entered. Execution of a batch file is automatic; the commands are executed just as if they had been typed in at the keyboard. Batch files may also contain the names of executable program files (i.e. those with a COM or EXE extension), in which case the specified program is executed and, provided the program makes a conventional exit to DOS upon termination, execution of the batch file will resume upon termination.

Batch file commands

MS-DOS provides a number of commands which are specifically intended for inclusion within batch files:

Command	Function
ECHO	The ECHO command may be used to control screen output during execution of a batch file. ECHO may be followed by ON or OFF or by a text string which will be displayed when the command line is executed. Examples: ECHO OFF disables the echoing (to the screen) of commands contained within the batch file; ECHO ON re-enables the echoing (to the screen) of commands contained within the batch file. (Note that there is no need to use this command at the end of a batch file as the reinstatement of screen echo of keyboard generated commands is automatic); ECHO Sorting data – please wait! displays the message: Sorting data – please wait! on the screen
FOR	FOR is used with IN and DO to implement a series of repeated commands. Examples: FOR %A IN (IN.ASM OUT.ASM MAIN.ASM) DO COPY %A LPT1: copies the files IN.ASM, OUT.ASM, and MAIN.ASM in the current directory to the

Command	*Function*
	printer; FOR %A IN (*.ASM) DO COPY %A LPT1: copies all the files having an ASM extension in the current directory to the printer. The command has the same effect as COPY *.ASM LPT1:
IF	If is used with GOTO to provide a means of branching within a batch file. GOTO must be followed by a label (which must begin with :). Example: IF NOT EXIST INPUT.DAT GOTO :EXIT transfers control to the label :EXIT if the file INPUT.DAT cannot be found in the current directory
PAUSE	The pause command suspends execution of a batch file until the user presses any key. The message: Press any key when ready ... is displayed on the screen
REM	The REM command is used to precede lines of text which will constitute remarks. Example: REM Check that the file exists before copying

Creating batch files

Batch files may be created using an ASCII text editor or a word processor (operating in ASCII mode). Alternatively, if the batch file comprises only a few lines, the file may be created using the MS-DOS COPY command

As an example, let us suppose that we wish to create a batch file which will:

1. Erase all of the files present on the disk placed in drive B.
2. Copy all of the files in drive A having a TXT extension to produce an identically named set of files on the disk placed in drive B.
3. Rename all of the files having a TXT extension in drive A so that they have a BAK extension.

The required operating system commands are thus;

ERASE B:*.*
COPY A:*.TXT B:\
RENAME A:*.TXT A:*.BAK

The following 'keystrokes' may be used to create a batch file named ARCHIVE.BAT containing the above commands:

COPY CON: ARCHIVE.BAT < ENTER >
ERASE B:*.* < ENTER >
COPY A:*.TXT B:\ < ENTER >
RENAME A:*.TXT A:*.BAK < ENTER >
< CTRL-Z > < ENTER >

If you wish to view the batch file which you have just created simply enter the command: TYPE ARCHIVE.BAT. Whenever you wish to execute the batch file simply type: ARCHIVE.

Note that, if necessary, the sequence of commands contained within a batch file may be interrupted by typing: < CTRL-C >. The system will respond by asking you to confirm that you wish to terminate the batch job. Respond with Y to terminate the batch process or N if you wish to continue with it.

Additional commands can be easily appended to an existing batch file. Assume that we wish to view the directory of the disk in drive A after running the archive batch file. We can simply append the extra commands to the batch files by entering: COPY ARCHIVE.BAT + CON:; the system displays the filename followed by the CON prompt. The extra line of text can now be entered using the following keystrokes: DIR A:\ < ENTER > and < CTRL-Z > < ENTER > .

Passing parameters

Parameters may be passed to batch files by including the % character to act as a place holder for each parameter passed. The parameters are numbered strictly in the sequence in which they appear after the name of the batch file. As an example, suppose that we have created a batch file called REBUILD, and this file requires two file specifications to be passed as parameters. Within the text of the batch file, these parameters will be represented by %1 and %2. The first file specification following the name of the batch file will be %1 and the second will be %2. Hence, if we enter the command: REBUILD PROC1.DAT PROC2.DAT < ENTER > during execution of the batch file, %1 will be replaced by PROC1.DAT whilst %2 will be replaced by PROC2.DAT.

It is also possible to implement simple testing and branching within a batch file. Labels used for branching should preferably be stated in lower case (to avoid confusion with operating systems commands) and should be preceded by a colon when they are the first (or only) statement in a line. The following example which produces a sorted list of directories illustrates these points:

```
ECHO OFF
IF EXIST %1 GOTO valid
ECHO Missing or invalid parameter
GOTO end
:valid
ECHO Index of Directories in %1
DIR %1 : FIND " < DIR > " : SORT
:end
```

The first line disables the echoing of subsequent commands contained within the batch file. The second line determines whether, or not, a valid parameter has been entered. If the parameter is invalid (or missing) the ECHO command is used to print an error message on the screen.

Disk copying

It is frequently necessary to make copies of floppy disks for backup and security purposes. The following procedure (which assumes a system fitted with a hard disk) is recommended:
1. Boot the system from the hard disk in the normal way.
2. When the system prompt (C>) appears, enter the command: SET PATH = C:\DOS (the command may be entered in either upper or lower case and should be immediately followed by the < ENTER > key). An alternative to using the SET PATH command is to make the DOS directory by entering the command: CD DOS. This step can be omitted if the DOS command utilities are present in the root directory (see page 148) of drive C.
3. Now enter the command: DISKCOPY A: A:. The system will respond with a message of the form:
    Insert SOURCE diskette in drive A:
    Press any key when ready ...
4. Now insert the distribution or master disk in drive A. Close the drive door and press any key (e.g. < SPACE >). The system will read information from the master disk and transfer the

contents of the disk to memory. At the start of this process a message of the form:

    Copying 80 tracks
    9 Sectors/Track, 2 Side(s)

will be displayed.

5. When all data has been transferred from the disk to memory, the system will prompt for insertion of the destination or target disk. The following message will appear:

    Insert TARGET diskette in drive A:
    Press any key when ready ...

The destination disk should then be inserted. This disk may be a blank (unformatted) disk or may be a disk which has been previously written to. In the latter case, the disk write protection should be removed. The drive door should then be closed and a key pressed. A blank (unformatted) disk will be formatted during the process, in which case the following message will appear:

    Formatting while copying

6. When the copying process has been completed, the user will be prompted with the following message:

    Copy another diskette (Y/N)?

Further disks may then be copied or the user may choose to exit from the DISKCOPY utility and return to the command prompt. In the latter case, the contents of the target disk may be checked by issuing the following command from the system prompt: DIR A:

7. If it is necessary to abort the copying process at any stage, the user should use the <CTRL-C> key combination (see page 138). It should also be noted that earlier versions of MS-DOS require the user to format disks before using DISKCOPY.

The MS-DOS debugger

One of the most useful tools available to the engineer and software developer within the MS-DOS environment is the debugger, DEBUG.COM. This program provides a variety of facilities including single-stepping a program to permit examination of the CPU registers and the contents of memory after execution of each instruction.

The debug command line can accept several arguments. Its syntax is as follows: DEBUG [filespec] [parm1] [parm2]; where [filespec] is the specification of the file to be loaded into memory, [parm1] and [parm 2] are optional parameters for the specified file.

As an example, the following MS-DOS command will load debug along with the file PROCESS.COM (taken from the disk in drive B) ready for debugging: DEBUG B:PROCESS.COM

When debug has been loaded, the familiar MS-DOS prompt is replaced by a hyphen (-). This indicates that DEBUG is awaiting a command from the user. Commands comprise single letter (in either upper or lower case). Delimiters are optional between commands and parameters. They must, however, be used to separate adjacent hexadecimal values.

<CTRL-BREAK> can be used to abort a DEBUG command whilst <CTRL-NUM.LOCK> can be used to pause the display (any other keystroke restarts the output). Commands may be edited using the keys available for normal MS-DOS command editing.

The following commands are available:

Command	Meaning	Function
A [addr]	Assemble	Assemble mnemonics into memory from the specified address. If no address is specified, the code will be assembled into memory from address CS: 0100. The <ENTER> key is used to terminate assembly and return to the debug prompt. Examples: A 200 starts assembly from address CS:0200; A 4E0:100 starts assembly from address 04E0:0100 (equivalent to a physical address of 04F00)
C range addr	Compare	Compare memory in the specified range with memory starting at the specified address
D [addr]	Dump	Dump (display) memory from the given starting address. If no start address is specified, the dump will commence at DS:0100. Examples: D 400 dumps memory from address DS:0400; D CS:0 dumps memory from address CS:0000
D [range]		Dump (display) memory within the specified range. Example: D DS:200 20F displays 16 bytes of memory from DS:0200 to DS:0210 inclusive
E addr [list]	Enter	Enter (edit) bytes into memory starting at the given address. If no list of data bytes is specified, byte values are displayed and may be sequentially overwritten. <SPACE> may be used to advance, and <-> may be used to reverse the memory pointer. Example: E 200, 3C, FF, 1A, FE places byte values of 3C, FF, 1A and FE into four consecutive memory locations commencing at DS:0200
F range list	Fill	Fills memory in the given range with data in the list. The list is repeated until all memory locations have been filled. Examples: F 100, 10F, FF fills 16 bytes of memory with FF commencing at address DS:0100; F 0, FFFF, AA, FF fills 65536 bytes of memory with alternate bytes of AA and FF

Command	Meaning	Function
G [= addr]	Go	Executes the code starting at the given address. If no address is specified, execution commences at address CS:IP. Example: G = 100 executes the code starting at address CS:0100.
G [= addr] [addr] [addr] ...		Executes the code starting at the given address with the specified breakpoints. Example: G = 100 104 10B executes the code starting at address CS:0100 and with breakpoints at addresses CS:0104 and CS:010B
H value value	Hexadecimal	Calculates the sum and difference of two hexadecimal values.
I port	Port input	Inputs a byte value from the specified I/O port address and displays the value. Example: I 302 inputs the byte value from I/O port address 302 and displays the value returned
L [addr]	Load	Loads the file previously specified by the Name (N) command. The file specification is held at address CS:0080. If no load address is specified, the file is loaded from address CS:0100
M range addr	Move	Moves (replicates) memory in the given range so that it is replicated starting at the specified address
N filespec	Name	Names a file to be used for a subsequent Load (L) or Write (W) command. Example: N B:PROCESS.COM names the file PROCESS.COM stored in the root directory of drive B for a subsequent load or write command
O port byte	Port output	Output a given byte value to the specified I/O port address. Example: O 303 FE outputs a byte value of FE from I/O port address 303
P [= addr] [instr]	Proceed	Executes a subroutine, interrupt, loop or string operation and resumes control at the next instruction. Execution starts at the specified address and continues for the specified number of instructions. If no address is specified, execution commences at the address given by CS:IP

Command	Meaning	Function
Q	Quit	Exits debug and returns control to the current MS-DOS shell
R [regname]	Register	Displays the contents of the specified register and allows the contents to be modified. If a name is not specified, the contents of all of the CPU registers (including flags) is displayed together with the next instruction to be executed (in hexadecimal and in mnemonic format)
S range list	Search	Search memory within the specified range for the listed data bytes. Example: S 0100 0800 20, 1B searches memory between address DS:0100 and DS:0800 for consecutive data values of 20 and 1B
T [=addr] [instr]	Trace	Traces the execution of a program from the specified address and executing the given number of instructions. If no address is specified, the execution starts at address CS:IP. If a number of instructions are not specified then only a single instruction is executed. A register dump (together with a disassembly of the next instruction to be executed) is displayed at each step. Examples: T traces the execution of the single instruction referenced by CS:IP; T=200, 4 traces the execution of four instructions commencing at address CS:0200
U [addr]	Unassemble	Unassemble (disassemble) code into mnemonic instructions starting at the specified address. If no address is specified, disassembly starts from the address given by CS:IP. Examples: U disassembles code starting at address CS:IP; U 200 disassembles code starting at address CS:0200
U [range]		Unassemble (disassemble) code into mnemonic instructions within the specified range of addresses. Example: U 200 400 disassembles the code starting at address CS:0200 and ending at address CS:0400

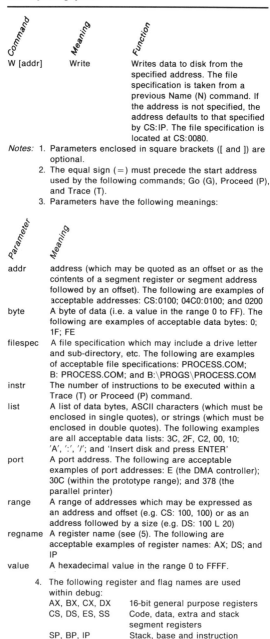

Command	Meaning	Function
W [addr]	Write	Writes data to disk from the specified address. The file specification is taken from a previous Name (N) command. If the address is not specified, the address defaults to that specified by CS:IP. The file specification is located at CS:0080.

Notes: 1. Parameters enclosed in square brackets ([and]) are optional.
2. The equal sign (=) must precede the start address used by the following commands; Go (G), Proceed (P), and Trace (T).
3. Parameters have the following meanings:

Parameter	Meaning
addr	address (which may be quoted as an offset or as the contents of a segment register or segment address followed by an offset). The following are examples of acceptable addresses: CS:0100; 04C0:0100; and 0200
byte	A byte of data (i.e. a value in the range 0 to FF). The following are examples of acceptable data bytes: 0; 1F; FE
filespec	A file specification which may include a drive letter and sub-directory, etc. The following are examples of acceptable file specifications: PROCESS.COM; B: PROCESS.COM; and B:\PROGS\PROCESS.COM
instr	The number of instructions to be executed within a Trace (T) or Proceed (P) command.
list	A list of data bytes, ASCII characters (which must be enclosed in single quotes), or strings (which must be enclosed in double quotes). The following examples are all acceptable data lists: 3C, 2F, C2, 00, 10; 'A', ':', '/'; and 'Insert disk and press ENTER'
port	A port address. The following are acceptable examples of port addresses: E (the DMA controller); 30C (within the prototype range); and 378 (the parallel printer)
range	A range of addresses which may be expressed as an address and offset (e.g. CS: 100, 100) or as an address followed by a size (e.g. DS: 100 L 20)
regname	A register name (see (5)). The following are acceptable examples of register names: AX; DS; and IP
value	A hexadecimal value in the range 0 to FFFF.

4. The following register and flag names are used within debug:

AX, BX, CX, DX	16-bit general purpose registers
CS, DS, ES, SS	Code, data, extra and stack segment registers
SP, BP, IP	Stack, base and instruction pointers

SI, DI	Source and destination index registers	
F	Flag register	

5. The following abbreviations are used to denote the state of the flags in conjunction with the Register (R) and Trace (T) commands:

Flag	Abbreviation	Meaning/status
Overflow	OV	Overflow
	NV	No overflow
Carry	CY	Carry
	NC	No carry
Zero	ZR	Zero
	NZ	Non-zero
Direction	DN	Down
	UP	Up
Interrupt	EI	Interrupts enabled
	DI	Interrupts disabled
Parity	PE	Parity even
	PO	Parity odd
Sign	NG	Negative
	PL	Positive
Auxiliary carry	AC	
	NC	

6. All numerical values within Debug are in hexadecimal.

Unix

Unix is a multi-user, multi-tasking operating system which was developed by the Computing Research Group at the Bell Laboratories in New Jersey. Unix was originated on a PDP-11 but is now available for the VAX as well as a number of high performance microcomputers.

Unix has now become synonymous with the C programming language, which has spread from what was essentially a research environment into the wider area of super-microcomputers. In this area it seems set to gain a large following among software developers.

Compared with many of its minicomputer operating system predecessors, Unix is a relatively small operating system. This, however, should not imply that it is in any way lacking in power.

Unix comprises the following main elements:

(a) the 'kernel', which is responsible for management of the resources of the system, including disk drives, printers, terminals, etc.;

(b) the 'file system', which is responsible for file management and the organization of all data storage;

(c) the 'shell' which acts as a bridge between the user and the remainder of the system.

A number of licensed versions of Unix have recently become available, most popular of which is Microsoft's operating system, Xenix.

Unix commands

Directory and file manipulation utilities

cat	concatenate and print files
cp	copy files
ln	create a link to a file
mkdir	make a new directory
mv	move or rename files and directories
rm	remove a file
rmdir	remove a directory
ls	lists contents of directory and information on files
pwd	print working directory
file	determine file type
pg	display the contents of a file a page at a time
cmp	compare two files
cd	change directory from the current one to your home directory
	if a directory name is included, it changes from the current directory to the directory specified
tail	read the last part of a file
cut	cut out selected fields of a file
grep	find patterns in a file
wc	counting things in a file
sort	sort files
split	split a file into pieces
pack	compress files
unpack	expand files
chmod	change the permission modes for files and directories
chown	change of owner of file
chgrp	change group of file

Communications utilities

mail	send or receive electronic mail
news	read news items
write	send messages
mesg	permit or deny messages

Help utilities

assist	assistance using operating system commands
assist assistwalk	brief introduction to assist
assist unixwalk	brief introduction to the Unix system
assist viwalk	brief introduction to Vi editor
help	on line help facility
man	displays the specified reference manual on the screen
readme	information on software/hardware, notes for users

Printing utilities

pr	formats and prints the contents of a file
lp	print the contents of a file on a line printer
lpstat	print LP status information
cancel	cancels line printer request

Editing utilities

sed	stream editor
ed	line editor
ex	line editor
vi	visual editor

User environment utilities

passwd	change password
env	list of environment/shell variables
export	put variable values in your environment
id	print user ID and group ID
info	displays your accounting record

Terminal utilities

stty	set the options for a terminal
tabs	set tabs on a terminal
tty	get the name of the terminal
tput	initialize a terminal

General utilities

banner	make posters
cal	print calendar
date	print current date and time
echo	echo arguments on your screen
kill	terminate a process
ps	report process status
who	who is on the system
nohup	run a command immune to hangups and quits

Programming utilities

svsp	Pascal compiler
cc	C compiler
awk	a pattern matching language and report generator
as	assembler
sh	shell command programming language

Software tools

Items of utility software which are available for most microcomputer systems include the following:

Assemblers

An assembler is used to generate machine code (object code) from assembly language source text (source code). The assembler normally needs to read the source text twice in order to accomplish his task. It is then known as a 'two-pass assembler'.

On the first pass, the assembler generates a symbol table which s stored in RAM. This table is used to equate each symbolic address (label) with an absolute address (which is usually not the address at which the program is finally loaded for execution). On he second pass, the assembler generates the machine code (object ode) for each instruction.

Various assembler directives can be included within the source code. These pseudo-mnemonics are not translated into object code but are recognized by the assembler during the assembly process. Their purpose is to allow the user to modify, in some way, the object code produced.

The following are some typical Z80 assembler directives:

DEFB exp.	define-byte (the expression or expressions which follow are to be loaded as a byte or bytes into the address held in the location counter; e.g. DEFB 42,64,42)
DEFM string	define-message (loads memory with ASCII values corresponding to a given character string; e.g. DEFM 'Press <ENTER>')
DEFS pppp	define-storage (increases the value held in the location counter by pppp, thus reserving a block of memory of size pppp for storage; e.g. DEFS 100)
DEFW exp.	define-word (as for define-byte but in each case two bytes are loaded and the location counter advances by two)
END	end (marks the end of the code to be assembled)
label EQU exp.	equate (sets the value of the label to be that of the expression; e.g. CR EQU 0DH)
ORG pppp	origin (sets the location counter to pppp and defines the start address in memory at which the following program segment will be resident; e.g. ORG 8000H)

Editors

An editor allows the user to create a text file in a form which may be easily modified. Editors are available in two forms: simple line editors (which only permit operations on a single line of text at a time), and full-screen editors (which permit full cursor control over the whole screen). The action of an editor is similar to that of a simple ASCII word processor. Most assemblers and high level language interpreters will accept pure ASCII text input; thus an editor can be used to create text for programs written in a variety of languages.

Interpreters

An interpreter translates a program written in a high level language (and normally presented in the form of an ASCII text file) into machine executable code. An important feature of an interpreter is that it acts on each statement of source text at a time, i.e. it reads each line, translates it into machine code, and then executes it immediately before fetching the next line of source text. (Where multi-statement lines are permitted each individual statement is interpreted separately.) It should be obvious from this that the interpreter must be used every time the program is run.

The advantage of using an interpreter is that flaws in the source text can be discovered immediately. A statement containing an obvious error will not be executed; the program will simply be halted, an appropriate error message generated, and the user prompted for a correction. The obvious disadvantage of this technique is that, since the interpreter has to act on each line, the program executes comparatively slowly (typically, at one-tenth of the speed when using a compiler). This may, or may not, be significant for a particular application.

Flowchart for an interpreter

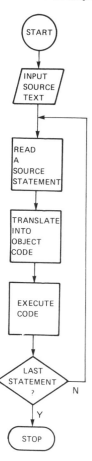

Compilers

A compiler can be used to generate a machine code program from source text written in a high level language. The process of compilation is carried out as a separate operation before the program is finally loaded in executable form.

Once the program has been fully debugged, the final compilation process is executed once only. Thereafter, the program is saved, loaded, and run as machine code. Compiled programs therefore run very much faster than those that need the services of an interpreter.

The obvious disadvantage of using a compiler is that, when an error occurs or a change is to be made to the program, the source code must be altered and the entire compilation process (including linking and loading) must be repeated. This tedious process can, to some extent, be shortened with the aid of a batch processing system, in which a single command line can be used to invoke the compiler, linker and loader.

Flowchart for a compiler

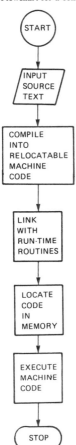

Linkers and loaders

After compilation, a program usually needs to be linked with the necessary I/O or mathematical routines contained in a 'run-time library'. The necessary routines are then simply added to the machine code. This process is achieved with the aid of a linker (sometimes also called a 'binder').

During compilation and assembly, symbolic labels are normally used to represent addresses. Programs can thus be made relocatable (i.e. they can be loaded anywhere in unreserved RAM). The final stage in the process involves replacing all symbolic ddresses with the absolute addresses to be used for final xecution. This is achieved with the aid of a loader.

Debuggers

Debuggers provide a means of testing programs interactively during run-time. Common features of debuggers include:

(a) displaying the contents of a given block of memory in hexadecimal or ASCII
(b) loading a program ready for execution
(c) filling a given block of memory with a given data value
(d) commencing execution with optional breakpoints
(e) performing hexadecimal arithmetic
(f) setting up a file control block and command tail
(g) disassembling a block of memory
(h) moving a block of memory from one location to another
(i) reading a disk file into memory
(j) tracing or single-stepping program execution
(k) showing memory layout of a disk file read
(l) writing the contents of a given block of memory to disk
(n) examining and modifying the CPU registers.

A typical 68000-based microcomputer development system would be provided with the following software tools:

AR68.PRG	archive utility (creates library modules that can be linked with LINK68 or LO68)
AS68.PRG	68000 assembler
CP68.PRG	
CO68.PRG	three-pass C compiler
C168.PRG	
LINK68.PRG	linker (combines assembled or compiled object modules with appropriate modules taken from the run-time library)
LO68.PRG	another linker
NM68.PRG	symbol table print utility
RELMOD.PRG	loader (produces a program file executable from the GEM operating system)
SID68.PRG	symbolic interactive debugger
SIZE68.PRG	program segment size utility

Note: The .PRG filename extension merely signifies a program file which can be executed directly from the command line interpreter.

Languages

High and low level languages

The choice of programming language required to solve any particular problem depends upon a number of factors, not least of which is the availability of a compiler or interpreter for the machine in question. Happily, a range of languages is available to most modern minicomputers and microcomputers. It is then necessary to make a choice based on such factors as compactness, speed of execution, ease of use, portability, ease of maintenance, etc.

It is fashionable to classify programming languages as either 'low level' or 'high level'. A better distinction would be made between those languages which are 'procedure oriented' and those which are 'machine oriented'.

The lowest level of all programming languages is machine code; i.e. the actual binary coded values that appear in the computer's program memory. The need to code programs in binary is thankfully a thing of the past; indeed, with today's powerful processors it represents a quite impossible task! The nearest approach to using machine code is that of writing programs in assembly language. This task involves using the processor's instruction set presented in mnemonic form.

Unlike assembly language, each statement contained within a program written in a high level language performs some recognizable function. Programs written in a high level language are thus eminently readable. The same cannot be said of assembly language programs unless, of course, they are regularly interspersed with comments.

One statement written in a high level language usually corresponds to many assembly language instructions. The source code for an assembly language program can thus be extremely lengthy. When assembled, however, this code will generally execut many times faster than an interpreted high level language program

Structured programming

Structured programs are both easier to understand and simpler to maintain than their unstructured counterparts. Most good programming languages contain a variety of logical structures which assist in this respect.

The essential features of structured programs are:

(a) The overall program flow should be sequential. Repeated jumps backwards and forwards within the code should be avoided
(b) Sections of code that are repeatedly executed should be used iteratively; i.e. they should be written out once only and contained within a loop
(c) All transfer of program control should be explicit, using such logical constructs as IF-THEN-ELSE, DO-WHILE, etc.

Assembly language

The most closely related language to that of the machine itself is assembly language. Assembly language programs use symbolic addresses (instead of actual memory locations) and mnemonic operational codes (opcodes). The assembly language program is translated into executable machine code by means of an assembler (see separate section).

The principal.disadvantage of assembly language is that programs are not readily transportable from one processor family to another. Furthermore, to be adept with assembly language programs the programmer must have an intimate knowledge of th hardware configuration of a system.

The advantage of assembly language programming is that code is extremely efficient; i.e. it is both fast in execution and very compact. Assembly language programs do not need the services of a compiler or interpreter and thus a minimum of additional software (an assembler and debugger) is required in order to produce a functional program. Indeed, in the case of 8-bit processors, short lengths of code may even be 'hand-assembled'; i.e. the machine code corresponding to a particular assembly language instruction is found by reference to the published instruction set and then simply entered directly into memory using a hexadecimal loader.

Sample assembly language program

```
;  *   SAMPLE ASSEMBLY LANGUAGE PROGRAM   *
;
;   PROGRAM DISPLAYS FULL CHARACTER
;   AND GRAPHIC SET ON THE VDU SCREEN
;
;   @ = SYSTEM CALLABLE ROUTINE
;   $ = POINTER TO STORAGE LOCATION
;
;   Z80 CODE
;
            ORG      0A000H    ;RELOCATABLE
$VIDMEM  EQU      3C00H
@DOS     EQU      5500H
            LD       D,9FH
            LD       E,21H
MAIN     LD       HL,$VIDMEM
            LD       BC,400H
LOOP1    LD       (HL),E
            INC      HL
            DEC      BC
            LD       A,B
            OR       C
            JR       NZ,LOOP1
            INC      E
            LD       HL,0FFFFH
LOOP2    DEC      HL
            LD       A,H
            OR       L
            JR       NZ,LOOP2
            DEC      D
            JR       NZ,MAIN
            JP       @DOS
            END
```

APL

APL stands for A Programming Language. For some time APL was used only within IBM and then only on mainframe machines. The reason for this is that the APL interpreter is not particularly compact and, furthermore, it requires a large workspace to run effectively. This fact alone has mitigated against its introduction among the early generations of 8-bit microcomputers. Now, with 16- and 32-bit processors and larger memories, 'micro-APL' is becoming increasingly attractive.

APL was first developed as a consistent notation for mathematics and became available as a programming language in the mid-sixties. APL has some limitations as a language for job processing but does contain an extensive set of operators and data structures. It is thus extremely useful as an investigative tool for use in research and in higher education. The standard APL is VS-APL, although a number of other variants are becoming available. IBM-APL and APL-PLUS are both currently available for use on the IBM PC.

BASIC

BASIC (Beginners All Purpose Symbolic Instruction Code) was developed at Dartmouth College by John Kemeny and Thomas Kurtz. The principal aim of its creators was to produce a language that the non-programmer would find both acceptable and usable.

BASIC statements therefore tend to use simple English words rather than abstract symbols.

BASIC is undoubtedly today's most popular language for home computing and secondary/tertiary education. In its more powerful forms it is capable of handling small business applications with reasonable efficiency.

BASIC exists in an almost infinite number of forms, but the one most widely used is that produced by Microsoft (M-BASIC). Other dialects of BASIC include BBC BASIC, C-BASIC (pseudo-compiled BASIC), Sinclair BASIC and X-BASIC (well suited to multi-user systems).

```
10      REM *** Sample BASIC Program ***
20      ERASE x()
30      INPUT "How many values ";r$
40      LET n=VAL(r$)
50      DIM x(n)
60      FOR i=1 TO n
70      INPUT "Value ";r$
80      LET x(i)=VAL(r$)
90      NEXT i
100     GOSUB 1000
110     GOSUB 2000
120     INPUT "Run again (y/n) ";r$
130     IF r$="n" OR r$="N" THEN END
140     GOTO 10
1000    REM *** Determine Average ***
1010    LET t=0
1020    FOR i=1 TO n
1030    LET t=t+x(i)
1040    NEXT t
1050    PRINT "Average of ";n;" values is ";
1060    RETURN
2000    REM *** Save Array ***
2010    INPUT "Filename for saving ";r$
2020    LET f$=LEFT$(r$,8)
2030    OPEN "O",1,f$
2040    WRITE £1,n
2050    FOR i=1 TO n
2060    WRITE £1,x(i)
2070    NEXT i
2080    CLOSE £1
2090    RETURN
```

BASIC keywords

Keyword	Purpose
LIST	Displays all program lines
LIST n	Displays line number n only
LIST −n	Displays line numbers up to n
LIST n−	Displays line numbers from n onwards
LIST n−m	Displays lines n to m
RUN	Executes program
RUN n	Executes program starting from line n

eyword	Purpose
EM	Non-executable remark or comment
ET	Keyword to prefix an assignment statement, but normally optional
N(X)	Calculates the sine of X X assumed in radians
OS(X)	Calculates the cosine of X X assumed in radians
AN(X)	Calculates tangent of X X assumed in radians
TN(X)	Calculates the arctangent of X. (The angle whose tangent is X.) X assumed in radians
T(X)	Truncates the floating-point number of X to the nearest lower integer
BS(X)	Converts X to its absolute value. (If X is negative it changes it to positive. If positive it leaves it alone.)
XP(X)	Calculates e^x. The symbol e is the base of Naperian logs and is approx 2.718
OG(X)	Calculates the logarithm of X to the base e
QR(X)	Calculates the square root of X. X MUST BE POSITIVE
IM A(n)	Reserve n memory locations for the subscripted array A
IM A(n,m)	Reserves n and m memory locations for the two-dimensional array A
RINT X	Prints on the screen, starting on a new line at left-hand edge, the value of X
RINT X;Y	Prints value of X and Y on same line with single space between them
RINT X,Y	Prints value of X in first zone and value of Y in second zone on the same line
RINT X;	Prints value of X and inhibits carriage return and line feed. This ensures that next print position is on the same line.
RINT''	Prints the literal characters enclosed within the quotes but not the quotes themselves
RINT A$	Prints the contents of the string variable A$
RINT	Prints a blank line
AB(N)	Used within a PRINT statement; it ensures the following variable is printed starting at column N
PC(N)	Leaves N spaces before printing the following variable
ET X	Places the single keyed character into the variable X. (Some BASICs wait, others do not wait, for the key to be pressed)
JPUT X	Wait until data has been entered at the keyboard and the RETURN key is pressed
JPUT'' '';X	Waits, displays the prompt message within the quotes until data is entered and RETURN key is pressed
OTO n	Go to line number n
' THEN	Used to provide alternative action/s. Only if the condition is true is the action/s after THEN executed

Keyword	Purpose
AND	Used to enforce both conditions in an IF THEN statement
OR	Used to allow either condition in an IF THEN statement
ON N GOTO	Goes to the Nth line number in the series of line numbers which follow the GOTO part
FOR NEXT	The FOR part is used at the head of the loop. The NEXT is the demarcation for the bottom of the loop. The FOR structure is: FOR N = S TO F STEP I
	N is the loop variable which starts at S, increases in increments of I until it reaches F. The NEXT part in some BASICs must be followed by the loop variable
GOSUB n	Go to subroutine situated at line n. It 'calls' the subroutine
RETURN	This must terminate all subroutines. It restores control back to the next statement after the call
ON GOSUB	Similar to ON GOTO but the line numbers refer to the start of subroutines
DATA	Part of the READ/DATA structure. DATA is followed by data items each separated by a comma
READ X	Reads into the numeric variable X the next sequential data item
READ X,Y,Z	Reads into X,Y and Z the three data items
READ A(N)	Reads into the subscripted array A(N) the next sequential data item
READ A$,B$	Reads into the strings
RESTORE	Once DATA items have been READ once they cannot be READ again unless RESTORE is used to reset the data pointer
CLR	Clears all numeric variables to zero and string variables to 'null string'
LEN (A$)	Calculates the length of the string (how many characters it contains, including spaces)
LEFT$(A$,n)	Takes the left-hand n characters of A$
CHR$(N)	Finds the character having the ASCII code N
RIGHT$(A$,n)	Takes the right-hand n characters of A$
MID$(A$,n,m)	Takes m characters, starting from the nth character
VAL(A$)	Finds the numeric value of the string up to the first non-numeric character. If the first character is non-numeric, the value is zero
STR$(X)	Converts the numeric variable X into string form
ASC("C")	Finds the ASCII code of the character in quotes
ASC("FGH")	Finds the ASCII code of the first character of the string
POKE n,m	Store the number m in the decimal machine address n
PEEK(n)	Finds the contents of the machine address n
RND(n)	Produces a random number. Meaning of n varies in different BASICs
DEF FN F(X)	The user-defined function. F is function name

Keyword	Purpose
	and X is dummy variable used only to define the function
N F(T)	Calls the previously defined function named F. T is the argument

C

The C language was developed at the Bell Laboratories in 1972 by Dennis Ritchie. C is based on a language called B, which was itself a development of BCPL (Basic Combined Programming Language).

C uses a relatively small amount of processor-dependent code and is thus highly flexible and portable. The commonly accepted standard for C language programming is the Portable C Compiler (PCC), written by Stephen Johnson. Many versions of Unix use PCC, including the Zilog, Onyx, Xenix, Berkeley Unix and Uniq systems. The Lattice C Compiler is currently the most popular C compiler for use with the IBM PC.

CP/M-68K can run most applications written in C for the Unix operating system, except programs that use the fork/exec multi-tasking primitives or read Unix file structures.

The accepted reference book for C programming is *The C Programming Language* by Brian Kernighan and Dennis Ritchie (Prentice-Hall).

SAMPLE C PROGRAM

```c
/*    SAMPLE C PROGRAM    */

#include "stdio.h"
#include "myfile.h"

#define QUIT 'Q'

char c;

main()
{
    printf("Press <Q> to quit\n");
    while ((c=getc(stdin))!=QUIT)
    if (isalnum(c))
        decide();
    pause();
    verify();
}

decide()
{
    printf("You pressed %c\n",c);
    if (isdigit (c))
        printf("Its a number!\n");
    else
        printf("Its not a number!\n");
}
```

```
verify()
{
     printf("Are you sure (Y/N)?\n");
     while ((c=getc(stdin))!=RETURN)
     switch(c){
     case 'Y':
          exit(0);
     case 'N':
          main();
     default:
          verify;
          break;
     }
}
```

COBOL

COBOL is an acronym for Common Business Oriented Language.
COBOL emanated from the Pentagon and is ideally suited to data
management. Despite its enormous popularity as an efficient
commercial language for use on mainframe and minicomputer
installations, COBOL has not made a great impact on the
microcomputing world. Despite this, a number of 'micro-COBOLs'
have appeared. These include COBOL-80, CIS-COBOL and RM/
COBOL.

FORTH

FORTH was invented by Charles Moore as a means of controlling
an astronomical telescope at the Kitt Peak Observatory. It is fair
to say that no other high level language is as comfortable or
versatile in real-time control applications as FORTH. The breadth
and scope of its applications are enormous, from controlling a
washing machine to managing a canning plant.
     A variety of FORTHs exist but most of these conform to the
Forth Interest Group 'FIG-FORTH' standard.
     FORTH makes extensive use of a resident dictionary and
parameter stack. The user is able to define new words and add
these to the dictionary. FORTH is thus extensible, and this feature
makes it extremely attractive because it allows the user to develop
his own application dictionary.
     The accepted reference book for the FORTH language is
Starting FORTH by Leo Brodie (Prentice-Hall).

Sample FORTH program

```
( * SAMPLE FORTH PROGRAM * )
( STEPPER MOTOR DRIVEN BY  )
( Z80 PIO LINES PAO TO PA2 )
31 CONSTANT DATA
93 CONSTANT CONTROL
: INIT 15 CONTROL OUTP ;
: PUT DATA OUTP ;
: CWSTEP 248 252 PUT PUT ;
: ACWSTEP 250 254 PUT PUT ;
: DELAY 200 0 DO LOOP ;
: CWREV 48 0 DO CWSTEP DELAY LOOP ;
: ACWREV 48 0 DO ACWSTEP DELAY LOOP ;
```

```
: CYCLE CWREV ACWREV ;

: PROCESS INIT 10 0 DO CYCLE LOOP ;
```

FORTRAN

FORTRAN is an abbreviation of FORmula TRANslation and has been widely used in science and engineering for more than twenty years. FORTRAN was developed in the 1950s by IBM and since then has been largely restricted to mainframe and minicomputers.

Various versions of FORTRAN are in common use, including FORTRAN IV and, more recently, FORTRAN 77. FORTRAN-80 is available as a microcomputer implementation of the language. This complies with the ANSI standard but does not permit double precision and complex data types. Version 2.00 of the IBM PC FORTRAN compiler conforms to the FORTRAN 77 standard.

LOGO

LOGO was invented by Seymour Papert and reflects the philosophy of the Swiss educationalist, Jean Piaget. LOGO is a graphics-oriented language (famous for its 'turtle') which is eminently suited to providing primary and secondary school children with a meaningful 'hands-on' experience of programming.

It is not surprising, therefore, that LOGO programming has been restricted almost exclusively to the educational world. This, however, belies the power of the language, which bears more than a passing resemblance to FORTH.

```
TO LOGO_DEMO
CLEARSCREEN
SHOWTURTLE
PENUP
MAKE "SIDE 200
MAKE "ANGLE 118
MAKE "INTERVAL 2
SETPOS [-100 0]
PENDOWN
RIGHT 135
LABEL "BEGIN
FORWARD :SIDE
LEFT :ANGLE
MAKE "SIDE :SIDE - :INTERVAL
FORWARD :SIDE
LEFT :ANGLE
MAKE "SIDE :SIDE - :INTERVAL
FORWARD :SIDE
LEFT :ANGLE
IF (:SIDE >= 0) [GO "BEGIN]
HIDETURTLE
END
```

Attributes and applications of ten common languages

Attributes

Language	Compactness	Ease of use	Ease of maintenance	Speed of execution
APL	★	★★★	★★★	★★★
ASSEMBLY LANGUAGE	★★★★	★	★	★★★★
BASIC	★	★★★★	★★★	★
C	★★★	★★	★★★★	★★★★
COBOL	★★★	★★★	★★★	★★★
FORTH	★★★★	★★★	★★★★	★★★★
FORTRAN	★★	★★	★★★	★★★
LOGO	★★	★★★★	★★★★	★★
PASCAL	★★	★★★★	★★★★	★★★
PL/M	★★★★	★★	★★★★	★★★★

★★★★ = Excellent/ideally suited
★★★ = Good/well suited
★★   = Poor/dubious choice
★   = Very poor/generally unsuitable

PASCAL

PASCAL was developed by Nicholas Wirth in the early 1970s. He named his language after the French mathematician Blaise Pascal.

The characteristics of PASCAL make it ideal for producing well-structured programs which can be both easily extended and debugged. PASCAL is thus well liked among educationalists and so must now be considered as a worthy contender to BASIC for teaching purposes. PASCAL compiles efficiently and runs several times faster than a comparable program written in FORTRAN or BASIC.

Various versions of PASCAL are currently available for most popular computer systems. Many of these (including PRO-PASCAL) conform to the ANSI/ISO standard with one notable exception, UCSD-PASCAL. This version of the language is highly portable and exhibits considerable machine independence over a wide range of 8- and 16-bit microcomputers.

```
{ *** SAMPLE PASCAL PROGRAM   *** }
PROGRAM average(input, output);
CONST
  flag = 0;
VAR
  number, total : REAL;
  count : INTEGER;
BEGIN
  total := 0.0;
  count := 0;
  WRITELN('Enter 0 to terminate input');
  READLN(number);
  WHILE number<>flag DO
  BEGIN
    total := total+number;
    count := count+1;
    READLN(number);
  END;
```

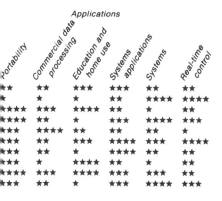

Applications

	Portability	Commercial data processing	Education and home use	Systems applications	Systems	Real-time control
	★★	★★	★★★	★★★	★★	★★
	★	★	★	★★	★★★★	★★★★
	★★★★	★★★	★★★★	★★	★	★★
	★★★★	★★	★	★★★	★★★★	★★★
	★★	★★★★	★★	★★	★★	★
	★★★	★★	★★★	★★★★	★★★	★★★★
	★★	★	★	★★★★	★★	★★
	★★	★★★★	★★	★	★★	★★
	★★★★	★★★	★★★★	★★★	★★★	★★
	★★	★★	★	★★★	★★★★	★★★

```
WRITELN('Average = ',total/count);
END.
```

PL/M

PL/M was devised by Intel in order to facilitate systems software development for its 8-bit microprocessor families. PL/M is itself based on PL/1 (a language which shares some of the features of FORTRAN and COBOL).

PL/M is a block-structured language that is ideally suited to producing modular code. Various PL/M implementations include PL/M-80 (the original 8080-based language) and PL/M-86 (for 8086 family devices). Other manufacturers have produced their own equivalents/alternatives to PL/M, including Motorola (MPL) and Zilog (PLZ).

Video display processing

A typical bit-mapped colour graphics display employs a number of logical memory planes each having a capacity equal to the total number of pixels within the display area.

The display area is given by the number of pixels which appear on the face of the CRT:

Display area $= V \times H$ (pixels)

where V is the number of display area pixels in the vertical direction, and H is the number of display area pixels in the horizontal direction.

Each pixel appearing within the display area is represented by b bits, where b is the number of logical memory planes. Thus, if b planes are provided, the total capacity of reserved video memory is given by:

Total memory required $= V \times h \times n \times b$ (bits) where h is the number of adjoining n-bit segments corresponding to a line of H pixels ($h = H/n$), and b is the number of logical bit planes.

h memory accesses are required per display line and each access loads b n-bit shift registers.

A simple eight-colour system can be realized using three memory planes (red, green and blue) with appropriate signals clocked out of three shift registers. In more sophisticated systems the shifted output (of four or more planes) is used as an index to a colour 'look-up' palette. The 'looked-up' value is then supplied to three digital to analogue converters which generate the final analogue RGB outputs.

Example 1: A high resolution display based upon the THOMSON-EFCIS EF9365 graphic display processor

$V = H = 512$ pixels
$h = 64$ (i.e. 64 8-bit words per line)
$n = 8$ bits
$b = 3$ (i.e. red, green, and blue memory planes providing 8 colours)

The total video display memory for such a system will be:

$512 \times 64 \times 8 \times 3 = 786\,432$ bits
$\qquad\qquad\qquad\quad\; = \;\; 98\,304$ bytes.

Example 2: Low resolution colour display option employed with the ATARI ST range of microcomputers

$V = 200$ pixels
$H = 320$ pixels
$h = 20$ (i.e. 20 16-bit words per line)
$n = 16$ bits
$b = 4$ (providing 16 colours)

The total video display memory for this system is:

$200 \times 20 \times 16 \times 4 = \;\; 256\,000$ bits
$\qquad\qquad\qquad\qquad\;\; = \;\; 32\,000$ bytes.

Logical organization of video memory

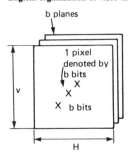

Video display processing (based on EF9365)

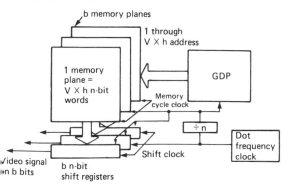

Video resolution

Terms such as 'high', 'medium' and 'standard' are often used to describe the resolution of video monitors. These terms are, however, somewhat misleading and it is advisable to refer to the actual pixel count wherever possible. A further point to note is that the display area produced by a microcomputer is somewhat smaller than the full-face area of the CRT. This imposes a further restriction on the suitability of a particular monitor.

In terms of the total number of pixels ($H \times V$), the following general standards apply:

High resolution   > 450 000 pixels
Medium resolution   300 000 to 450 000 pixels
Low (standard) resolution < 300 000 pixels

Typical high resolution video display

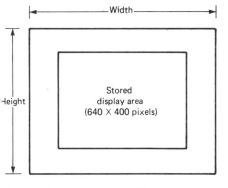

(Aspect ratio = Width/Height = 4/3)

Typical video display ASCII character set (based on a 5 × 8 matrix)

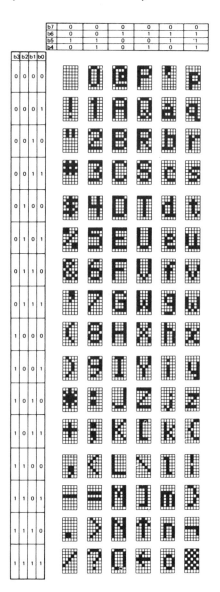

Typical video standards

	UK	USA
Lines per field	312	260
Lines per frame	312	260
Fields per frame	1	1
Line period	64.1025 μs	64.1025 μs
Line frequency	15.600 kHz	15.600 kHz
Frame period	20 ms	16.666 ms
Frame frequency	50 Hz	60 Hz
Field period	20 ms	16.666 ms
Field frequency	50 Hz	60 Hz
INTERLACED		
Lines per field	312.5	262.5
Lines per frame	625	512
Fields per frame	2	2
Line period	64 μs	63.492 μs
Line frequency	15.625 kHz	15.750 kHz
Frame period	40 ms	33.333 ms
Frame frequency	25 Hz	30 Hz
Field period	20 ms	16.666 ms
Field frequency	50 Hz	60 Hz

Non-interlaced scanning

Start of field

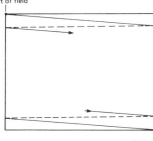

End of field

Interlaced scanning

Start of odd numbered fields   Start of even numbered fields

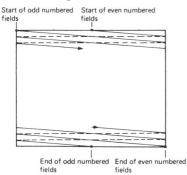

End of odd numbered fields   End of even numbered fields

Typical video waveforms

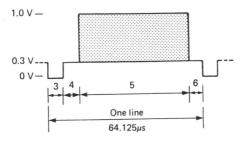

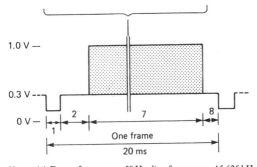

Notes: (a) Frame frequency = 50 Hz, line frequency = 15.625 kHz
     (b) Line sync. pulses not shown on frame waveform
     (c) 1 = frame/vertical sync. pulse
       2 = frame/vertical blanking period
       3 = line/horizontal sync. pulse
       4 = line/horizontal blanking period
       5 = line/horizontal scan/display period
       6 = line/horizontal flyback period
       7 = frame/vertical scan/display period
       8 = frame/vertical flyback period
     (d) Video lines are normally terminated with an impedance
       of 75 ohms

Screen colours and TTL RGB video signals

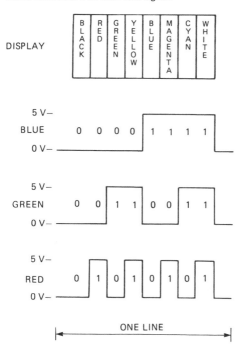

Colour mixing chart

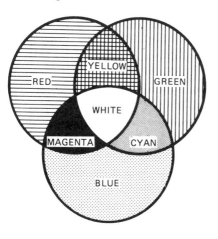

SCART connector pin connections

Shield — 21
Composite video output — 19
GND (composite video out) — 17
Red input — 15
GND (red input) — 13
Green input — 11
GND (green input) — 9
Blue input — 7
GND (blue input) — 5
L. audio output — 3
R. audio output — 1

20 — Composite video/sync.
18 — GND (fast video blanking)
16 — Fast video blanking
14 — GND (data bus)
12 — Data bus
10 — Data bus
8 — Source switching
6 — L. audio input
4 — GND (audio)
2 — R. audio input

(Pin view of chassis mounting female connector)

Bus systems

The word 'bus' is a contraction of 'omnibus' which itself is a latin word which simply means 'to all'. This aptly and succinctly describes the function of a bus, i.e. the linking of components within a complex system by means of a common highway. Not only does such an arrangement minimize the total number of connecting paths but it also prevents duplication by allowing intelligent devices shared access to ancillary sub-systems (such as memories and I/O cards).

A backplane bus system generally comprises of a number of identical sized cards mounted in a frame and linked together at the rear of the card frame by tracks on a printed wiring board mounted at right angles to the cards. This form of bus is used to link together the sub-system components (each comprising of a PCB card and a number of VLSI devices) within a more complex system. Such a system may incorporate several microprocessors (each with its own support devices and local bus system) or may just involve a single microprocessor (again with support devices and its own local bus) operating in conjunction with a number of less intelligent supporting cards.

Backplane bus systems are inherently flexible and present the designer with a huge range of options for optimizing performance without compromising system compatability. The modular nature of the bus allows a large number of permutations and a system can be readily expanded to cope with changing requirements and new demands. Modularity also allows cards to be exchanged when faults develop or interchanged between racks for testing. The end-user is thus able to minimize system down-time and need not be concerned with the board level servicing as cards can be returned to manufacturers or service agencies whilst the system remains fully operational.

At the conceptual level, the functional elements of a bus systems can be divided into 'bus masters' (intelligent controlling devices which can generate bus commands), 'bus slaves' (devices which generally exhibit less intelligence and cannot themselves generate bus commands), and 'intelligent slaves' (these are slaves which have their own intelligent controlling device but which do not themselves have the capacity to place commands on the bus).

The ability to support more than one master is clearly a desirable facility and one which more fully exploits the potential of a bus system. Such an arrangement is known as a 'multiprocessor system'. Whilst several bus masters may be connected in a bus configuration it should be clear that ONLY ONE can command the bus at any time. The resources offered by the slaves must be shared between several bus masters.

In systems which support more than one potential bus master, a system of 'bus arbitration' must be employed to eliminate possible contentions for the control of the bus. Several techniques are used to establish bus priority and these generally fall into two classes: 'serial' and 'parallel'.

In a serially arbitrated system, bus access is granted by a priority determined by the physical slot location. Each master present notifies the next lower priority master when it needs to gain access to the bus. It also monitors the bus request status of the next higher-priority master. The masters thus pass bus requests along from one to the next in a daisy-chain fashion.

In a parallel arbitrated system, external hardware is used to establish the priority of each bus master. Both systems have their advantages and disadvantages and some bus standards permit the use of both techniques.

Before introducing some of the most popular bus standards, it is worthwhile summarizing some of the most desirable characteristics of a bus system. These features are not presented in any particular order and their relative importance will, of course, vary according to the application that one has in mind.

In general, a bus system should:

(a) be processor and manufacturer independent
(b) allow the use of multiple masters
(c) permit asynchronous operation
(d) employ simple non-multiplexed data transfer protocol
(e) use a simple low-cost backplane
(f) maintain constant impedance of signal tracks within the backplane
(g) permit as high a bus data rate as possible (thus minimizing processing delays)
(h) allow as wide an addressing range as possible (both in relation to memory and I/O space)
(i) support as wide a range of processors as possible (including 8, 16 and 32-bit types)
(j) use a reliable connector (preferably an indirect type)
(k) use standard card sizes (e.g. single or double Eurocard)
(l) require no 'off-bus' connections or links between bus cards
(m) incorporate some means for signalling bus errors

S-100 bus

The S-100 bus was developed by MITS for use in their Altair 8080-based microcomputer system. The system used a number of printed circuit card modules connected into a card frame chassis by means of a double-sided 50-way PCB edge connector. The S-100 bus quickly became the *de facto* standard for the early 8080-based modular microcomputer systems.

The S-100 bus was later refined so that a number of incompatibility problems were reduced (if not eliminated altogether) and the revised standard appears under IEEE-696.

The following points are worthy of note:

(a) The various supply rails are unregulated and thus on-board regulators are required.

(b) There is a risk of cross-talk between some adjacent bus lines on the backplane. For this reason, and to reduce propagation delays in the backplane, the electrical length of the backplane must be reasonably short.

(c) Care must be taken, when inserting and removing cards, to prevent inadvertent shorting of supply rails and signal lines. (In any event this task should *always* be performed with the power off and the reservoir capacitors in a fully discharged state.)

(d) Data lines are unidirectional (rather than bidirectional). Thus two sets of eight data lines ('data in' and 'data out') are provided. If necessary, these two sets of lines can be combined to provide a bidirectional data bus using an 8-bit bidirectional bus transceiver.

(e) The revised S-100 standard (IEEE-696) makes provision for 16-bit processors by extending the address bus from 16 to 24 bits and by ganging the 8-bit data-in and data-out buses into a 16-bit bidirectional bus. Additional handshake lines are included in order to permit intermixing of 8 and 16-bit memory cards.

(f) The data rate of any signal on the bus should not exceed 6 MHz.

(g) The overall structure of the bus is:
  (i)   16 data lines
  (ii)   16 (or 24) address lines
  (iii)   8 status lines
  (iv)   19 control lines (5 output, 6 input and 8 DMA)
  (v)   8 vectored interrupt lines
  (vi)   20 utility bus lines
  (vii)   5 power lines.

(h) Four lines are reserved for future use and three further lines are undefined and are thus available for use by individual manufacturers who should clearly specify their logical function. The voltage level of any signal on these lines should not exceed 5 V.

The S-100 Bus Handbook by Dave Bursky (Hayden) provides a useful reference to the S-100 bus and includes a number of circuit diagrams of representative S-100 card modules.

S-100 pin assignment

Pin No.	Abbreviation	Active level	Signal/function
1	+8 V		Unregulated supply rail
2	+18 V		Unregulated supply rail
3	XRDY	H	Ready input to bus master

4	VI0	L*	Vectored interrupt line 0
5	VI1	L*	Vectored interrupt line 1
6	VI2	L*	Vectored interrupt line 2
7	VI3	L*	Vectored interrupt line 3
8	VI4	L*	Vectored interrupt line 4
9	VI5	L*	Vectored interrupt line 5
10	VI6	L*	Vectored interrupt line 6
11	VI7	L*	Vectored interrupt line 7
12	NMI	L*	Non-maskable interrupt
13	PWRFAIL	L	Power fail signal (pulled low when a power failure is detected)
14	DMA3	L*	DMA request line with highest priority
15	A18		Extended address bus line 18
16	A16		Extended address bus line 16
17	A17		Extended address bus line 17
18	SDSB	L*	Status disable (tri-states all status lines)
19	CDSB	L*	Command disable (tri-states all control input lines)
20	GND		Common 0 V line
21	NDEF		Undefined
22	ADSB	L*	Address disable (tri-states all address lines)
23	DODSB	L*	Data out disable (tri-states all data output lines)
24	∅		Bus clock
25	pSTVAL	L	Status valid strobe (indicates that status information is true)
26	pHLDA	H	Hold acknowledge (signal from the current bus master which indicates that control will pass to the device seeking bus control on the next bus cycle)
27	RFU		Reserved for future use
28	RFU		Reserved for future use
29	A5		Address line 5
30	A4		Address line 4
31	A3		Address line 3
32	A15		Address line 15
33	A12		Address line 12
34	A9		Address line 9
35	DO1/Data 1		Data out line 1/bidirectional data line 1
36	DO0/Data 0		Data out line 0/bidirectional data line 0
37	A10		Address line 10
38	DO4/Data 4		Data out line 4/bidirectional data line 4
39	DO5/Data 5		Data out line 5/bidirectional data line 5
40	DO6/Data 6		Data out line 6/bidirectional data line 6
41	DI2/Data 10		Data in line 2/bidirectional data line 10
42	DI3/Data 11		Data in line 3/bidirectional data line 11
43	DI7/Data 15		Data in line 7/bidirectional data line 15
44	sM1	H	M1 cycle (indicates that the current machine cycle is an operation code fetch)
45	sOUT	H	Output (indicates that data is being transferred to an output device)
46	sINP	H	Input (indicates that data is being fetched from an input device)
47	sMEMR	H	Memory read (indicates that the bus master is fetching data from memory)
48	sHLTA	H	Halt acknowledge (indicates that the

Pin No.	Abbreviation	Active level	Signal/function
			bus master is executing an HLT instruction)
49	CLOCK		2 MHz clock
50	GND		Common 0 V
51	+8 V		Unregulated supply rail
52	-16 V		Unregulated supply rail
53	GND		Common 0 V
54	SLAVE CLR	L*	Slave clear (resets all bus slaves)
55	DMA0	L*	DMA request line (lowest priority)
56	DMA1	L*	DMA request line
57	DMA2	L*	DMA request line
58	sXTRQ	L*	16-bit data request (requests slaves to assert SIXTN)
59	A19		Address line 19
60	SIXTN	L*	16-bit data acknowledge (slave response to sXTRQ)
61	A20		Extended address bus line 20
62	A21		Extended address bus line 21
63	A22		Extended address bus line 22
64	A23		Extended address bus line 23
65	NDEF		Not defined
66	NDEF		Not defined
67	PHANTOM		Phantom (disables normal slaves and enables phantom slaves which share addresses with the normal set)
68	MWRT	H	Memory write
69	RFU		Reserved for future use
70	GND		Common 0 V
71	RFU		Reserved for future use
72	RDY	H*	Ready input to bus master
73	INT	L*	Interrupt request
74	HOLD	L*	Hold request (request from device wishing to have control of the bus)
75	RESET	L*	Reset (resets bus master devices)
76	pSYNC	H	Synchronizing signal which indicates the first bus state of a bus cycle
77	pWR	L	Write (indicates that the bus master has placed valid data on the DO bus/data bus)
78	pDBIN	H	Data bus in (indicates that the bus master is requesting data on the DI bus/data bus)
79	A0		Address line 0
80	A1		Address line 1
81	A2		Address line 2
82	A6		Address line 6
83	A7		Address line 7
84	A8		Address line 8
85	A13		Address line 13
86	A14		Address line 14
87	A11		Address line 11
88	DO2/DATA 2		Data out line 2/bidirectional data line 2
89	DO3/DATA 3		Data out line 3/bidirectional data line 3

Pin No.	Abbreviation	Active level	Signal/function
90	DO7/DATA 7		Data out line 7/bidirectional data line 7
91	DI4/DATA 12		Data in line 4/bidirectional data line 12
92	DI5/DATA 13		Data in line 5/bidirectional data line 13
93	DI6/DATA 14		Data in line 6/bidirectional data line 14
94	DI1/DATA 9		Data in line 1/bidirectional data line 9
95	DI0/DATA 8		Data in line 0/bidirectional data line 8
96	sINTA	H	Interrupt acknowledge
97	sWO	L	Write output (used to gate data from the bus master to a slave)
98	ERROR	L*	Error (indicates that an error has occurred during the current bus cycle)
99	POC	L	Power on clear (clears all devices attached to the bus when power is first applied)
100	GND		Common 0 V

Notes: 1. * = open collector
   H = active high
   L = active low
   2. p   precedes control line mnemonics
      s   precedes status line mnemonics

S-100 pin numbering

(Pin view of motherboard connector)

Intel Multibus

In recent years Intel's Multibus has gained considerable support as an industrial bus standard. The system is based on an 86-way edge connector and is ideally suited to multiprocessor applications.

The following points are worthy of note:

(a) Signals have been grouped together according to their logical function and placed physically adjacent on the edge connector.

(b) All signals are active low.

(c) 20 address lines and 16 bidirectional data lines are provided (the 20 address lines being those normally associated with the 8086/80186 processor families).

(d) When a processor seeks control of the bus it asserts a bus request signal (BREQ) together with its bus priority output signal (BPRO). A parallel or serial priority encoder uses these signals to determine which processor has control of the bus at any particular time. A suitable bus controller is Intel's 8218 or 8288.

(e) Hexadecimal numbering is used to distinguish address and data bus lines.

Intel Multibus pin assignment

Component side

Pin No.	Signal group	Abbreviation	Signal/function
1	Supply	GND	Ground/common 0 V
3	rails	+5 V	+5 V d.c. supply rail
5		+5 V	+5 V d.c. supply rail
7		+12 V	+12 V d.c. supply rail
9		−5 V	−5 V d.c. supply rail
11		GND	Ground/common 0 V
13	Bus	BCLK	Bus clock
15	control	BPRN	Bus priority input
17		BUSY	Bus busy
19		MRDC	Memory read command
21		IORC	I/O read command
23		XACK	Transfer acknowledge
25			Reserved
27		BHEN	Byte high enable
29		CBRQ	Common bus request
31		CCLK	Constant clock
33		INTA	Interrupt acknowledge
35	Interrupt	INT6	Parallel interrupt
37		INT4	requests
39		INT2	
41		INT0	
43	Address	ADRE	Address lines
45	bus	ADRC	
47		ADRA	
49		ADR8	
51		ADR6	
53		ADR4	
55		ADR2	
57		ADR0	
59	Data	DATE	Data lines
61	bus	DATC	
63		DATA	
65		DAT8	
67		DAT6	
69		DAT4	
71		DAT2	
73		DAT0	
75	Supply	GND	Ground/common 0 V
77	rails		Reserved
79		−12 V	−12 V d.c. supply rail
81		+5 V	+5 V d.c. supply rail
83		+5 V	+5 V d.c. supply rail
85		GND	Ground/common 0 V

Track side

Pin No.	Signal group	Abbreviation	Signal/function
2	Supply	GND	Ground/common 0 V
4	rails	+5 V	+5 V d.c. supply rail
6		+5 V	+5 V d.c. supply rail
8		+12 V	+12 V d.c. supply rail
10		−5 V	−5 V d.c. supply rail
12		GND	Ground/common 0 V
14	Bus	INIT	Initialize
16	control	BPRO	Bus priority output
18		BREQ	Bus request
20		MWTC	Memory write command
22		IOWC	I/O write command
24		INH1	Inhibit 1 (disable RAM)
26		INH2	Inhibit 2 (disable ROM)
28	Address	AD10	Address lines
30	bus	AD11	
32		AD12	
34		AD13	
36	Interrupt	INT7	Parallel interrupt
38		INT5	requests
40		INT3	
42		INT1	
44	Address	ADRF	Address lines
46	bus	ADRD	
48		ADRB	
50		ADR9	
52		ADR7	
54		ADR5	
56		ADR3	
58		ADR1	
60	Data	DATF	Data lines
62	bus	DATD	
64		DATB	
66		DAT9	
68		DAT7	
70		DAT5	
72		DAT3	
74		DAT1	
76	Supply	GND	Ground/common 0 V
78	rails		Reserved
80		−12 V	−12 V d.c. supply rail
82		+5 V	+5 V d.c. supply rail
84		+5 V	+5 V d.c. supply rail
86		GND	Ground/common 0 V

The G-64 bus

The G-64 bus concept was created by GESPAC S.A. of Geneva in 1979 and it arose from a need to provide industry with an up-to-date bus standard. The G-64 bus was originally designed for 6809 processor signals but the specification has been extended to cope with a wider range of processors. Hence the G-64 bus now caters for 8 and 16-bit processors (16 individual data lines are provided) and permits asynchronous as well as synchronous data transfer. The G-64 bus is based on the single Eurocard format with a standard module size of 100mm × 160mm. The connector specified for use with the G-64 bus is the popular and highly reliable IEC 603-2 (DIN 41612 type b). This connector is an indirect type double-sided 64-way connector with ground connections at each end of the connector (pins 1 and 32 on each side). The G-64 bus employs an unterminated backplane and this limits the speed of data transfer on the bus.

STD bus

The STD bus system was another early contender for the low-cost, 8-bit bus market. It provides a 8-bit data path and 16-bit address path. The memory addressing range is 64K whilst the I/O space is only 256 bytes (though this has been expanded in an number of implementations). The bus will not directly support multiple masters (unless an off-bus connection is employed). The system is non-Eurocard based (unlike most of its rivals) and it uses a direct edge connector.

As with S-100, various modifications and extensions have been made to the STD standard with a view to extending its life. Unfortunately, these modifications have created a number of problems for end-users relating to compatability of system cards. The STE bus standard provides a far superior environment for the development of an eight bit system and many users of the STD bus are converting to this new standard.

STE bus

The STE bus was originally conceived as a Eurocard replacement for the STD bus. Many of the shortcomings of earlier 8-bit bus standards (such as G-64 and STD) have been eliminated. The system was first specified in 1982 and the first STE cards appeared in 1984. Since 1985 the standard has attracted considerable support and many users of earlier 8-bit bus systems have changed to STE. In 1987 the system was defined under the IEEE-1000 specification which further establishes it as an internationally recognized standard.

The STE bus provides for an 8-bit data path and 20 address lines (permitting 1M byte of directly addressable memory space). The system provides for an I/O space of 4K bytes and up to three potential bus masters may be present within a system.

STE bears more than a passing resemblance to VME and, some enthusiastic users have likened it to a 8-bit implementation of the VME standard. One of the beauties of the STE bus is that, whilst the system is flexible enough to permit mixing of a wide variety of processors from different manufacturers, it is definitive in terms of bus signals and protocol. System designers can thus have every confidence that STE bus products obtained from a variety of sources can be interconnected and the whole system will operate as planned.

The connector specified for use with STE boards is a 64-pin male connector utilizing rows a and c (the inside row is not used). This connector is specified in IEC 603–2 and the corresponding female connector is specified for the STE backplane. The function of the signals present are as follows:

D0 to D7	Eight data lines
A0 to A19	Twenty address lines
ADRSTB*	Address strobe. This line is taken low to indicate that a valid address has been placed on the bus.
DATSTB*	Data strobe. This line is taken low to indicate that valid data has been placed on the bus.
CM0 to CM2	Command modifiers which indicate the current type of bus cycle
BUSRQ0* and BUSRQ1*	Bus request lines. These lines are taken low when a potential bus master wishes to gain access to the bus.
BUSAK0* and BUSAK1*	Bus acknowledge lines. These lines are taken low to indicate that the bus request has been granted. A potential bus master may only drive the bus when it has received an acknowledge signal on the bus request line.
DATACK*	This handshake line is asserted by a bus slave on a write cycle in order to indicate that it has accepted data or, on a read cycle, to indicate that its data is valid.
TRFERR*	A bus slave asserts this signal instead of DATACK* if an error is detected.
ATNRQ0* to ATNRQ7*	Attention request/interrupt lines. (ATNRQ0* has the highest priority).
SYSCLK	16MHz system clock.
SYSRST*	System reset.

STE bus connector

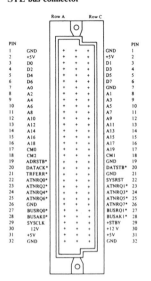

Comparison of three popular 8-bit backplane buses

	STD	G-64	STE
Signal lines	56	64	64
Address range (bytes)	64K*	64K	1M
Data path (bits)	8	8	8
I/O space (bytes)	256*	1K	4K
Multiple masters	off bus connection required	yes	up to 3
Error checking	none	yes	error line
Normal card size (mm)	114 × 165	100 × 160	100 × 160
Connector	direct edge	DIN 41612 (type b)	DIN 41612 (type c)

*various expansion schemes have been employed

Multibus

Multibus was developed by the Intel Corporation and forms the basis for the IEEE-796 bus standard. Multibus permits both 8 and 16-bit data transfers and has a 24-bit address bus. Daisy chain bus priority usually allows for the presence of up to four bus masters. Eight interrupt lines are provided and these may be decoded on a master CPU card in order to generate the appropriate vectored service routine.

Multibus cards have two connectors; an 86-way edge connector (P1) on which all signal lines are defined and an auxilliary 60-pin connector (P2) for customized functions. The main connector offers regulated power rails of +5V and +12V together with eight separate ground connections (see page 168).

Bus signals are grouped together according to their logical function and placed physically adjacent on the edge connector. 20 address lines and 16 data lines are provided and all bus signals are active low (ground true).

Multibus is now defined under IEEE-796 and the successful transition from 8 to 16-bit operation has gained it a wide measure of support in industry today. The system is based on an 86-way edge connector and is ideally suited to multiprocessor applications.

Q-bus and euro Q-bus

Q-bus traces its origins from DEC's unibus system which was prominent in the 1970s and implemented on the popular DEC PDP-11 minicomputer. The system is now used in conjunction with DEC's LSI-11 microcomputer.

Euro Q-bus is based on the Q-bus and employs a single DIN 41612 connector (three rows are used) provides 22-bit addressing, DMA, and a priority interrupt structure. Euro-Q bus cards are double height (6U) eruocards derived from DEC LSI-11 modules. Ground connections are made at the ends of the connector (pins 1 and 32 of all three rows) and at four points in row A. In common with most modern bus systems, the bus is fitted with terminating networks.

Versabus

Versabus is an elegant asynchronous bus system which was primarily designed for use with Motorola's 16/32-bit 68000 microprocessor. The bus is not, however, confined to the 68000 device and has considerable capacity for further expansion. Two double edge connectors are used; the basic 16-bit data path being associated with one and the necessary bus lines for a full 32-bit data path and 32-bit addressing being provided on the second connector.

VME bus

The VME bus standard resulted from a joint effort by semi-conductor manufacturers Mostek, Motorola, and Signetics. The bus supports very fast data transfer rates (up to 24MHz) and uses a single 96-way DIN 41612 type c indirect connector to provide a 16-bit data path. A second 96-way indirect connector may be used to provide a full 32-bit operation. The basic system incorporates a 24-bit address bus whilst the extended bus supports 32-bit addresses.

The VME bus has its roots in Versabus and is arguably the highest performing, currently available 16/32 bit microprocessor bus system, offering true 'state of the art' performance. The bus is, however, expensive to implement and is thus inappropriate in a number of more basic applications.

IBM PC expansion bus

The immense popularity of the IBM PC has ensured a wide market for compatible expansion cards and it is therefore not surprising that the IBM PC expansion bus has established itself as a standard in its own right.

The IBM expansion bus uses a double sided 31-way connector (62-ways in total). The address and data bus are grouped together on one side of the connector while the control bus and power rails occupy the other side of the connector.

IBM PC expansion bus pin assignment

Pin No.	Abbreviation	Signal/function
1	GND	Ground/common 0 V
2	$\overline{\text{CHCK}}$	Channel check output (when low this indicates that some form of error has occurred)
3	RESET	Reset (when high this line resets all expansion cards)
4	D7	Data line 7
5	+5 V	+5 V d.c. supply rail
6	D6	Data line 6
7	IRQ2	Interrupt request input 2
8	D5	Data line 5
9	−5 V	−5 V d.c. supply rail
10	D4	Data line 4
11	DRQ2	DMA request input 2
12	D3	Data line 3
13	−12 V	−12 V d.c. supply rail
14	D2	Data line 2
15		Reserved
16	D1	Data line 1
17	+12 V	+12 V d.c. supply rail
18	D0	Data line 0
19	GND	Ground/common 0 V
20	BCRDY	Ready input (normally high, pulled low by a slow memory or I/O device to signal that it is not ready for data transfer to take place)
21	$\overline{\text{IMW}}$	Memory write output
22	AEN	Address enable output
23	$\overline{\text{IMR}}$	Memory read output
24	A19	Address line 19
25	IIOW	I/O write output
26	A18	Address line 18
27	$\overline{\text{IIOR}}$	I/O read output
28	A17	Address line 17

Pin No.	Abbreviation	Signal/function
29	DACK3	DMA acknowledge output 3 (see notes)
30	A16	Address line 16
31	DRQ3	DMA request input 3
32	A15	Address line 15
33	DACK1	DMA acknowledge output 1 (see notes)
34	A14	Address line 14
35	DRQ1	DMA request input 1
36	A13	Address line 13
37	DACK0	DMA acknowledge output 0 (see notes)
38	A12	Address line 12
39	XCLK4	4 MHz clock (CPU clock divided by two, 200 ns period, 50% duty cycle)
40	A11	Address line 11
41	IRQ7	Interrupt request line 7 (see notes)
42	A10	Address line 10
43	IRQ6	Interrupt request line 6 (see notes)
44	A9	Address line 9
45	IRQ5	Interrupt request line 5
46	A8	Address line 8
47	IRQ4	Interrupt request line 4 (see notes)
48	A7	Address line 7
49	IRQ3	Interrupt request line 3
50	A6	Address line 6
51	DACK2	DMA acknowledge 2
52	A5	Address line 5
53	TC	Terminal count output (pulsed high to indicate that the terminal count for a DMA transfer has been reached)
54	A4	Address line 4
55	ALE	Address latch enable output
56	A3	Address line 3
57	+5 V	+5 V d.c. supply rail
58	A2	Address line 2
59	14 MHz	14.31818 MHz clock (fast clock with 70 ns period, 50% duty cycle)
60	A1	Address line 1
61	GND	Ground/common 0 V
62	IA0	Address line 0

Notes: (a) Signal direction is quoted relative to the motherboard
(b) IRQ4 is generated by the motherboard serial interface
IRQ6 is generated by the motherboard disk interface
IRQ7 is generated by the motherboard parallel interface
(c) DACK0 is used to refresh dynamic memory, while DACK1 to DACK3 are used to acknowledge DMA requests.

IBM PC expansion bus pin numbering

Small computer systems interface (SCSI)

SCSI is a local I/O bus which is commonly used to interface mass storage devices (such as hard disk and tape drives) to a host computer system. The SCSI bus supports a total of eight devices (including the host computer). Communication is allowed between two devices at any one time. Each device present must have its own unique SCSI ID (invariably selected by means of links or DIP switch settings). The ID is established by placing a single data bit (driven low) onto the bus according to the following table:

Data bit	SCSI ID
DB(0)	0
DB(1)	1
DB(2)	2
DB(3)	3
DB(4)	4
DB(5)	5
DB(6)	6
DB(7)	7

When two devices communicate on the SCSI bus, the unit originating the operation is designated as the 'initiator'. The unit performing the operation, on the other hand, is known as the target. Any desired combination of initiators and targets may be present in an SCSI bus system (provided, of course, that the total number of devices present does not exceed eight). Data transfers on the SCSI bus are asynchronous and follow a defined handshake protocol in which signals are exchanged on the request ($\overline{REQ}$) and acknowledge ($\overline{ACK}$) lines. The SCSI interface employs a total of nine control signals and nine data signals (including an optional parity bit).

SCSI signals and bus phases

Signal	Abbreviation	Function
Busy	$\overline{BSY}$	Asserted to indicate that the bus is in use (these lines are OR-tied).
Select	$\overline{SEL}$	Asserted by an initiator when selecting a target or by a target to reselect an initiator.
Control/data	$\overline{C}/D$	Driven by a target to indicate whether control information or data is present on the bus.
Input/output	$\overline{I}/O$	Driven by a target to determine the direction of data flow on the data bus. The direction is quoted relative to the initiator. True (low) indicates input to the initiator.
Message	$\overline{MSG}$	Driven by the target during the message phase.
Request	$\overline{REQ}$	Driven by the target to indicate a request for a data transfer handshake sequence.

Signal	Abbreviation	function
Acknowledge	ACK	Driven by an initiator to acknowledge a data transfer sequence.
Attention	ATN	Driven by an initiator to indicate the attention condition.
Reset	RST	An OR-tied signal which indicates a reset condition.

The following table indicates the source of each SCSI signal during each of the eight bus phases:

Bus phase	BSY	SEL	Signal C/D, I/O	ACK/ATN	DB (7-0, P)
Bus free	None	None	None	None	None
Arbitration	All	Winner	None	None	ID
Select	Both	Init	None	Init	Init
Reselect	Both	Target	Target	Init	Target
Command	Target	None	Target	Init	Init
Data-in	Target	None	Target	Init	Target
Data-out	Target	None	Target	Init	Init
Status	Target	None	Target	Init	Target
Message-in	Target	None	Target	Init	Target
Message-out	Target	None	Target	Init	Init

Notes:

All the signal must be driven by all actively participating devices.

Both the signal is driven by the initiator and/or target as specified in the arbitration and selection phases

Init Driven only by the active initiator.

None this signal must not be driven by any device (the bias circuitry within the bus terminator will ensure that the signal is pulled into the false state).

ID SCSI ID (a unique data bit) must be placed on the bus by a device that is arbitrating.

The following truth table applies to the Data, Command, and Message phases:

Phase	MSG	C/D	I/O	Direction of transfer
Data-out	1	1	1	Initiator to target
Data-in	1	1	0	Target to initiator
Command	1	0	1	Initiator to target
	1	0	0	Target to initiator
Message-out	0	0	1	Initiator to target
Message-in	0	0	0	Target to initiator

Signal levels and bus termination

SCSI signals are either 'true' (low) or 'false' (high). A bus terminator ensures that each signal line assumes the false state by pulling the line high when it is not driven into the low (asserted) state.

Each signal driven on to the bus by a device should conform to the following electrical specification:

Voltage (asserted state) = 0.0V min. and 0.4V max.

(released state) = 2.5V min. and 5.25V max.

Signals received by a device from the bus, on the other hand, should conform to the following electrical specification:

Voltage (true state) = 0.0V min. and 0.8V max.

(false state) = 2.0V min. and 5.25V max.

A terminator must be installed on the last (furthermost) device connected to the bus. The maximum physical length of the bus cable is 6 metres (approx. 20 feet) and the characteristic impedance should be 100 ohms ± 10%.

SCSI connector

The SCSI interface uses a 50-way connector arranged in two rows, each of 25-ways. Typical part numbers for the female cable-mounting connector with integral strain relief are AMP 1-499506-2 and DuPont 66900-350. The connector pin assignment is as follows:

Signal	Pin no.
$\overline{DB}$ (0)	2
$\overline{DB}$ (1)	4
$\overline{DB}$ (2)	6
$\overline{DB}$ (3)	8
$\overline{DB}$ (4)	10
$\overline{DB}$ (5)	12
$\overline{DB}$ (6)	14
$\overline{DB}$ (7)	16
$\overline{DB}$ (P)	18
GND	20
GND	22
GND	24
Terminator power	26
GND	28
GND	30
$\overline{ATN}$	32
GND	34
$\overline{BSY}$	36
$\overline{ACK}$	38
$\overline{RST}$	40
$\overline{MSG}$	42
$\overline{SEL}$	44
$\overline{C}/D$	46
$\overline{REQ}$	48
$\overline{I}/O$	50

Note: 1 All odd numbered pins, with the exception of pin-25, are connected to ground (GND). Pin-25 is not connected.

2 Pin-1 is marked by a triangle indentation on the 50-way connector.

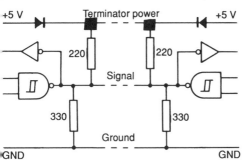

Typical SCSI bus interface circuitry

IEEE-488/GPIB bus

Whilst not strictly a backplane bus, the IEEE-488 bus is worthy of
mention in the general context of bus systems by virtue of its
immense popularity in the field of instrumentation.
The IEEE-488 bus was originally developed by Hewlett-Packard
and is now known simply as the General Purpose Instrument Bus
(GPIB). The bus provides a means of interconnecting instruments
in automatic test equipment (ATE) configurations where data can
be exchanged between a number of participating devices.

The IEEE-488 bus provides for the following types of device:

(a) Listeners (which receive data from other instruments but are
    not themselves capable of generating data),
(b) Talkers (which are only capable of outputing data onto the
    bus),
(c) Talker/listeners (which can both generate data and receive
    data), and
(d) Controllers (which manage the flow of data on the bus and
    provide processing facilities).

While only one talker can be active at any given instant, it is
possible for several listeners to be receiving data simultaneously.

The IEEE-488 bus uses eight multi-purpose bidirectional data
lines. These lines are used to transfer data, addresses, commands
and status bytes. In addition, five bus management and three
handshake lines are provided.

Commands are signalled by taking the Attention Line (ATN)
low. Commands may be directed to individual devices by placing a
unique address on the lower five data bus lines. Alternatively,
universal commands may be simultaneously directed to all
participating devices.

The format for a command byte (ATN low) is as follows:

Bit 8   Don't care
Bits 6 and 7   Command code bits
Bits 5 to 1   Addresses

The following command byte truth table is obeyed:

D8	D7	D6	D5	D4	D3	D2	D1	Meaning
X	0	0	0	B4	B3	B2	B1	Universal commands
X	0	1	A5	A4	A3	A2	A1	Listen addresses
X	0	1	1	1	1	1	1	Unlisten command
X	1	0	A5	A4	A3	A2	A1	Talk addresses
X	1	0	1	1	1	1	1	Untalk command
X	1	1	A5	A4	A3	A2	A1	Secondary commands
X	1	1	1	1	1	1	1	Ignored

Notes: (a) Command codes are only valid when ATN is low.
(b) Address 11111 cannot be used for a talker or listener.

The specified maximum data rate for the bus is normally either 1
or 2 Mbyte/s but, in practice, typical data transfer rates are
250 kbyte/s or less. The maximum terminated bus length is
normally assumed to be 20 m.

An important feature of the bus is that it provides for data
transfer between devices having widely different response times. In
practice, therefore, the slowest listener determines the rate at which
data transfer takes place.

A variety of dedicated VLSI GPIB bus interface devices are
available. These include Intel's 8291 GPIB Listener/Talker and
8292 GPIB Controller, as well as Motorola's 68488 GPIB
Adaptor.

The IEC-625 bus is similar to the IEEE-488 bus but employs a
different connector (25-way D-type rather than the 24-pin
connector originally specified by Hewlett-Packard).

IEEE-488/GPIB bus system

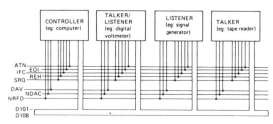

IEEE-488/GPIB pin assignment

Pin No.	Signal group	Abbreviation	Signal/function
1	Data	DIO1	Data line 1
2		DIO2	Data line 2
3		DIO3	Data line 3
4		DIO4	Data line 4
5	Management	EOI	End or identify (sent by a talker to indicate that transfer of data is complete)
6	Handshake	DAV	Data valid (asserted by a talker to indicate that valid data is present on the bus)

Pin No.	Signal group	Abbreviation	Signal/function
7		NRFD	Not ready for data (asserted by a listener to indicate that it is not ready for data)
8		NDAC	Not data accepted (asserted while data is being accepted by a listener)
9	Management	IFC	Interface clear (asserted by the controller in order to initialize the system in a known state)
10		SRQ	Service request (sent to the controller by a device requiring attention)
11		ATN	Attention (asserted by the controller when placing a command onto the bus)
12		SHIELD	Shield
13	Data	DIO5	Data line 5
14		DIO6	Data line 6
15		DIO7	Data line 7
16		DIO8	Data line 8
17	Management	REN	Remote enable (enables an instrument to be controlled by the bus controller rather than by its own front panel controls)
18		GND	Ground/common
19		GND	Ground/common
20		GND	Ground/common
21		GND	Ground/common
22		GND	Ground/common
23		GND	Ground/common
24		GND	Ground/common

Notes: (a) Handshake signals (DAV, NRFD and NDAC) are all active low open collector and are used in a wired-OR configuration.

(b) All other signals are TTL compatible and active low.

IEEE-488/GPIB pin connections

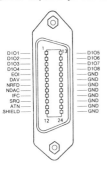

Centronics printer interface

The Centronics interface has established itself as the standard for
parallel data transfer between a microcomputer and a printer. The
standard is based on 36-way Amphenol connector (part no: 57–
30360) and is suitable for distances of up to 2 m.

Parallel data is transferred into the printer's internal buffer when
a strobe pulse is sent. Handshaking is accomplished by means of
acknowledge (ACKNLG) and busy (BUSY) signals.

Centronics printer interface pin assignment

Pin No.	Abbreviation	Signal/function
1	STROBE	Strobe (active low to read data)
2	DATA 1	Data line 1
3	DATA 2	Data line 2
4	DATA 3	Data line 3
5	DATA 4	Data line 4
6	DATA 5	Data line 5
7	DATA 6	Data line 6
8	DATA 7	Data line 7
9	DATA 8	Data line 8
10	ACKNLG	Acknowledge (pulsed low to indicate that data has been received)
11	BUSY	Busy (taken high under the following conditions: (a) during data entry (b) during a printing operation (c) when the printer is OFF-LINE (d) during print error status)
12	PE	Paper end (taken high to indicate that the printer is out of paper)
13	SLCT	Select (taken high to indicate that the printer is in the selected state)
14	AUTO FEED XT	Automatic feed (when this input is taken low, the printer is instructed to produce an automatic line feed after printing. This function can be selected internally by means of a DIP switch)
15	n.c.	Not connected (unused)
16	0 V	Logic ground
17	CHASSIS GND	Printer chassis (normally isolated from logic ground at the printer)
18	n.c.	Not connected (unused)
19 to 30	GND	Signal ground (originally defined as 'twisted pair earth returns' for pin numbers 1 to 12 inclusive)
31	INIT	Initialize (this line is pulsed low to reset the printer controller)
32	ERROR	Error (taken low by the printer to indicate: (a) PAPER END state (b) OFF-LINE state (c) error state)

33	GND	Signal ground
34	n.c.	Not connected (unused)
35	LOGIC 1	Logic 1 (usually pulled high via 3.3 kohm)
36	$\overline{\text{SLCT IN}}$	Select input (data entry to the printer is only possible when this line is taken low, but this function may be disabled by means of an internal DIP switch)

Notes: (a) Signals, pin numbers, and signal directions apply to the printer.

(b) Alternative types of connector (such as 25-way D type, PCB edge, etc.) are commonly used at the microcomputer.

(c) All signals are standard TTL levels.

(d) $\overline{\text{ERROR}}$ and $\overline{\text{ACKNLG}}$ signals are not supported on some interfaces.

Centronics interface pin connections

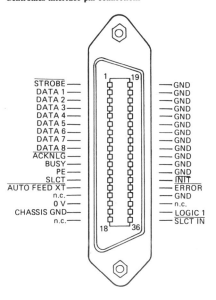

Serial data transmission

In serial data transmission one data bit is transmitted after another. In order to transmit a byte of data it is therefore necessary to convert incoming parallel data from the bus into a serial bit stream which can be transmitted along a line.

Serial data transmission can be synchronous (clocked) or asynchronous (non-clocked). The latter method has obvious advantages and is by far the most popular method. The rate at which data is transmitted is given by the number of bits transmitted per unit time. The commonly adopted unit is the 'baud', with 1 baud roughly equivalent to 1 bit per second.

It should, however, be noted that there is a subtle difference between the bit rate as perceived by the computer and the baud rate present in the transmission medium. The reason is simply that some overhead in terms of additional synchronizing bits is required in order to recover asynchronously transmitted data.

In the case of a typical RS-232C link, a total of 11 bits is required to transmit only seven bits of data. A line baud rate of 600 baud thus represents a useful data transfer rate of only some 382 bits per second.

Many modern serial data transmission systems can trace their origins to the 20 mA current loop interface which was once commonly used to connect a teletype unit to a minicomputer system. This system was based on the following logic levels:

Mark = logic 1 = 20 mA current flowing

Space = logic 0 = no current flowing

where the terms 'mark' and 'space' simply refer to the presence or absence of a current.

This system was extended to cater for more modern and more complex peripherals for which voltage, rather than current, levels were appropriate.

RS-232C/CCITT V24

The RS-232C/CCITT V24 interface is the most widely used method of providing serial communication between microcomputers and peripheral devices. The interface is defined by the Electronic Industries Association (EIA) standard and relates to the connection of data terminal equipment (DTE) and data communication equipment (DCE). For many purposes the DTE and DCE are the computer and peripheral respectively although the distinction is not always clear as, for example, in the case where two microcomputers are linked together via RS-232C ports. In general, the RS-232C system may be used where the DTE and DCE are physically separated by up to 20 m or so. For greater distances telephone lines are usually more appropriate.

The EIA specification permits synchronous or asynchronous communication at data rates of up to 19.2 kb/s. Furthermore, character length and bit codes may be varied according to the particular application. The specification allows for the following signals:

(a) serial data comprising
   (i)   a primary channel providing full duplex data transfer (i.e. simultaneous transmission and reception), and
   (ii)   a secondary channel also capable of full duplex operation;
(b) handshake control signals;
(c) timing signals.

The RS-232C system may thus be configured for a variety of operating modes including transmit only (primary channel), receive only (primary channel), half-duplex, full-duplex, and various primary and secondary channel transmit/receive combinations.

From this, it should be clear that the RS-232C is versatile and highly adaptable. Unfortunately, such flexibility does carry a penalty — the wide variation in interpretation, which can result in some bewildering anomalies in the physical connection and control protocol of practical RS-232C systems.

The RS-232C interface is usually distinguished by its connector — a 25-way 'D' connector. DCE equipment is normally fitted with a female connector while DTE equipment is fitted with a male connector.

In practice, few systems involving personal computers make use of the full complement of signal lines; indeed, many arrangements use only eight lines in total (including the protective ground and signal return).

The most common arrangement for a microcomputer RS-232C interface involves six signal lines and two ground connections. These use pins 1 to 7 and 20 of the D-connector and their functions, assuming that we are dealing with the computer side of the interface, are as follows:

PROTECTIVE GROUND	Connected to the equipment frame or chassis (may be connected to an outer screening conductor).
TD (TxD)	Serial transmitted data output.
RD (RxD)	Serial received data input.
RTS	Request to send. Output. Peripheral to transmit data when an 'on' condition is present.
CTS	Clear to send. Input. When 'on' indicates that the peripheral can receive data.
DSR	Data set ready. Input. When 'on' indicates that handshaking has been completed.
SIGNAL GROUND	Acts as a common signal return. Normally connected to a ground point within the RS-232C interface and should not be linked directly to the protective ground (even though these may appear to both be at zero potential).
DTR	Data terminal ready. Output. When 'on' indicates that the peripheral should be connected to the communication channel.

Serial RS-232C data is transmitted asynchronously (i.e. it is not clocked) and each data word represents a single ASCII character. Most systems provide for seven data bits although some may be configured for any number of bits between five and eight. The number of stop bits may also range between 1, $1\frac{1}{2}$ and 2. Parity may be even, odd or disabled.

The voltage levels in an RS-232C system are markedly different from those which appear within the computer. In the transmit and receive data paths, for example, a positive voltage of between 3 V and 25 V is used to represent logic 0 while a negative voltage of similar magnitude is used to represent logic 1.

In the control signal paths, however, conventional positive logic is employed; a high voltage in the range 3 V to 25 V indicates the active or 'on' state while a negative voltage of similar magnitude indicates the inactive or 'off' state. It should be noted that some 'quasi RS-232C' systems exist in which conventional TTL logic levels are employed. Such systems are obviously not directly

compatible with the original EIA system and considerable damage
can be caused by inadvertent interconnection of the two.

The maximum open-circuit voltage on any RS-232C line must
not be allowed to exceed ± 25 V (relative to signal ground) and the
maximum short-circuit current between any two lines must not
exceed 500 mA. The effective loading resistance of any circuit must
be between 3 kohm and 7 kohm with an effective shunt capacitance
not exceeding 2.5 nF.

RS-423/RS-422

In order to improve the performance of the RS-232C specification,
several further standards have been introduced. These provide for
better line matching, thereby reducing reflections which are
otherwise present on a mismatched line.

RS-422 is a balanced system (differential signal lines are used)
while RS-423 is unbalanced (a single signal line is used in
conjunction with signal ground). Both systems allow several
remote peripherals to be driven from a common line in a simple
serial bus configuration.

RS-423 allows for a line terminating resistance of 450 ohm
(minimum) while RS-422 caters for a line impedance of as low as
50 ohm. The improvement in matching permits the use of much
faster data rates. Data rates of up to 125 kbaud and distances of
over 1000 m can be tolerated (though not necessarily at the same
time!).

RS-449

RS-449 is a further enhancement of RS-422 and RS-423 which has
been developed to cater for very fast data rates (up to 2 Mbaud).
Compared with RS-232C, ten extra circuit functions have been
provided while three of the original interchange circuits have been
abandoned. Protective ground is also no longer provided.

In order to minimize confusion, and since certain changes have
been made to the definition of circuit functions, a completely new
set of mnemonics has been provided. In addition, the system
requires 37-way and 9-way 'D' connectors, the latter being
necessary where use is made of the secondary channel interchange
circuits.

RS-232C/CCITT V24 pin assignment

Pin No.	Abbrev.	Direction	Circuit CCITT	Circuit EIA	Function
1	FG	—	101	AA	Frame ground
2	TD	To DCE	103	BA	Transmitted data
3	RD	To DTE	104	BB	Received data
4	RTS	To DCE	105	CA	Request to send
5	CTS	To DTE	106	CB	Clear to send
6	DSR	To DTE	107	CC	Data set ready
7	SG	—	102	AB	Signal ground
8	DCD	To DTE	109	CF	Data carrier detect
9		To DTE			Positive d.c. test voltage
10		To DTE			Negative d.c. test voltage
11	QM	To DTE	Note 1		Equalizer mode
12	SDCD	To DTE	122	SCF	Secondary data carrier detect
13	SCTS	To DTE	121	SCB	Secondary clear to send
14	STD	To DCE	118	SBA	Secondary transmitted data
	NS	To DCE	Note 1		New synchronization

Pin No.	Abbrev.	Direction	Circuit CCITT	Circuit EIA	Function
15	TC	To DTE	114	DB	Transmitter clock
16	SRD	To DTE	119	SBB	Secondary received data
	DCT	To DTE	Note 1		Divided clock transmitter
17	RC	To DTE	115	DD	Receiver clock
18	DCR	To DTE	Note 1		Divided clock receiver
19	SRTS	To DCE	120	DCA	Secondary request to send
20	DTR	To DCE	108.2	CD	Data terminal ready
21	SQ	To DTE	110	CG	Signal quality detect
22	RI	To DTE	125	CE	Ring indicator
23		To DCE	111	CH	Data rate selector
		To DCE	112	CI	Data rate selector
24	TC	To DCE	113	DA	External transmitter clock
25		To DCE	Note 2		Busy

Notes: 1. Bell 208A
2. Bell 113B

RS-232C pin connections

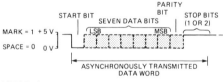

SECONDARY TRANSMIT DATA — 14 — 1 — PROTECTIVE GROUND
TRANSMIT CLOCK (DCE SOURCE) — 15 — 2 — TRANSMIT DATA, TXD
SECONDARY RECEIVE DATA — 16 — 3 — RECEIVE DATA, RXD
RECEIVE CLOCK — 17 — 4 — REQUEST TO SEND, RTS
UNASSIGNED — 18 — 5 — CLEAR TO SEND, CTS
SECONDARY REQUEST TO SEND — 19 — 6 — DATA SET READY, DSR
DATA TERMINAL READY, DTR — 20 — 7 — SIGNAL GROUND
SIGNAL DETECT — 21 — 8 — CARRIER DETECT
BELL DETECT — 22 — 9 — RESERVED (DATA SET TESTING)
BAUD RATE SELECT — 23 — 10 — RESERVED (DATA SET TESTING)
TRANSMIT CLOCK (DTE SOURCE) — 24 — 11 — UNASSIGNED
UNASSIGNED — 25 — 12 — SECONDARY CARRIER DETECT
13 — SECONDARY CLEAR TO SEND

Serial data format

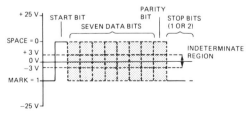

(a) TTL levels

(b) RS–232C signal levels

Data rates and distances for RS-232C

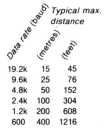

Data rate (baud)	Typical max. distance (metres)	(feet)
19.2k	15	45
9.6k	25	76
4.8k	50	152
2.4k	100	304
1.2k	200	608
600	400	1216

RS-232C/CCITT V24 voltage levels
Mark = logic 1 = 'off' = -3 V to -25 V (typically -6 V)
Space = logic 0 = 'on' = $+3$ V to $+25$ V (typically $+6$ V)

Null modems

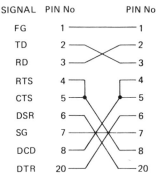

Note: The above alternative 'null modems' may be used to link
two computers together where each device is configured as a
DTE.

Typical serial data communication support devices

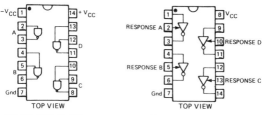

1488 RS-232C Line Driver

1489 RS-232C Line Receiver

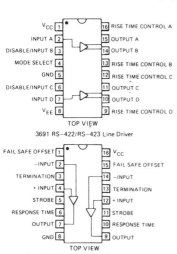

3691 RS-422/RS-423 Line Driver

88LS120 RS-422/RS-423 Line Receiver

Typical baud rate generator circuit

74LS259 output	Baud rate
Q_0	110
Q_1	9600
Q_2	4800
Q_3	1800
Q_4	1200
Q_5	2400
Q_6	300
Q_7	150

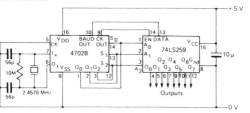

Modem standards

Classification	Data rate (baud)	Mode	Tone frequencies (Hz)				
			Transmit		Receive		Answer
			0	1	0	1	
CCITT V21 Orig.	300	Duplex	1180	980	1850	1650	—
CCITT V21 Answ.	300	Duplex	1850	1650	1180	980	2100
CCITT V23 Mode 1	600	Half duplex	1700	1300	1700	1300	2100
CCITT V23 Mode 2	1200	See note	2100	1300	2100	1300	2100
CCITT V23 Back	75	See note	450	390	450	390	—
Bell 103 Orig.	300	Duplex	1070	1270	2025	2225	—
Bell 103 Answ.	300	Duplex	2025	2225	1070	1270	2225
Bell 202	1200	Half	2200	1200	2200	1200	2025

Note: V23 Mode 2 permits full-duplex when the 'back' data rate is 75 baud.
When the 'back' rate is 1200 baud the system operates in half-duplex.

S5/8 interface

The RS-232C and V.24 standards are unnecessarily complex for
many applications and a simpler serial interface using conventional
TTL levels has much to recommend it. A minimal but nevertheless
elegant solution is offered by the new S5/8 standard. This standard
(currently awaiting BS approval) uses 5 V levels in conjunction
with a standard 8-pin DIN connector.

The S5/8 standard specifies two classes of device. A D-device
incorporates its own power supply and can provide power (+ 5 V
at up to 20 mA) at the S5/8 connector. An S-device, on the other
hand, does not have a supply of its own but may derive its power
from an associated D-device. A typical example of an S-device
connected to a D-device would be a line-powered modem
connected to a personal computer.

Although there is an obvious difference between D and S-devices
as regards power supplies, they are considered to be on an equal
footing as far as data transfer is concerned; neither device is
considered to be a sender or receiver (a perennial bugbear of RS-
232C systems!).

The pin assignment of the standard 8-way DIN connector used
by S5/8 is as follows:

Pin No.	Abbreviation	Signal/function
1	DINP	Data input
2	GROUND	Signal ground (common)
3	DOUT	Data output
4	HINP	Handshake input
5	HOUT	Handshake output
6	SINP	Secondary input
7	SOUT	Secondary output
8	V+	+5 V (20 mA max.)
Screen	EARTH	Earthed screen

The above arrangement ensures that input and output signals are paired on opposite sides of the connector (as in audio practice). It should also be noted that a standard 180 degree 5-pin DIN plug will mate with the 8-pin DIN connector specified in S5/8. This arrangement will give access to all signals with the exception of the secondary communication circuits (SINP and SOUT) and $+5$ V (V +).

The electrical characteristics of the S5/8 interface are as follows:

Inputs

Input resistance:	47 k ohm
Input low threshold:	+ 0.9 V maximum
Input high threshold:	+ 3.85 V minimum
Input protection:	± 25 V minimum

Outputs

Output low voltage:	+ 0.15 V maximum
Output high voltage:	+ 4.35 V minimum
Capacitive load drive capability:	2.5 nF minimum
Short-circuit protection:	to any other signal on the interface

S5/8 uses a conventional serial data structure and, in the same sense as RS-232C, the line rests low (0 V) and goes high for the start bit. Thereafter, transmitted data bits are inverted. Each frame (serially transmitted data word) comprises one start bit, eight data bits, and one stop bit (i.e., 10 bits total). There is no parity bit and hence error detection should be performed on a block-by-block basis using checksum or CRC techniques.

S5/8 specifies a data transfer rate of 9600 bit/s (the fastest widely used bit rate) and simple handshaking is provided using the HINP and HOUT lines. A full software flow-control specification is currently awaited.

Undoubtedly the most attractive feature of S5/8 is that an interface can be very easily realized using nothing more than a UART and a high-speed CMOS inverting buffer (e.g. 74HC14). There is no need for the line drivers and level shifters that would be essential to the correct operation of a conventional RS-232C interface.

Finally, whilst an S5/8 input will safely and correctly receive RS-232C signal levels, the reverse is not necessarily true. Depending upon the popularity of the new standard, it is expected that many manufacturers will not only implement their RS-232C ports using 8-way DIN connectors but will also change their line receivers for high-speed CMOS Schmitt inverters. Such an arrangement should readily permit interworking of the two systems.

KERMIT

The KERMIT file transfer protocol was developed by Bill Catchings and Frank da Cruz at the Columbia University Centre for Computing Activities (CUCCA). The initial objective was to allow users of DEC-20 and IBM timesharing systems to archive their files on microcomputer floppy disks. The design owes much to the ANSI and ISO models and ideas were incorporated from similar projects at Stanford University and the University of Utah.

KERMIT has grown to support over fifty different operating systems and is now in constant use in many sites all over·the world. The KERMIT software is free and available to all but, to defray costs of media, printing, postage, etc., a distribution fee is requested from sites that order KERMIT directly from the University of Columbia. Other sites are, however, free to distribute KERMIT on their own terms subject to certain stipulations.

Further details can be obtained from:

KERMIT distribution,
Columbia University Centre for Computing Activities,
7th Floor Watson Laboratory,
612 West 115th Street,
New York,
NY 10025

Prospective microcomputer KERMIT users should note that CUCCA can only provide 9-inch tapes (usually 1600 bit/in). Bootstrapping procedures are, however, provided to allow microcomputer versions to be downloaded from the mainframe for which the tape is produced. The tape includes all source programs and documentation. One copy of the KERMIT manual is also provided with each tape.

KERMIT is designed for the transfer of sequential files over ordinary serial telecommunication lines. It is not necessarily better than many other terminal-oriented file transfer protocols but it is free, well documented, and has been implemented on a wide variety of microcomputers and mainframes.

KERMIT transfers data by encapsulating it in 'packets' of control information which incorporate a synchronization marker, packet number (to facilitate detection of 'lost' packets), length indicator, and a checksum to allow verification of the data. Retransmission is requested when lost or corrupt data packets are detected; duplicate packets are simply discarded. In addition, special control packets allow co-operating KERMITs to connect and disconnect from each other and to exchange various kinds of information. Very few assumptions are made concerning the capabilities of either of the participating computers and hence the KERMIT protocol is effective with many different types of system.

KERMIT uses a simple set of basic commands which include SEND (followed by a filespec), RECEIVE, CONNECT (i.e., establish a virtual terminal connection to the remote system), SET (establish non-standard settings such as parity and flow-control), and HELP (displays a summary of KERMIT commands and actions). A ? typed anywhere within a KERMIT command lists the commands, options, or operands that are possible at that point. This particular command may, or may not, require a carriage return depending upon the operating system employed.

Useful interface circuits

Bipolar transistor relay driver

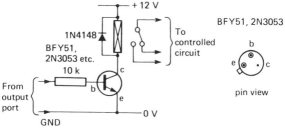

A logic 1 from the output port operates the relay.
Max. recommended relay operating current = 50 mA

VMOS FET relay driver

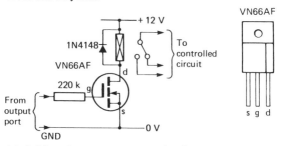

A logic 1 from the output port operates the relay.
Max. recommended relay operating current = 500 mA

VMOS FET motor driver

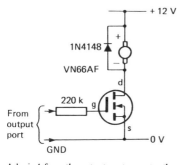

A logic 1 from the output port operates the motor.
Max. recommended motor current (stalled)   = 1 A
Max. recommended motor current (operating) = 500 mA

VMOS FET audible transducer driver

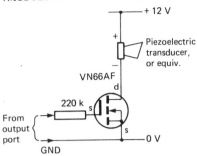

A logic 1 from the output port produces an audible output.
Max. recommended transducer current (operating) = 500 mA

A.C. mains controller using a solid state relay

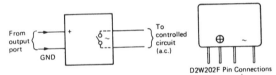

D2W202F Pin Connections

A logic 1 relay will switch the main circuit 'on'.
Typical solid state controller input resistance = 1.5 kohm
(It will therefore interface directly with most TTL devices)
Controlled voltages can be between 60 V and 280 V a.c. at up to
2 A.
Max. 'off' state leakage current = 5 mA
Max. isolation = 2.5 kV a.c.
(The D2W202F is available from International Rectifier)

Bipolar transistor LED driver

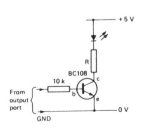

R	Typical diode current
220 Ω	13 mA
270 Ω	10 mA
330 Ω	8.5 mA
390 Ω	7 mA

BC108

pin view

Switch input

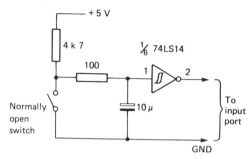

Switch 'open' generates a logic 0 at the input port.
Switch 'closed' generates a logic 1 at the input port.
The circuit is unsuitable for very noisy switches (i.e. where contact
bounce is severe) in which case additional software 'de-bouncing'
will be required.

Optically isolated data coupler

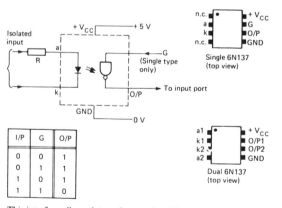

I/P	G	O/P
0	0	1
0	1	1
1	0	1
1	1	0

This interface allows data to be transferred between two
electrically isolated systems.
A suitable isolator is the 6N137 (also available in a dual version).
Typical propagation delay = 45 ns
Max. data transfer rate = 10 Mbit/s
Input current = 10 mA typical (therefore necessitating a TTL buffer
driver)
Typical value for R = 120 ohm (TTL logic level input)
The enable input (G) is normally held high.

Photodiode light sensor interface

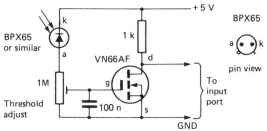

A logic 0 is generated when the light level exceeds the threshold setting, and vice versa.

Semiconductor temperature sensor interface

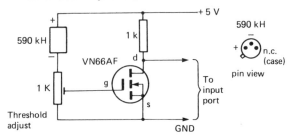

A logic 0 is generated when the temperature level exceeds the threshold setting, and vice versa.

Stepper motor interface

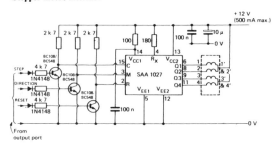

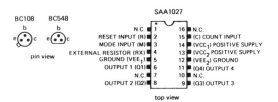

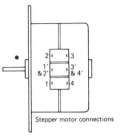

Stepper motor connections

The interface is suitable for driving a four-phase two-stator stepper motor having the following characteristics:

Supply voltage = 12 V
Resistance per phase = 47 ohm
Inductance per phase = 400 mH
Max. working torque = 50 mNm
Step rotation = 7.5 degrees per step

The STEP input is pulsed low to produce a step rotation.

A low (logic 0) on the DIRECTION input selects clockwise rotation. A high (logic 1) on the DIRECTION input selects anticlockwise rotation.

The RESET input is taken high to reset the driver. During normal operation the RESET input must be held low (logic 0).

Resistor colour code

Four band resistors

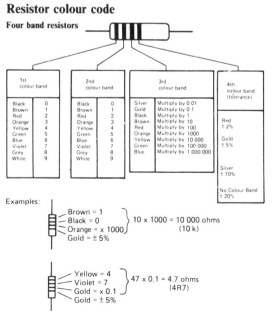

1st colour band		2nd colour band		3rd colour band		4th colour band (tolerance)
Black	0	Black	0	Silver	Multiply by 0 01	
Brown	1	Brown	1	Gold	Multiply by 0.1	
Red	2	Red	2	Black	Multiply by 1	
Orange	3	Orange	3	Brown	Multiply by 10	Red ± 2%
Yellow	4	Yellow	4	Red	Multiply by 100	
Green	5	Green	5	Orange	Multiply by 1000	Gold ± 5%
Blue	6	Blue	6	Yellow	Multiply by 10 000	
Violet	7	Violet	7	Green	Multiply by 100 000	
Grey	8	Grey	8	Blue	Multiply by 1 000 000	Silver ± 10%
White	9	White	9			
						No Colour Band ± 20%

Examples:

Brown = 1
Black = 0
Orange = x 1000 } 10 x 1000 = 10 000 ohms (10 k)
Gold = ± 5%

Yellow = 4
Violet = 7
Gold = x 0.1 } 47 x 0.1 = 4.7 ohms (4R7)
Gold = ± 5%

Five band resistors

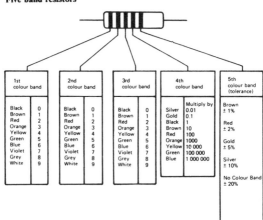

1st colour band		2nd colour band		3rd colour band		4th colour band		5th colour band (tolerance)
Black	0	Black	0	Black	0	Silver	Multiply by 0.01	Brown ± 1%
Brown	1	Brown	1	Brown	1	Gold	0.1	
Red	2	Red	2	Red	2	Black	1	Red ± 2%
Orange	3	Orange	3	Orange	3	Brown	10	
Yellow	4	Yellow	4	Yellow	4	Red	100	Gold ± 5%
Green	5	Green	5	Green	5	Orange	1000	
Blue	6	Blue	6	Blue	6	Yellow	10 000	Silver ± 10%
Violet	7	Violet	7	Violet	7	Green	100 000	
Grey	8	Grey	8	Grey	8	Blue	1 000 000	No Colour Band ± 20%
White	9	White	9	White	9			

Examples:

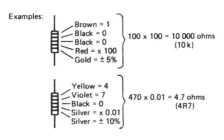

Brown = 1
Black = 0
Black = 0
Red = x 100
Gold = ± 5%
} 100 x 100 = 10 000 ohms
(10 k)

Yellow = 4
Violet = 7
Black = 0
Silver = x 0.01
Silver = ± 10%
} 470 x 0.01 = 4.7 ohms
(4R7)

Capacitor colour code

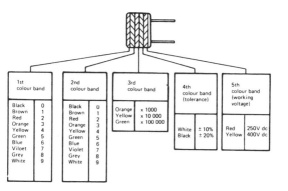

1st colour band		2nd colour band		3rd colour band		4th colour band (tolerance)		5th colour band (working voltage)	
Black	0	Black	0	Orange	x 1000				
Brown	1	Brown	1	Yellow	x 10 000				
Red	2	Red	2	Green	x 100 000				
Orange	3	Orange	3						
Yellow	4	Yellow	4			White	± 10%	Red	250V dc
Green	5	Green	5			Black	± 20%	Yellow	400V dc
Blue	6	Blue	6						
Viloet	7	Violet	7						
Grey	8	Grey	8						
White	9	White	9						

Examples:

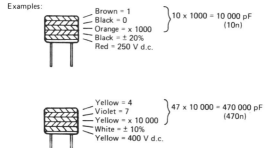

Brown = 1
Black = 0
Orange = x 1000   } 10 × 1000 = 10 000 pF
Black = ± 20%   (10n)
Red = 250 V d.c.

Yellow = 4
Violet = 7
Yellow = x 10 000   } 47 × 10 000 = 470 000 pF
White = ± 10%   (470n)
Yellow = 400 V d.c.

Cassette drive stock faults

Symptom	Cause
Motor not turning	Power supply defective
	Motor control relay/series transistor
	Defective speed regulator
	Defective cable or connector
	Motor defective
Motor turning but tape not moving	Drive belt broken or excessively worn
No read or write	Power supply failure
	Read/write head open circuit
	I/O failure
	Defective cable or connector
	Read/write head dirty or worn
Read but no write (previous data not erased)	Erase head open-circuit
	Erase circuitry not functioning
	Erase head dirty or worn
Read but no write (previous data erased)	Write amplifier defective
Write but no read (tape can be read on a similar machine)	Read amplifier defective
Inability to read tapes made on other machines	Speed incorrect
	Worn drive belt
	Incorrect reading level
Intermittent data errors	Speed irregular
	Worn drive belt
	Worn or eccentric pinch wheel
	Insufficient pinch wheel pressure
	Flywheel defective
	Insufficient erase current
	Incorrect recording or reading levels
	Faulty ALC circuitry
Intermittent data errors with particular media	Inconsistent magnetic oxide coating
	Tape stretched or creased
	Cassette pressure pad defective
Gradual deterioration in performance, increasing number of data errors	Heads contaminated with oxide
	Residual magnetism in read/write head
	Incorrect azimuth of read/write head

Action

Check supply rail
Replace relay/series transistor

Check regulator
Check for d.c. at appropriate points, check
continuity with multimeter
Replace motor
Replace belt

Check supply rails and regulators
Check head for continuity, check head
connections to PCB
Check I/O device, including address decoding
and chip select signals
Check using multimeter or logic probe at
appropriate points
Check read/write head, clean or replace

Check head for continuity, check head
connections to PCB
Check erase oscillator or d.c. feed to erase
head
Check erase head, clean or replace
Check for write signal at the read/write head
and work backwards to the I/O device
Check for read signal at the read/write head
and work forwards to the I/O device
Check motor speed regulator, adjust if possible

Replace belt
Adjust gain control
Check motor speed regulator
Replace belt
Replace pinch wheel

Adjust pinch wheel

Check for excessive play on flywheel
Check erase signal or d.c. feed to erase head
Check levels and, if possible, adjust

Check ALC detector and time constant
Replace cassette

Replace cassette
Adjust or replace pressure pad

Clean heads

De-magnetize read/write head

Adjust head azimuth

Symptom	*Cause*
Wind or rewind too slow	Cassette defective
	Friction plate worn
	Friction lever worn
	Torque low
Tapes damaged	Excessive take-up torque
	Excessive pinch wheel pressure
Tape spillage	Pinch wheel not disengaging correctly
	Friction plates worn
Pause inoperative	Pinch wheel not disengaging
Eject inoperative	Eject linkage or eject spring faulty

Disk drive stock faults

Symptom	*Cause*
Drive motor not turning	Power supply defective
	'Motor on' signal not active
	Defective speed regulator
	Defective cable or connector
	Motor defective
Motor turning but disk not moving	Drive belt broken or excessively worn
	Head load bail arm defective
No read or write	Power supply failure
	Head not loading
	Head not stepping
	Pressure pad assembly defective
	Index hole not located
	Read amplifier defective
	Read/write head open circuit
	Drive not selected
	Read/write head dirty or worn
Read but no write	Disk write-protected
	Write-protect circuitry faulty
	Write amplifier defective

Action

Replace cassette
Replace or adjust friction plate
Replace or adjust lever
Check and adjust pulley assembly
Adjust or replace assembly
Adjust pinch wheel pressure

Check pinch wheel assembly

Replace or renew friction plates
Check pinch wheel assembly and slider linkage

Check linkage or replace spring

Action

Check supply rail
Check disk controller and disk bus (pin 16)

Check regulator
Check for d.c. at appropriate points

Replace motor
Replace belt

Check arm and adjust or replace

Check supply rails and regulators
Check head load mechanism and solenoid.
Check disk bus (pin 4) and work towards
solenoid driver
Check stepper motor mechanism. Check disk
bus (pin 20) and work towards stepper motor
drivers
Check pressure pad and spring tension. Renew
if necessary
Check LED and photo-detector circuitry
Check read amplifier and move towards disk
controller. Check disk bus (pin 30)
Check head for continuity, check head
connections to PCB
Check drive select lines using logic probe
Check read/write head, clean or replace

Remove write-protect tab
Check write-protect LED and photo-detector.
Check disk bus (pin 26)
Check for write signal at the read/write head
and work backwards to the disk controller.

Cause

Symptom	Cause
	Disk controller failure
Inability to read disks made on other machines	Speed incorrect
Intermittent data errors	Disk format incorrect
	Speed irregular
	Worn drive belt
	Pressure pad worn
	Data separation fault
	Flywheel defective
	Incorrect recording or reading levels
	Read/write head dirty or worn
Intermittent data errors with particular disks	Inconsistent magnetic oxide coating
	Disk hub rings damaged or off-centre
	Excessive internal friction between disk and envelope
Gradual deterioration in performance, increasing number of data errors	Read/write head contaminated with oxide
	Read/write head worn
	Head assembly out of alignment
	Head carriage worn
	Insufficient head pressure
	Speed incorrect
Disk damaged	Excessive head pressure
	Head worn or damaged
	Drive spindle and platen out of alignment
	Foreign body lodged in pressure pad

Printer stock faults

Symptom	Cause
Printer non-functional. Controls and indicators inoperative	Mains input fuse blown
	Mains switch defective
	Input filter defective
	Mains transformer open-circuit

Action

Check disk bus (pin 20)
Check disk bus (pin 24)
Check motor speed and adjust
Drive and/or DOS incompatible
Check motor speed regulator
Replace belt
Adjust or renew pressure pad
Check data separation circuitry using
oscilloscope and test disk
Check for excessive play on flywheel
Check read/write amplifiers

Check read/write head, clean or replace

Replace disk

Replace disk

Replace disk

Clean head

Replace head
Check head azimuth with analogue alignment
disk
Adjust or replace head carriage
Adjust pressure pad
Check motor speed and adjust. Soak test and
measure speed after drive has reached its
normal working temperature
Adjust pressure pad
Replace head
Re-align

Replace pressure pad

Action

Check and replace. If fuse still blown check
input filter, mains transformer, and power
supply
Disconnect from mains supply and test mains
switch for continuity
Check filter inductors for continuity
Check resistance of winding with an ohmmeter.
(Typical values of primary and secondary
winding resistance are 40 ohm and 1 ohm
respectively)

Symptom

Cause

Power supply defective

Head carriage moves but no characters are printed

Head driving pulse absent or too narrow

Incorrect head gap

Head carriage moves but printing is faint or inconsistent

Incorrect head gap

Worn ribbon

Head carriage moves but one or more of the dot positions is missing

Defective head driver transistor or open circuit print head

Defective print head

Defective driver or buffer

Head carriage does not move, 'out of paper' indicator is illuminated

Paper end detector faulty

Head carriage does not move or moves erratically

Timing belt broken or worn

Timing belt tension incorrect

Timing sensor defective

Defective carriage motor or driver transistor

Action

Check individual raw d.c. rails. Check rectifiers and regulators

Check the head driving pulse using an oscilloscope

Check the head pulse monostable and/or the head trigger from the master CPU

Check positive supply rail to head driver transistors

Check and adjust

Check and adjust

Replace ribbon

Check the waveform at the collector and base of each driver transistor. If any collector waveform is found to be permanently high while the base is normal, remove the transistor, test and replace. If any collector waveform is found to be permanently low while the base is normal, disconnect the print head ribbon cable and measure the resistance of the actuator solenoid in question (typically 22 ohm)

Replace the print head if the actuator solenoid is found to be open circuit, otherwise remove the driver transistor, test and replace

If all waveforms are normal and all actuator solenoids measure approximately 22 ohm, it is possible that one or more of the needles has become seized or broken. It will then be necessary to remove and replace the print head. A substitution test should thus be carried out

If one or more of the base waveforms is incorrect, check the driver using an oscilloscope and work backwards to the master CPU

Check PE signal and paper end sensor

Check and replace

Adjust tension plate assembly

Check PTS signal. Check position timing sensor

Check waveforms at the collector of the four carriage motor driver transistors and verify the correct phase relationship. If one of the collector waveforms is permanently high whilst the base waveform is normal, remove, test and replace the transistor in question. If one of the collector waveforms is permanently low while the base waveform is normal, check the resistance of the relevant winding on the stepper motor (typically 40 to 50 ohm). If necessary compare with values obtained from the other windings. Remove and replace the carriage motor if any one of the windings is

Symptom	*Cause*
	Defective driver or buffer
Paper feed abnormal or not feeding at all	Defective paper release mechanism or sprocket drive
	Defective line feed motor or driver transistor
	Defective driver or buffer
Printer executes 'self-test' but will not accept printing instructions from the host computer	Interface faulty
Abnormal indication on switch panel. 'LF', 'FF' or 'OFF-LINE' switches inoperative	Control switch or indicator defective

Monitor stock faults

Symptom	*Cause*
No raster displayed, controls inoperative	Power supply failure
	Horizontal output stage failure

found to be abnormal, otherwise check the
driver transistor for a collector-emitter short-
circuit

If one or more of the base waveforms is
incorrect, check the driver using an
oscilloscope and work backwards to the slave
CPU

Check friction feed and sprocket drive
assembly. Adjust or repla

Check waveforms at the collector and base of
each of the four line feed motor driver
transistors and verify the correct phase
relationship. If one of the collector waveforms
is permanently high while the base waveform is
normal, remove, test and replace the transistor
in question. If one of the collector waveforms is
permanently low while the base is normal,
check the resistance of the relevant winding on
the line feed stepper motor (typically 40 to
50 ohm). If necessary, compare with values
obtained from the other windings. Remove and
replace the line feed motor if any of the
windings is found to be abnormal, otherwise
check the driver transistor for a collector-
emitter short-circuit

If one or more of the base waveforms is
incorrect, check the driver with an oscilloscope
and work backwards to the CPU

Check interface cable and connectors. Check
interface circuitry and, in particular, the BUSY
(pin 11) and ERROR (pin 32) status signal lines

Remove and check switch panel. Check switch
panel connector and interconnecting cable to
main PCB

Clean or replace any defective switch

Test and replace any defective indicator

Check fuses, d.c. supply rails, mains
transformer windings for continuity, rectifiers
and regulators

Check supply rail to horizontal output stage.
Check waveform at the collector of the driver
stage and at the collector of the horizontal
output stage. If the former is normal while the
latter is abnormal, remove and test the output
transistor. Replace if defective, otherwise check

Symptom	Cause
	Horizontal oscillator or driver faulty
	CRT defective
Raster is displayed but no video information is present	Video amplifier stage faulty
Data is displayed but focus is poor	Focus control adjustment Focus anode supply defective CRT defective
Data is displayed but brightness is low. Display size may increase and focus worsen as brightness is increased	Poor EHT regulation, horizontal output stage defective
Data is displayed but contrast is poor	Video amplifier or video output stage faulty
	Contrast control out of adjustment
Data is displayed but brightness is low. Display size remains constant and focus correct as brightness control is varied	Incorrect bias voltage on CRT
No horizontal sync, display contains a number of near horizontal bars	Horizontal sync stage defective
No horizontal or vertical sync, display consists of rolling horizontal bars	Sync separator defective
Reduced height, good vertical linearity	Height control out of adjustment
Poor vertical linearity, height normal	Vertical linearity out of adjustment
Vertical foldover, abnormal height accompanied by poor linearity	Vertical oscillator, driver or output stage defective

Action

the windings of the flyback transformer for
continuity

If, in the above procedure, the signal at the
collector of the driver stage is abnormal, check
the driver stage and work backwards to the
oscillator

Check CRT heaters for continuity. Check d.c.
voltages at the CRT electrodes. Note that a high
voltage probe will be needed to measure the
final anode supply. If the d.c. voltages are
abnormal, and particularly if any two of the
voltages are identical, remove the CRT
connector and check for shorts or leakage
between the electrodes. Remove and replace
the CRT if found to be defective. Take great
care when handling the CRT since there is a
risk of implosion if subjected to a mechanical
shock

Check d.c. supply voltage to video amplifier
stage. Check input connector. Check video
waveform at input and work towards video
output stage

Adjust focus control

Check d.c. supply to focus anode

Check for internal short between first anode
and focus anode

Check d.c. supply voltage to horizontal output
stage. Check d.c. voltages at CRT electrodes
using a high voltage probe for the final anode
measurement

Check horizontal flyback transformer for short-
circuited turns.

Check EHT rectifier arrangement

Check d.c. voltages on video amplifier stages.
Check video waveform at input connector and
work forwards to the video output stage

Adjust contrast control

Adjust preset brightness control. Check d.c.
supply to video output stage

Check waveforms at sync input and work
towards the horizontal oscillator

Check waveform at sync input and work
towards horizontal and vertical oscillators.
Check d.c. voltages on sync separator stage

Adjust height control

Adjust vertical linearity

Adjust vertical linearity. Check d.c. supply to
vertical stages. Check waveforms on vertical
stages

	Vertical yoke defective
No vertical scan, display consists of a bright horizontal line	Vertical oscillator, driver or output stage defective
	Vertical yoke defective
Reduced width, good horizontal linearity	Width control out of adjustment
No horizontal scan, display consists of a bright vertical line	Horizontal yoke defective, linearity or width coil open circuit
Horizontal linearity poor, width normal	Linearity control out of adjustment
Horizontal linearity poor, width and brightness may be reduced	Horizontal flyback transformer defective, horizontal yoke defective

Typical adjustment procedure for a monochrome monitor

Adjustment	*Preset control*
Horizontal sync	H-hold preset resistor; H-osc. inductor
Horizontal linearity	H-lin. inductor
Horizontal width	Width inductor
Vertical sync	V-hold preset resistor
Vertical linearity and vertical height	V-lin. preset resistor; V-height preset resistor
Contrast	Contrast preset resistor
Brightness	Brightness preset resistor
Focus	Dynamic focus preset resistor; focus preset resistor

heck inductance of vertical yoke (typically 5 to
5 mH)
heck d.c. supply to vertical stages. Check
aveforms and d.c voltages
heck vertical yoke for continuity (typically 2 to
0 ohm)
djust width control

heck horizontal yoke for continuity (typically
5 to 1.5 ohm). Check width and linearity coils
or continuity (typically 0.5 to 2 ohm)
djust linearity control

heck horizontal flyback transformer and
orizontal yoke for shorted turns (typical
orizontal yoke inductance is 100 to 300 μH)

rocedure

djust H-hold preset to mid-position; adjust
H-osc. inductor to centre of range over which
icture achieves sync
djust for equal width character H at the left,
ight, and centre of the display
djust for correct width of display. (Note that
his adjustment interacts with the linearity and
t will be necessary to repeat the previous
djustment)
djust to the centre of the range over which
icture achieves sync
djust V-height preset to obtain a display of
pproximately 70 per cent of the normal height
Use V-lin. preset to obtain equal height
haracters at the bottom, middle, and top of the
display
djust V-height preset to obtain a full height
display
djust for satisfactory display contrast
djust external brightness control to maximum
at which point the display raster should be
clearly visible)
djust brightness preset to the point where the
background raster just disappears
djust dynamic focus preset to minimum
djust focus preset to ensure that the display is
ocused uniformly
djust the dynamic focus preset for uniform
ocus at the edges of the display

Adjustment	*Preset control*
Screen centring	Centring magnet
Image deformation	Correction magnet

Repeat the two previous adjustments for optimum focusing

Adjust the magnet to provide a display which has the same periphery at the bottom and top, and at the left and right

Rotate the four correction magnets to gradually correct any deformation of the display

Glossary

Access time
The time taken to retrieve data from a memory/storage device, i.e. the elapsed time between the receipt of a read signal at the device and the placement of valid data on the bus. Typical access times for semiconductor memory devices are in the region 100ns to 200ns whilst average access times for magnetic disks typically range from 10ms to 50ms.

Accumulator
A register within the central processing unit (CPU) in which the result of an operation is placed.

Acknowledge (ACK)
A signal used in serial data communications which indicates that data has been received without error.

Active high
A term used to describe a signal which is asserted in the high (logic 1) state.

Active low
A term used to describe a signal which is asserted in the low (logic 0) state.

Address
A reference to the location of data in memory or within I/O space. The CPU places addresses (in binary coded form) on the address bus.

Address bus
The set of lines used to convey address information. The IBM PC-XT, for example, has twenty address lines (A0 to A19) and these are capable of addressing more than a million address locations. One byte of data may be stored at each address.

Address decoder
A hardware device (often a single integrated circuit) which provides chip select or chip enable signals from address patterns which appear on an address bus.

Address selection
The process of selecting a specific address (or range of addresses). In order to prevent conflicts, expansion cards must usually be configured (by means of DIP switches or links) to unique addresses within the I/O address map.

Analogue
The representation of information in the form of a continuously variable quantity (e.g. voltage).

Archive
A device or medium used for storage of data which need not be instantly accessible (e.g a tape cartridge).

American Standard Code for Information Interchange (ASCII)
A code which is almost universally employed for exchanging data

between microcomputers. Standard ASCII is based on a seven-bit binary code and caters for alphanumeric characters (both upper and lower case), punctuation, and special control characters. Extended ASCII employs an eighth bit to provide an additional 128 characters (often used to represent graphic symbols).

Assembly language
A low-level programming language which is based on mnemonic instructions. Assembly language is often unique to a particular microprocessor or microprocessor family.

Asserted
A term used to describe a signal when it is in its logically true state (i.e. logic 1 in the case of an active high signal or logic 0 in the case of an active low signal).

Asynchronous transmission
A data transmission method in which the time between transmitted characters is arbitrary. Transmission is controlled by start and stop bits and no additional synchronizing or timing (i.e. clock) information is required).

Backplane
A printed circuit board assembly used in computer bus systems (e.g. STE, VME, etc) in which bus card connectors are mounted at regular intervals. The backplane links all cards together and normally provides access to data and address bus lines as well as the control bus and power rails.

Backup
A file or disk copy made in order to avoid the accidental loss, damage, or erasure of programs and/or data.

Bank switching
A technique employed in microcomputer memory management systems in which one of several banks of memory may be switched into the same memory address space by writing a particular bit pattern to a specified I/O port address.

Batch file
A file containing a series of DOS commands which are executed when the file name is entered after the DOS prompt. Batch files are given a BAT file extension. A special type of batch file (AUTOEXEC.BAT) is executed (when present) whenever a system is initialized.

Basic input output system (BIOS)
The BIOS is the part of an operating system which handles communications between the microcomputer and peripheral devices (such as keyboard, serial port, etc.). The BIOS is supplied as firmware and is contained in a read-only memory (ROM).

Bit
A contraction of 'binary digit'; a single digit in a binary number

Boot
The name given to the process of loading and initializing an operating system (part of the operating system is held on disk and must be loaded from disk into RAM on power-up).

Boot record
A single-sector record present on a disk which conveys
information about the disk and instructs the computer to load the
requisite operating system files into RAM (thus booting the
machine).

Buffer
In a hardware context, a buffer is a device which provides a degree
of electrical isolation at an interface. The input to a buffer usually
exhibits a much higher impedance than its output (see also
'Driver'). In a software context, a buffer is a reserved area of
memory which provides temporary data storage and thus may be
used to compensate for a difference in the rate of data flow or
time of occurrence of events.

Bus
An electrical highway for signals which have some common
function. Most microprocessor systems have three distinct buses;
an address bus, data bus and control bus. Some bus systems are
associated with particular backplane configurations (e.g. STE and
VME).

Byte
A group of eight bits which are operated on as a unit.

Central processing unit (CPU)
The part of a computer that decodes instructions and controls the
other hardware elements of the system. The CPU comprises a
control unit, arithmetic/logic unit and internal storage. In
microcomputers, a microprocessor acts as the CPU (see also
'Microprocessor').

Channel
A path along which signals or data can be sent.

Chip
The term commonly used to describe an integrated circuit.

Clock
A source of timing signals used for synchronizing data transfers
within a computer system.

Cluster
A unit of space allocated on the surface of a disk. The number of
sectors which make up a cluster varies according to the DOS
version and disk type (see also 'Sector'). Standard MS-DOS or
PC-DOS uses clusters of eight sectors for hard disks of up to 16M
bytes and clusters of four sectors for larger disks (e.g. 40M byte).

Command
An instruction (entered from the keyboard or contained within a
batch file) which will be recognised and executed by a system (see
also 'Batch file').

Common
A return path for a signal (usually 'ground').

Controller
A sub-system within a microcomputer which controls the flow of
data between the system and an I/O or storage device (e.g. a CRT

controller, hard disk controller, etc.). A controller will generally be based on one, or more, programmable VLSI devices.

Coprocessor
A second processor which shares the same instruction stream as the main processor. The coprocessor handles specific tasks (e.g. mathematics) which would otherwise be performed less efficiently (or not at all) by the main processor.

Daisy chain
A method of connection in which signals move in a chained fashion from one device to another. This form of connection is commonly used with disk drives.

Data
A general term used to describe numbers, letters and symbols present within a computer system.

Data bus
A highway (in the form of multiple electrical conductors) which conveys data between the different elements within a microprocessor system.

Device driver
A term used to describe memory resident software (specified in the CONFIG.SYS system file) which provides a means of interfacing specialized hardware (e.g. expanded memory adapters).

Direct memory access (DMA)
A method of fast data transfer in which data moves between a peripheral device (e.g. a hard disk) and main memory without direct control of the CPU.

Directory
A catalogue of disk files (containing such information as filename, size, attributes, and date/time of creation). The directory is stored on the disk and updated whenever a file is amended, created, or deleted. A directory entry usually comprises 32 bytes for each file.

Disk operating system (DOS)
A group of programs which provide a low-level interface with the system hardware (particularly disk I/O). Routines contained within system resident portions of the operating system may be used by the programmer. Other programs provided as part of the system include those used for formatting disks, copying files, etc.

Driver
In a software context, a driver is a software routine which provides a means of interfacing a specialized hardware device (see also 'Device driver'). In a hardware context, a driver is an electrical circuit which provides an electrical interface between an output port and an output transducer. A driver invariably provides power gain (i.e. current gain and/or voltage gain), see also 'amplifier'.

Expanded memory
Additional memory which is effectively paged into a window within the existing memory map of the system. Several blocks of memory may be paged (or 'bank switched') into the same window (at different times) by writing data to an I/O port which is reserved for memory control.

Extended memory
Memory which is added to the base memory of a system (typically 640K in the case of a PC or PC-compatible) in order to increase the linear addressing range of the machine (the additional memory simply extends the upper address limit of the memory map).

File
Information (which may comprise ASCII encoded text, binary coded data and executable programs) stored on a floppy or hard disk. Files may be redirected from one logical device to another using appropriate DOS commands.

Filter
In a software context, a filter is a software routine which removes or modifies certain data items (or data items within a defined range). In a hardware context, a filter is an electrical circuit which modifies the frequency distribution of a signal. Filters are often categorized as low-pass, high-pass, band-pass, or band-stop depending upon the shape of their frequency response characteristic.

Firmware
A program (software) stored in read-only memory (ROM). Firmware provides non-volatile storage of programs.

Fixed disk
A disk which cannot be removed from its housing. Note that, whilst the terms 'hard' and 'fixed' are often used interchangeably, some forms of hard disk are exchangeable.

Format
The process in which a magnetic disk is initialized so that it can accept data. The process involves writing a magnetic pattern of tracks and sectors to a blank (uninitialized) disk. A disk containing data can be reformatted, in which case all data stored on the disk will be lost. An MS-DOS utility program (FORMAT.COM) is supplied in order to carry out the formatting of floppy disks (a similar utility is usually provided for formatting the hard disk).

Graphics adapter
An option card which provides a specific graphics capability (e.g. CGA, EGA, HGA, VGA). Graphics signal generation is not normally part of the functionality provided within a system mother board.

Handshake
An interlocked sequence of signals between peripheral devices in which a device waits for an acknowledgement of the receipt of data before sending new data.

Hard disk
A rigid (non-flexible) disk used for the magnetic storage of data and programs (see also 'Fixed disk').

Hardware
The physical components (i.e. printed circuit boards, integrated circuits, resistors, capacitors, etc) of a microcomputer system.

High state
The more positive of the two voltage levels used to represent binary logic states. A high state (logic 1) is generally represented by a voltage in the range 2.0V to 5.0V.

Interface
A shared boundary between two or more systems, or between two or more elements within a system. In order to facilitate interconnection of systems, various interface standards are adopted (e.g. RS-232 in the case of asynchronous data communications).

Input/output (I/O)
Devices and lines used to transfer information to and from external (peripheral) devices.

Integrated circuit
An electronic circuit fabricated on a single wafer (chip) and packaged as a single component.

Interface system
The functional elements required for unambiguous communication between two or more devices. Typical elements include: driver and receiver circuitry, signal line descriptions, timing and control conventions, communication protocols, and functional logic circuits.

Interleave
A system of numbering the sectors on a disk in a non-consecutive fashion in order to optimize data access times.

Interrupt
A signal generated by a peripheral device when it wishes to gain the attention of the CPU. The Intel 8086 family of microprocessors support both software and hardware interrupts. The former provide a means of invoking BIOS and DOS services whilst the latter are generally managed by an interrupt controller chip (e.g. 8259).

Joystick
A device used for positioning a cursor, pointer, or output device using switches or potentiometers which respond to displacement of the stick in the X and Y directions.

Logical device
A device which is normally associated with microcomputer I/O, such as the console (which comprises keyboard and display) and printer.

Low state
The more negative of the two voltage levels used to represent the binary logic states. A low state (logic 0) is generally represented by a voltage in the range 0V to 0.8V.

Memory
That part of a microcomputer system into which information can be placed and later retrieved. Storage and memory are interchangeable terms. Memory can take various forms including semiconductor (RAM and ROM), magnetic (floppy and hard

disks), and optical disks. Note that memory may also be categorized as read-only (in which case data cannot subsequently be written to the memory) or read/write (in which case data can both be read from and written to the memory).

Microprocessor
A central processing unit fabricated on a single chip.

Motherboard
A main circuit board (or system board) to which a number of expansion or adapter cards may be fitted.

Multitasking
A process in which several programs are running simultaneously.

Negative acknowledge (NAK)
A signal used in serial data communications which indicates that erroneous data has been received.

Network
A system which allows two or more computers (or intelligent controllers) to be linked via a physical communications medium (e.g. coaxial cable) in order to exchange information and share resources.

Noise
Any unwanted signal component which may appear superimposed on a wanted signal.

Operating system
A control program which provides a low-level interface with the system hardware. The operating system thus frees the programmer from the need to produce hardware specific I/O routines (e.g. those associated with disk filing). See also 'Disk operating system'.

Option card
A printed circuit board (adapter card) which complies with the physical and electrical specification for a particular system and which provides the system with additional functionality (e.g. asynchronous communications facilities).

Peripheral
An external hardware device whose activity is under the control of the microcomputer system.

Personal computer (PC)
A term used to describe a general purpose single-user computer system. The term encompasses equipment which ranges from low-cost 8-bit home computers to sophisticated 32-bit machines used in scientific, business, management and engineering applications.

Port
A general term used to describe an interface circuit which facilitates transfer of data to and from external devices (peripherals).

Propagation delay
The time taken for a signal to travel from one point to another. In the case of logic elements, propagation delay is the time interval

between the appearance of a logic state transition at the input of a gate and its subsequent appearance at the output.

Protocol
A set of rules and formats necessary for the effective exchange of data between intelligent devices.

Random access
An access method in which each word can be retrieved in the same amount of time (i.e. the storage locations can be accessed in any desired order). This method should be compared with sequential access in which access times are dependent upon the position of the data within the memory.

Random access memory (RAM)
A term which usually refers to semiconductor read/write memory (in which access time is independent of actual storage address). Note that semiconductor read-only memory (ROM) devices also provide random access.

Read
The process of transferring data to a processor from memory or I/O.

Read-only memory (ROM)
A memory device which is permanently programmed. Erasable-programmable read only memory (EPROM) devices are popular for storage of programs and data in stand-alone applications and can be erased under ultraviolet light to permit reprogramming.

Register
A storage area within a CPU, controller, or other programmable device, in which data (or addresses) are placed during processing. Registers will commonly hold 8, 16 or 32-bit values.

Relay
An electromechanical device which opens or closes one or more sets of switching contacts in response to an electrical input. Relays typically permit switching of currents several orders of magnitude greater than the input current. They can also provide a high degree of electrical isolation between the input and the controlled circuits. (See also 'Solid-state relay').

Root directory
The principal directory of a disk (either hard or floppy) which is created when the disk is first formatted. The root directory may contain the details of further sub-directories which may themselves contain yet more sub-directories, and so on.

Run length limited (RLL)
An encoding technique which is commonly used to increase the storage capacity of a hard disk. In this technique, the 'run length' (number of consecutive zero bits which are recorded before a logic 1 bit is inserted within the bit stream) is allowed to vary between two fixed limits (usually 2 and 7, or 3 and 9). Under 2, 7 RLL from two to seven consecutive 0 bits are allowed whereas, under 3, 9 RLL from three to nine adjacent 0 bits are allowed. Note that 2, 7 RLL offers a theoretical 50% increase in drive capacity whilst 3, 9 RLL offers a theoretical 100% increase in drive capacity over conventional MFM encoding.

Sector
The name given to a section of the circular track placed (during formatting) on a magnetic disk. Tracks are commonly divided into ten sectors (see also 'Format').

Shell
The name given to an item of software which aims to provide a user interface to the system (e.g. the program COMMAND.COM is the standard DOS shell).

Software
A series of computer instructions (i.e. a program).

Solid-state relay
A relay which is based on optically coupled semiconductor switching devices (see also 'Relay').

Sub-directory
A directory which contains details of a group of files and which is itself contained within another directory (or within the root directory).

System board
The system board is the mother printed circuit board which provides the basic functionality of the microcomputer system including CPU, RAM, and ROM. The system board is fitted with connectors which permit the installation of one, or more, option cards (e.g. graphics adapters).

Validation
A process in which input data is checked in order to identify incorrect items. Validation can take several forms including range, character, and format checks.

Verification
A process in which stored data is checked (by subsequent reading) to see whether it is correct.

Visual display unit (VDU)
An output device (usually based on a cathode ray tube) on which text and/or graphics can be displayed. A VDU is normally fitted with an integral keyboard in which case it is sometimes referred to as a console.

Volume label
A disk name (comprising up to 11 characters). Note that hard disks may be partitioned into several volumes, each associated with its own logical drive specifier (i.e. C:, D:, E:, etc.).

Write
The process of transferring data from a CPU to memory or to an I/O device.

Index

Note: within each letter, capitalized entries, acronyms, etc, have been listed before conventional entries.